America's Environmental Crisis

Why We Are Winning the Battle but Losing the
War to Avoid a Climate Catastrophe

By

Peter S. Wellenberger

CENTRAL PARK SOUTH PUBLISHING

Publisher: **Central Park South Publishing**
website: www.langtonsinternational.com

Book Layout: **alienartifacts**

America's Environmental Crisis by Peter S. Wellenberger ©
2020 1st ed.
ISBN 978-1-7352964-1-8

"Treat the earth well: it was not given to you by your parents, it was loaned to you by your children. We do not inherit the Earth from our ancestors, we borrow it from our Children."

– Chief Crazy Horse -

Dedication

This book is dedicated to my grandchildren, Jameson and Maddox Lockhart, andmy wife Kathy's grandchildren, Ariana and Jailyn Mulder-Arroyo, as well as Kiana, Jayce and Logan Mulder. May they inherit a world that is habitable to both humans and animals.

It is also dedicated to the incredible men and woman who work with the National Estuarine Research Reserve System – a network of 29 protected areas established through partnerships between NOAA and numerous coastal states. The Reserves represent different biogeographic regions of the U.S. and they protect more than 1.3 million acres of coastal and estuarine habitats for long-term research, water-quality monitoring, education, and coastal stewardship.

A portion of the profits from the sale of this book will be used to support the National Estuarine Research Reserve Association (NERRA), which is dedicated to protecting our nation's estuaries for generations to come and serving as a critical ally in combatting the effects of climate change.

Acknowledgements

I would like to thank my daughter, Kristin Adele Lockhart, for her support and assistance during the writing process. Her skills as a public-school teacher were invaluable. Thanks as well to Kelle Loughlin at the Great Bay National Estuarine Research Reserve for her help with the environmental history of Seacoast New Hampshire and Alynna Hartmann, professor of Political Science at the University, for her insights and proof-reading skills. Finally, I am most grateful to my four former classmates and still friends from Antioch-New England Graduate School in Keene, New Hampshire. First to Clif Read and Mike Zettek for their support and enthusiasm, and especially to David Wickline and Richard Donovan for their initial editing and fact checking. This book would not have been possible without David and Rich's professional expertise.

Endorsements

"Peter Wellenberger presents a compelling analysis of the tragic impacts of endless development and drive for profit that threaten human health and well-being and compromises the Earth's capacity. From flooding in Coastal New England to droughts in the Southwest, the declining bee population, fracking, mountain top mining practices and agribusiness, he documents almost 300 years of exploitation of the natural resources in the United States. This is a dark tale of imminent climate collapse and the reckless drive for profit often labeled as 'progress' and 'development'. Wellenberger paints a picture that highlights the toxic intersection of economics, culture, politics, and natural systems. Overall, the book provides an elegant map of how we got here with insights on how to move towards a sustainable future. This is a well-written and highly accessible must-read for anyone interested in the future of humanity and the planet."

Alynna Lyon -Political Science Professor, University of New Hampshire.

Preface

"You think you can destroy the planet? What intoxicating vanity. We've been residents here for the blink of an eye. If we're gone tomorrow, the earth will not miss us."

-Michael Crichton -

Growing up on Long Island in New York, I came to the realization there was too much -- too many people, cars, stores and everything else man has invented. I was bewildered by all the congestion and determined to move to a more "natural" environment. To escape the suburban jungle, I moved to and have lived in New Hampshire for most of my adult life. Here I found a more appealing landscape.

The county where I grew up is called Nassau. According to the 2010 census, the county's population was 1,339,532 – the most densely populated in New York State outside of New York City. In 2012, *Forbes* magazine, in an article based on the American Community Survey, reported Nassau County is the most expensive county in New York with one of the highest incomes in the United States (U.S.).[1]

I had the privilege of growing up in a wealthy community that offered superior schools, beautiful tree-lined streets, one that had been well planned from its inception. Founded in 1869 and aptly named Garden City, the town was the brainchild of multi-millionaire Alexander Stewart. As technology advanced, they had the foresight to locate the power lines and telephone poles in backyards to maintain the town's pastoral setting. Located smack in the middle of Nassau County, Garden City remains an oasis for those who can afford to live there (houses were a lot less expensive when my parents moved there in 1963).

It was not until high school when I bought my first car – a '65 Mustang convertible – that I began to recognize that life outside of Garden City was not the same as within it. With only one gas station in town, I would travel south to a road known as Hempstead Turnpike that offered more options. The road stretches across the county west to east, some 18 miles from Floral Park in Queens all the way out to East Farmingdale in Suffolk County.

The Turnpike crosses an area previously known as the Hempstead Plains. Back then, it was an open expanse of native grassland estimated to comprise about 60,000 acres – one of the few natural prairies east of the Allegheny Mountains created by an outwash of glacial sediment more than 10,000 years ago. Glaciation played a major role in shaping the topography of Long Island, its beautiful ocean beaches delineating the southern extent of the last ice age.[2]

The early Dutch and English settlers converted the Plains with its rich soil to farmland and the first horse races in North America date back to 1665 in a section of the Plains near Garden City.

In the early 1900s, the area had earned the reputation as the "Cradle of Aviation." The most famous flight from there was Charles Lindbergh's 1927 epic journey to France.[3] He took off from Roosevelt Field, Garden City, and my maternal grandfather was there to witness the event.

Today, Roosevelt Field is a massive shopping mall that seems to grow bigger every time I return to my hometown.

South of Roosevelt Field, Hempstead Turnpike continues its journey to the west. About halfway along the route is Hofstra College, which provides a break from today's monotonous strip malls and commercial activity. The Turnpike then cuts through East Meadow before splitting the hamlet of Levittown in half. You will learn more about this so-called "Birthplace of Suburbia" and the roots of suburban sprawl in Chapter Four. From Levittown, there are only a few more communities before one reaches the Suffolk County line.

My definition of discontentment is to drive along Hempstead Turnpike. It is 18 miles of redundant stores, congestion, traffic lights, telephone poles and wires, signs, trash and anything else that takes away from the beauty of a community. None of it was ever planned with sustainability in mind. America features lots of similarly congested roads, but this turnpike is the one most deeply rooted in my environmental consciousness. My wife and I recently attended a family wedding in Skokie, Illinois. We flew into Midway Airport and, instead of driving through downtown via the expressway, we took the shorter route through the neighborhoods west of Chicago. The journey – about 24 miles – took over an hour.

I had been to Chicago previously and found the city to be appealing – what some call "Midwestern Charm." But my visit was limited primarily to the tourist areas of the city and it was not until my drive to Skokie that I realized what life is really like for most Chicagoans. Not the glitz found on the Gold Coast along Lake Michigan, but miles of congestion, litter, urban decay, noise and foul air. It is what I call a desecrated landscape where people live in poverty.

My work as a coastal resource manager included travelling to Ireland five times to establish a "Sister Reserve" program. It was my distinct pleasure to share ideas with them about coastal zone management. During one visit, I travelled to Strangford Lough, a large estuary off the eastern coast of Northern Ireland. I was struck not only by its pristine natural state, but the fact that the shoreline was devoid of development. I asked our guide if this was the result of strong regulations regarding coastal development. He replied, "Not at all. We just don't build too close to the water as that is the custom. It is how we preserve the natural beauty of the estuary." These were words that I have never heard uttered in the U.S.

Therefore, this book is very personal for me. Sprawl has ruined much of Long Island and its current population of nearly eight million (including Brooklyn and Queens) is not sustainable. Chicago is no different.

The Chicago River is so absent of water, locks are needed to reach Lake Michigan. While New Hampshire is not immune from sprawl, it has just taken longer to get there. Some lessons from what has gone wrong in other places have been learned; in other cases, ignored. Americans continue to leave large and growing footprints across every state.

We face other acute challenges as well – water shortages, loss of habitat and wildlife, polluted air and water, and, perhaps most important, a culture that seems to care more about the individual than the community. These issues are tied to climate change in varying degrees, a growing crisis that will continue to dominate our public policy for decades to come.

Just as unfettered population growth is in juxtaposition to protecting our environment, our nation continues to pursue economic expansion at any cost. This path is alien to the idealism of my youth and the optimistic viewpoints expressed by Charles Reich in his ground-breaking 1970 publication, *The Greening of America*. Reich argued then that a social revolution was underway and, as a result, these radical changes would cause a fundamental shift in our culture. It would mean the end of what he called the "dominate corporate state" which exploits and destroys nature and eventually mankind itself.

And why not make such a bold claim? The 1970s represent the highpoint of American environmentalism. Congress passed such landmark legislation as the Clean Air Act, the Clean Water Act, the Coastal Zone Management Act (CZMA) and the Endangered Species Act (ESA). President Nixon, a Republican, established the Environmental Protection Agency (EPA), and the nation observed its first Earth Day on April 22, 1970. People were committed to a better future.

Now, nearly 50 years later, we have turned back the clock and no longer embrace the values of the 1970s. Instead, we have regressed to the notion of individual enrichment and growth at any cost. While many Americans assert their concern for the environment – and a great many people are doing all they can to protect it – the people we vote into office often have a contrarian point of view.

Therefore, all our institutions need to be challenged. Not only have our politicians failed us but our religious institutions as well. One of the most shocking statistics I discovered in writing this book is the number of Americans who believe in creationism opposed to evolution (see Chapter Sixteen). Fortunately, that number has been on the decline recently as science and technology play a vital role in discussing and surviving the impending climate crisis. At the same time, we need to reconnect children with nature so they will develop a strong bond with the natural world.

Some people will argue this book paints a bleak picture. Perhaps they are right, but the rationale that the environment should always take a back seat to the economy is why we face a climate catastrophe. Our wildlife is being used as a scapegoat in the name of prosperity with the potential of causing mass extinctions. Those who seek a greener future for their grandchildren are tired of fossil fuel companies claiming we cannot afford to switch to renewables and the plastic manufacturers saying if we eliminate plastic bags, it will cost jobs. In a sustainable economy, renewable energy will create jobs and people will make reusable packaging products.

While we win many of the battles, we are losing the war to save our environment. I came to write this book because we can do better – much better. Following a short introduction, our story begins with how we got it wrong from the day Europeans first landed in America. The following chapters then discuss the many environmental issues we face and how we got to this point. A much more comprehensive review of these issues is needed to fully understand their impact. Instead, my purpose is to take stock of the current situation and potential solutions.

There are numerous chapters on energy and the relationship to climate change dispersed throughout the book. The last section makes recommendations for the future including an overview of the "New Green Deal" as proposed by Sen. Ed Markey (D-MA) and Rep. Alexandria Ocasio-Cortez (D-NY). Throughout the book there are inserts (shown in grey) with news items about current environmental conditions and events as well as how some efforts are making a difference. These accounts are taken directly from their source with only minor edits.

Authors Note:
Statistics Are Funny Things

Americans today are bombarded with statistics that are often manipulated to present a certain point of view. Politicians are especially skilled at using statistics that fit their narrative. And achieving consistency with numbers can be tricky depending on the source. People also interpret data according to his/her own beliefs.

The most eye-opening book I read in college was called *How to Lie With Statistics* and when it comes to climate change, understanding statistics becomes imperative. It is where critical thinking skills come into play. As noted by former U.S. Senator Patrick Moynihan (D-NY), "everyone is entitled to his own opinion, but not his own facts."

The most basic fact about climate change is that the planet is getting hotter. But climate deniers will use a long cold wave as proof that temperatures fluctuate and have for hundreds of years. This is known as confirmation bias – only using data that proves a viewpoint. The fact that the planet has been slowly heating up since the Industrial Revolution and getting hotter as the years go by is irrefutable. Cold waves are becoming anomalies that occur in a defined region. What matters are long-term trends across the globe, not a "colder than usual" spring in the Midwest.

Some scientists have argued that there was a "pause" in the rate of global warming recorded from 1998 to 2013. In December 2019, the Climate News Network, which publishes a daily news story on climate and energy, reported there was no pause. After a team of researchers analyzed all the data, they found "a divergence between the rate of actual global warming and the model projections which was caused by various biases in the model interpretation and in the observations." In other words, there was no statistical evidence of a pause highlighting the complexity of climate research.

Readers should also keep in mind that a "big number" needs to be viewed in context. As referenced, part of the pro-coal agenda is to protect the 50,000 miners who would lose their jobs if we no longer burned coal. According to the U.S. Department of Labor, there were over 128 million Americans working full-time in the U.S. as of 2018. While 50,000 sounds like a big number, put in perspective it is much smaller. For comparison, the country's largest private employer, Walmart, has some 1.4 million U.S. employees – providing 28 times as many jobs as coal mining. As cheaper natural gas has replaced the use of coal, there are efforts to retrain coal miners for better jobs in the green energy sector. These are recent developments rarely mentioned by the coal industry.

One final note. Sometimes when using multiple references, there is not always agreement on the numbers being used. For example, when looking at the impact of methane – a more potent but short-lived greenhouse gas – as a contributing factor of climate change compared to carbon dioxide which is far more prevalent, there is a wide range of figures cited by various sources. For the purposes of this book, I used the most conservative number to avoid any claims of perceived bias or lack of objectivity on the author's part.

Abbreviations

CAFE – Corporate Average Fuel Economy

CDC – Center for Disease Control and Prevention

CEQ – Council on Environmental Quality

CZMA – Coastal Zone Management Act

DDT – Dichloro-Diphenyl-Trichloroethane

EPA – Environmental Protection Agency

ESA – Endangered Species Act

EV – Plug-In Electric Vehicles

FDA – Food and Drug Administration

FEMA - Federal Emergency Management Agency

GDP – Gross Domestic Product

IPCC – Intergovernmental Panel on Climate Change

MLP – Master Limited Partnership

MPG – Miles Per Gallon

NEPA – National Environmental Policy Act

NPR – National Public Radio

NOAA – National Oceanic and Atmospheric Administration

NRC – Nuclear Regulatory Commission

PCBs - Polychlorinated Biphenyls

PPM – Parts Per Million

PV – Photovoltaic

SUVs – Sport Utility Vehicles

USDA – United States Department of Agriculture

ZEVs – Zero-emission vehicles

Table of Contents

Part Two – What a Sustainable Future Looks Like

Figures

Part One:
How We Got Here

"Nature is relentless and unchangeable, and it is indifferent as to whether its hidden reasons and actions are understandable to man or not."

- Galileo Galilei -

Introduction

"We are living on this planet as if we had another one to go to."

- Terri Swearingen -

When my children were young, they loved to play Jenga – a game where players take turns removing one block at a time from a tower constructed of 54 blocks. Each removed block is then placed on top of the tower, creating a progressively taller structure. Eventually, the tower becomes unstable and collapses.

Our environment is no different, only far more complicated with thousands of building blocks.

Man keeps removing these blocks, one by one, to create something else. Only just like Jenga, we have no idea when things might collapse and how whole ecosystems will be lost when too many pieces are detached.

Modern capitalism in the U.S. is often in direct opposition to sustainability and the protection of our natural environment. While there is frequent discussion about the emerging "green economy," the rich and powerful continue to control the direction of our economy and everyday consumers are happy to participate. At the end of the day, too many of us want the least expensive toaster oven or latest Smartphone with no thought to the environmental consequences related to making, transporting, or disposing of these products.

Many people will cite hundreds of examples of ecological-friendly products available on the market and the current interest in organic and fresh foods. But the fundamentals of our economy are based on continual growth and output. Hence the tag line of this book. We are winning the battle but losing the war.

The highly reputable Pew Foundation conducted a study in 2016 of Americans' attitudes towards protecting the environment. More than half (55%) of Americans ranked the environment as a top policy issue for President Donald Trump and Congress to address; Democrats (72%) were twice as likely as Republicans (35%) to cite protecting the environment as top priority, a partisan gap that has widened considerably over the past ten years.[1]

In a 2014 study, millennials indicated a strong concern for the environment but were also found to be less likely than older generations to view themselves as "environmentalists." A somewhat surprising revelation when one considers their generation will experience the greatest number of impacts resulting from climate change.[2]

While most Americans believe it is important to protect the environment, defending the country from future terrorist attacks (76%) and strengthening the economy (73%) were at the top of the public's priorities in 2017.[3] It is no surprise these issues lead the list along with health care, education, crime, race relations, etc. that all finished above the environment as a top priority. Subsequent polls have only slightly changed the order with the economy or health care most often finishing on top. In exit polls following the 2018 midterm elections, rarely did voters mention the environment as a priority with climate change finishing a distant seventh.[4] In 2019, climate change has risen in the polls as a top priority, but is it too late?

When we grow the economy at the expense of the environment, it shifts future clean-up costs to the taxpayer. In a sustainable economy, the offender pays or does no harm; but if growth and profit are the primary intentions, protecting the environment frequently takes a back seat. As a result, we have incurred a pollution deficit that has put Americans' health at risk.

Even when society moves in the right direction, we usually fail to consider the bigger picture. The development of LEDs (light-emitting diode) resulted in a far superior light bulb compared to an incandescent and, in general, Americans seem to have accepted the transition. But these bulbs also have a dark side as they contain a litany of dangerous and toxic substances. Electric cars (hybrids share some of the same problems) seem like a good idea, as well, until one looks more closely under the hood. While these vehicles save on the use of gasoline, the batteries need to be recharged and their production and disposal leads to other environmental impacts.

Most of our electricity continues to be generated from fossil fuels with coal providing up to a third of the power supply. According to the U.S. Energy Information Administration, coal provides the largest generation share in 18 states (as of 2017). While down from 28 states ten years earlier, most of the conversions from coal have been to natural gas – also a fossil fuel or to nuclear energy which poses its own environmental issues; renewables, while on the rise, provide only a small percentage of our electrical power.[5]

We can pat ourselves on the back for doing something we perceive as the smarter choice, but it does not change what matters most – carbon emissions continue to rise to levels not seen since the dawn of man. On October 8, 2018, the United Nations-sponsored Intergovernmental Panel on Climate Change (IPCC) released its highly anticipated report on what needs to be done to limit global warming to minimize the devastating impacts that lie ahead. Most alarming, the report offers a narrow window for rapid climate action stating: "By 2030, emissions would have to fall to 45 percent below 2010 levels and by 2050, all or nearly all coal burning must stop."[6]

To reduce emissions by almost 50 percent from levels last seen in 2010 and to do so in just ten years will require massive structural changes that affect every American. Thanks to President Trump's pro-fossil fuel agenda, we are unprepared to accept the challenge and are headed in the opposite direction. Congress seems no more willing to address climate change than it does to tackle Medicare spending or the solvency of Social

Security just as the federal government is running up huge deficits.

From the day English colonists first settled in the new land known as America, we have believed that nature is there to serve us. While Native Americans lived in harmony with the environment, the English and other colonists wanted to live as they had done in Europe by exploiting the natural resources and altering the landscape. After almost 300 years of abuse and neglect, we have reached an environmental crossroads and it is time to pay the piper.

Protecting the environment is not an elitist position any more than a desire to safeguard our health from the poisons being released into the air and waterways. It is possible to develop clean energy and not live in the dark or freeze, but the transition will not be easy and it will require sacrifices. Some companies and industries will adapt more quickly than others and with so much at stake, the resistance will be fierce; it means holding capitalism accountable.

We need to ask ourselves how did we wind up here, what choices can we make that will lead to sustainable options and who can make it happen? As it relates to climate change, given the complexity of our natural systems and the force that drive them, it is difficult to predict the outcomes as we have never seen anything like this before. This is not a partisan issue and our collective failure to respond quickly may mean there is not enough time left to make the requisite changes. We may only get one shot at saving ourselves from a bleak future and, as the Trump Presidency moves the country dangerously backwards, it becomes even more imperative that we act on this national emergency.

There are lots of prominent people today who espouse the virtues of travel to Mars. With all the complex problems we face here on Earth, it is disheartening how people get so excited about such a costly adventure while ignoring what is happening right in front of them. In December 1968, Apollo 8 became the first manned spacecraft to orbit the moon. It sent back one of the most iconic photographs ever taken – a planet awash in blue and white swirls. This photo gave impetus to the environmental movement of the 1970s as we got to see what our majestic planet looks like from space. Do we really want Mars to be our lifeboat? Instead, wouldn't it be better to create a healthier and sustainable Earth that supports all living things, not a place to run away from?

6   Peter Wellenberger

Chapter One
How We Got It All Wrong From the Start

"I like the dreams of the future better than the history of the past."

- Thomas Jefferson -

The Great Bay estuary transforms New Hampshire's modest 18 miles of coastline into 150 miles of tidal shoreline. The rivers that flow into the estuary drain a watershed that extends more than 1,000 square miles and includes parts of New Hampshire and Maine. Formed by the glaciers some 15,000 years ago, the estuary features five tidally-influenced habitats – eelgrass beds, mudflats, saltmarsh, channel bottom and rocky intertidal. Today, it serves as a nursery to many fish species as well as an important resting spot along the Atlantic Flyway.[1]

The first humans to enjoy Great Bay's bounty were the Abenaki Indians, one of the Algonquian-speaking peoples of northeastern North America. As hunter gatherers, they were satisfied to harvest only what was necessary for survival. Evidence of their presence in the form of oyster and clam shell piles – called middens – still exists today.

From a conservation perspective, what is most revealing about the region is its cultural history. The first known European to explore and write about the area was Martin Pring in 1603. The Piscataqua River, which links the interior regions of the estuary to the Gulf of Maine, features a good natural harbor. The west bank of the harbor was settled by English colonists in 1630 and named Strawbery Banke (as spelled by the English) after the many wild strawberries growing there in what is now known as the City of Portsmouth.[2]

These early settlers found a region rich in natural resources, both on land and in the water. The estuary teemed with fish and the adjacent upland forests flourished with majestic trees. Deer and other wild game were abundant as well. During the spring and fall migrations the skies were darkened by waterfowl. Salt hay from the marshes was harvested and used to feed livestock and transported as far away as Boston. Oysters and clams were so plentiful they were fed to hogs.[3]

Active fur, fish, waterfowl and lumber trades soon developed around these natural resources. A thriving fish industry was present through the first half of the eighteenth century. Salmon were particularly abundant in several of the tidal rivers. Salted alewives were shipped to Boston. Other fish species harvested in the estuary and nearby coastal waters were cod, haddock, bass, shad, mackerel, herring, flounder and sturgeon. The cured fish was then exported to other American coastal cities, Canada and Europe.[4]

Commercial fishing was not limited to the estuary and near shore. The Gulf of Maine, which includes the nutrient-rich Georges Bank, provided what seemed like an endless supply of Atlantic cod – the most abundant and important groundfish along the Atlantic coast. Haddock, pollock, and flatfish, such as flounder, were also common.[5]

Much of this early fishing occurred out of the Isles of Shoals - a group of small islands and tidal ledges situated approximately 6 miles off the coast straddling the border of the states of Maine and New Hampshire. The Isles of Shoals were named by English explorer Captain John Smith after sighting them in 1614. According to his account, fewer than two dozen men could hook 60,000 fish in a month. By 1623, the islands had become a valuable fishing base.[6]

Once the early settlers had cleared the land to plant food crops and the demand for cordwood and lumber increased exponentially, the forests quickly became another resource exploited for profit. For thousands of years there were giant pine trees that stood 250 feet and higher. It was 1634 when the first shipment of tall pines arrived in England to be made into masts for the ships of the King's Navy. The King of England wanted the best ones saved as masts and were marked with the King's Broad Arrow.[7]

As the demand for lumber grew, sawmills were powered by the tidal waters. By 1700, an estimated 90 sawmills were in operation. The raw wood was then transported along the waterways to local shipyards for shipbuilding and for export to other places. The sawdust from these sawmills presented an early disposal problem as it smothered finfish spawning beds and buried oyster beds. For each 1,000 feet of lumber cut, approximately 40 bushels of sawdust were produced and dumped into the estuary. By 1750, one local merchant remarked the Atlantic salmon were no longer returning to the Piscataqua River like they did in the past.[8]

The massive clear-cutting of the land also led to widespread erosion. The constant flow of sediment altered water depths throughout the estuary. Newmarket is a town located on the Lamprey River some 12 miles from the mouth of the estuary. At one time, four-masted schooners loaded with coal could sail up to the town dock.[9] The health of the estuary was also on a downward path as excessive amounts of sediment choked eelgrass and oyster beds.

As the forests disappeared, manufacturing began to take hold. These trades included ale breweries and mills that made everything from cloth and woolen goods to gunpowder and snuff. The contaminated waste was then dumped into the rivers or pits along the shore. Disposing of polluted waste into the water was a common practice for other emerging industries. Newmarket was also home to one of the earliest iron works in the nation. Opened in 1719, it exploited "bog iron" dug from the estuary in the marshes and tidal channels. These impure iron deposits were used to produce tools and other metal products.[10]

Another valuable natural resource found in the estuary was blue marine clay, which was ideally suited for making bricks. By the late 1800s, over 40 brickyards were churning out thousands of bricks that were used in the construction of houses, mills and factories throughout New England. Many of the finest homes on Beacon Street in Boston were built with bricks from Great Bay.

The brickyard kilns burned up to 30,000 cords of wood a year, leading to the cutting of massive tree lots (a cord of wood is 128 cubic feet). "However, since the clay was a limited resource, the clay banks were eventually exhausted closing down the brickyards. Extraction of the blue clay resulted in permanent modification of the estuarine shoreline."[11]

Other resources were being exhausted as well. By the 1850s, the advent of efficient fishing gear accelerated the taking of cod when fishermen began to set longlines. Better gear led to elevated catches (called landings). In 1870, over a million pounds of cod had been recorded at one wharf in Portsmouth from just a winter's harvest. Cod landings for the entire Gulf of Maine in the same year were over 145 million pounds.[12]

By 1902, landings had fallen to approximately 56 million pounds. By the late 1930s when most fishing was done by draggers, total landings of cod dropped to around 22 million pounds. As we move into the 21st century, landings in 2007 were less than 9 million pounds. In a span of not even 140 years, cod landings in the Gulf fell from 145 million to a mere 9 million pounds.[13]

As the wilderness was gradually transformed into a domesticated rural landscape, subsistence and commercial harvesting significantly reduced not just cod but other fish, waterfowl and game populations. As a result, the self-sufficient settlers of earlier times could no longer feed themselves and had to resort to importing many of their food staples.

In their 2012 draft comprehensive management plan, the Great Bay National Wildlife Refuge under the U.S. Fish and Wildlife Service, noted the following wildlife impacts across the region:

"Many wildlife species declined because of habitat loss (e.g., forest clearing), bounty and market hunting, millinery trade (for feathers to use in hats), and natural history specimen collecting. The millinery trade in the late 1800s, and hunting and egg collecting (for food and bait) decimated Arctic, common, and roseate tern populations in the Gulf of Maine. Mountain lion, gray wolf, elk, and caribou were extirpated from the area by the mid-1800s or early 1900s and have not recolonized the region. The heath hen, passenger pigeon, great auk, Labrador duck, and sea mink became extinct at the hand of humans."[14]

The hunting of waterfowl was a major pursuit in the estuary during the 1800s. Market gunners filled the skies with rounds of shot from what were known as punt guns, an extremely heavy shotgun used in the nineteenth and early twentieth centuries for shooting large numbers of waterfowl for commercial harvesting operations. A single shot could kill over 50 waterfowl sitting on the water's surface. Because of the sizeable recoil and weight of the guns, they were mounted on the "punts" – a small flat-bottomed skiff boat used for hunting.[15]

"The term 'used for duck hunting' isn't the right expression for aiming this piece of artillery in the general direction of a flock of ducks, firing, and spending the rest of the day picking up the carcasses. The mass hunting of waterfowl to supply commercial markets with meat became a widely accepted practice. In addition to the market for food, women's fashion in the mid-1800s added a major demand for feathers to adorn hats."[16]

As the estuary's bounty continued to dwindle, the region turned to manufacturing to support its growing population. Large mill complexes were constructed along the shores of the tidal rivers. Dover, New

Hampshire, on the Cocheco River – a major tributary in the estuary – boomed in the first part of the nineteenth century. In the decade between 1820 and 1830, Dover's population almost doubled from about 2,870 to 5,450 as workers were drawn to the multiple cotton mills that were built along the river. Mills were built in other towns within the estuary, dramatically altering the many riverfronts. By "common consent," these mills released industrial waste and other pollutants that contaminated the estuarine ecosystem.[17]

Tanneries along the tidal tributaries were another industry that became established providing leather for shoes, saddles and other products important to the region's economy. At first, tanners relied on tannin from tree bark to process the hides before switching to a chemical tanning process that produced chrome sludge and acid solution wastes that were discharged into the waterways. Natural plant dyes were replaced by chemicals using arsenic and chromium.[18]

Human settlements and activities brought about other changes as well. While timbering and agriculture changed the watershed's landscape, threats to human health grew as the estuary became a dumping ground for raw sewage. By the 1950s, Great Bay was no longer seen as a valuable natural resource. As factories closed, the larger mill towns fell into disrepair. Only with the addition of sewage treatment plants beginning in the 1960s did water quality finally begin to improve.

For most of the past 50 years, New Hampshire has been the fastest growing state in the northeast. With its easy access to metropolitan Boston, much of this growth has been concentrated within the Great Bay watershed. Between 1980 and 2008, the average population size of the 45 New Hampshire municipalities in the Great Bay watershed increased by 83 percent. While this growth has slowed during the past ten years, the renewed interest in the Great Bay as a place to live and work has led to new challenges.[19]

The most significant threat came in the fall of 1973 when Aristotle Onassis proposed to build a large oil refinery on Durham Point, an area that features wide expanses of freshwater wetlands that drain into the estuary. The citizens of Durham, New Hampshire, rallied against the project and it was eventually defeated in 1974. This close call set in motion efforts to protect the area from future development. In 1989, the National Oceanic and Atmospheric Administration (NOAA) designated Great Bay as an estuary of national importance and, in partnership with the State of New Hampshire Fish and Game Department, created the Great Bay National Estuarine Research Reserve.[20]

While much of the shoreline around Great Bay is now protected, nearby commercial and industrial development created a rise in the amount of impervious surface such as roads and parking lots in the Great Bay watershed. An analysis by the Piscataqua Region Estuaries Partnership (PREP) determined that the coverage of impervious surfaces in the watershed (NH towns only) increased from 29,914 acres in 1990 to 50,934 acres in 2005.

As this rate continues to outpace population growth, it exacerbates the amount of pollution that flows into the estuary due to runoff (e.g. "non-point" sources such as dog waste, automobile fluids, and lawn fertilizers often associated with stormwater runoff).[21] This is the same type of sprawl development found in densely-populated urban areas.

Despite the federal and state protections now in place, the estuary's future remains uncertain. There are no more "giant" trees. Native oyster populations are only a fraction of what they once were due to the introduction of disease. Eelgrass beds are dying off from excessive nitrogen due to pollution, which could lead to a collapse of Great Bay's intertwined food webs; regional cod populations will likely never return to their historical levels. Stricter local and state regulations to limit non-point sources of pollution are needed to ensure a cleaner and healthier estuary.

Why is the history of man's impacts on Great Bay relevant today? For one simple reason – it is a story that has been and continues to be repeated, a thousand times in a thousand places across our nation. While the details may differ, the long-lasting effects are the same and ultimately threaten our very existence. It is a story of exploitation and extraction leading to depletion and potential collapse.

If a country is born out of easy access to an abundance of natural resources, and prospers and expands by exploiting these same resources over hundreds of years, there will be a breaking point. All the sea walls in the world cannot stop a massive rise in sea level. We might be able to partially overcome the harm that has already occurred by switching to a more sustainable economy that is in harmony with the environment. These are the challenges we must face sooner rather than later.

A Fish in Peril

NOAA Fisheries, 2018: A century ago, streams in coastal New England teemed each spring with small silvery fish called rainbow smelt. By the millions, rainbow smelt swam from the ocean into rivers and brooks, spawned, and then returned to sea. They were so plentiful farmers caught them by the barrelful and had enough to eat, use as bait, and even spread on their fields as fertilizer.

In a springtime ritual, adults and children went to their local streams and caught great quantities of the small fish. Prized as one of the best-tasting fried fish, smelt were brought home for dinner, sold locally, and shipped to distant markets. Many animals—seals, striped bass, codfish, great blue herons, and others—feasted on rainbow smelt during the springtime bonanza. Although small in size, this fish played a big role in the ecosystem and economy.

Now rainbow smelt are declining, even in streams that once hosted abundant runs each spring. In many places, it would be difficult to fill a single barrel with rainbow smelt. The species has largely disappeared from the southern part of its geographic range, and its numbers along the coast of the Gulf of Maine have dropped dramatically. Reliable data on population size are not available, but Maine fishery data show that rainbow smelt landings have dropped significantly since the 1800s. While a decrease in fishing may contribute to the decline in landings, the overall trend is clear: rainbow smelt are in trouble. Recognizing the plight of the rainbow smelt, the U.S. government listed it in 2004 as a federal Species of Concern.[22]

While other saltwater species are also in decline, over 90 percent of the nearly 500 managed fish stocks in the U.S. are sustainable according to the NOAA's 2018 status report to Congress. This brings the total number of rebuilt U.S. marine fish stocks to 45 since the year 2000. In part, this success is the result of fishing restrictions and fewer commercial fishing boats.[23]

Chapter Two

The Wildlife We Will Never Know

"If you pluck a chicken one feather at a time nobody notices."

- Benito Mussolini -

America was once blessed with an abundance of wildlife. The lower 48 states – an area of nearly three million square miles – supported some of the richest fish and wildlife habitat on Earth. Wildlife was so abundant that no one could comprehend any single species ever disappearing.

The following description was published in 2012 written by the Virginia Department of Game and Inland Fisheries in a report about the legacy of America's wildlife:

> "By the time the first Transcontinental railway system broke open the West in 1869, vast herds of 100 million bison and 40 million pronghorn antelope pounding across the plains had vanished. An estimated 60 million beavers had been reduced to 100,000. There were once 30 to 40 million passenger pigeons, so dense in numbers that reports said it took literally hours for the skies to clear during their migrations, only to totally disappear.
>
> Waterfowl populations had plummeted. Swamps had been drained, prime habitat converted to agriculture, and market hunting continued unabated. Women in America and in Europe were parading the street in hats festooned with the feathers of egrets, herons

and 40 varieties of native birds. They would soon be wearing the entire bodies of birds on their heads. We were plucking America bare. Nevertheless, most Americans at the time were not storming the Capitol, demanding conservation reform from their legislatures. Rather, they were toasting their good fortune built on the incalculable wealth of their land's rich soil, their free access to the silver and gold veins to be mined just under America's skin, and the seemingly limitless forests thrown over the country's mountains and lowlands like a cloak hiding a treasure of wildlife.

America was just too vast, too fabulously abundant a landscape to succumb to the pinprick of mere mortals – or so we believed. We couldn't have been more wrong. It was a matter of taking too much with too little knowledge of the consequences – and far too little restraint. From New York to California, from North Dakota to Florida, we all were to blame."[1]

As noted elsewhere in the article, "We simply did not understand the intricate workings of the natural systems we were destroying. We did not understand predator/prey relationships, or habitat or range requirements. We did not understand the interrelatedness of all living things."[2]

The American bison, more commonly known as the buffalo, once roamed North America's vast grasslands that stretched from the Gulf of Mexico to Alaska and along much of the Atlantic Seaboard as far north as New York. While Native Americans lived in harmony with the buffalo, the white men who followed nearly hunted them out of existence. In addition to the commercial slaughter of the nineteenth century, the introduction of bovine diseases took their toll as well. It is estimated the buffalo population exceeded 60 million before the hunters arrived; at its lowest point, the species was down to a mere 541 animals. Thanks to recent recovery efforts, the buffalo survives today with its population closer to 31,000.[3]

Many of us learned about the plight of the buffalo in school; some of us were taught about the cruel demise of the passenger pigeon. However, few people know about the other bird species that have gone extinct. Once the only parrot species native to the eastern U.S., Carolina parakeets had the unfortunate habit of remaining beside injured or dead flock members, making them easy targets for hunters. "Although flocks were still occasionally observed in the early 1900s, they had disappeared by 1918. The last captive Carolina parakeet died at the Cincinnati Zoo – in the same cage where the last passenger pigeon had died four years earlier."[4]

Heath hens, native to the northeast U.S., were extremely common in historical times. A member of the grouse family, the hens were an important food source for folks with limited means. Although New York passed legislation back in 1791 protecting the species, they continued to be hunted. By the mid-1800s, they could only be found on Martha's Vineyard in Massachusetts. Within 50 years, poaching, disease and feral cats led to their near demise. A fire at a preserve killed off most of the only remaining population. The last surviving heath hen, Booming Ben, died in 1932.[5]

The eastern elk was a subspecies (or distinct population) of elk that inhabited the northern and eastern parts of the U.S., and southern Canada. The last eastern elk was shot in Pennsylvania on September 1, 1877.[6]

The ivory-billed woodpecker, one of the largest woodpeckers in the world, was native to the virgin forests of the Southeastern U.S. Due to the wide-spread destruction of their original habitats, they have only been linked to bottom land swamp forests over the past 100 years as almost no forests today can maintain an ivory-billed woodpecker population. Because of habitat destruction and, to a lesser degree, hunting, the species is thought to be extinct. While there have been reports of limited sightings in this century, no universally-accepted evidence exists for the continued existence of this once beautiful bird.[7] Waterfowl, while not extinct, have been greatly reduced in their numbers. Early European settlers in America hunted waterfowl with great zeal, as the supply of waterfowl seemed unlimited in the coastal Atlantic regions. During the fall migrations, the skies would turn black with thousands of black ducks and many other species taking wing.

As more immigrants came to America starting in the nineteenth century, the need for more food supplies increased considerably. This is when market hunting began to thrive. Men would use wooden boats to go out into the bays hunting for ducks and geese. With the advent of punt guns – massive, boat-mounted shotguns that could fire a half-pound of lead shot at a time – hunters could slaughter dozens of birds with a single blast. Bringing home several wooden barrels of birds was not uncommon. Like Great Bay, places along the eastern seaboard such as Chesapeake Bay, Delaware Bay, and Barnaget Bay were hunted extensively.[8] This period of intense commercial waterfowl hunting is vividly depicted in James Michener's historical novel, *Chesapeake*.[9]

Here is a short summary of waterfowl hunting that occurred on Long Island, New York:

> "Long Island is located on the eastern flyway for waterfowl. At the turn of the nineteenth century, all first-class hotels and restaurants served game dinners. Many local hunters supplemented their meager income by market gunning. Hunting ducks for fancy New York restaurants was just one way to survive.
>
> This wholesale slaughter of waterfowl took place from around 1840 until 1918 when a new conservation law went into effect preventing the practice of market gunning. The numbers killed were astounding. In the 1800s, Captain Wilbur Corwin of Bellport and one other gunner

killed 640 ducks in one day according to his written log."[10]

Fish populations have suffered much the same fate as their terrestrial brethren. Commercially-important chinook salmon in the Pacific Northwest, also known as king salmon, are estimated to be ten percent of their historic numbers, with some local populations much lower. The factors contributing to their decline include dams, logging, agriculture, over fishing and climate change.

Bob Strauss, author of *A Field Guide to the Dinosaurs of North America*, wrote about recently extinct fish in the U.S. These include:

> "Blackfin cisco, a 'salmonid' fish that is closely related to salmon and trout, were once plentiful in the Great Lakes. They succumbed to a combination of overfishing and predation by not one, but three, invasive species (the alewife, the rainbow smelt, and a genus of sea lamprey). The blackfin cisco didn't disappear from the Great Lakes all at once: the last attested Lake Huron sighting was in 1960, the last Lake Michigan sighting in 1969, and the last known sighting of all (near Thunder Bay, Ontario) in 2006.
>
> Also known as the blue pike, the blue walleye was fished out of the Great Lakes by the bucket load from the late nineteenth century to the middle twentieth, the last known specimen being sighted in the early 1980s. It was not only overfishing that led to the blue walleye's demise; we can also blame the rainbow smelt which were introduced from landlocked populations, and industrial pollution from surrounding factories.
>
> Compared to other species, the thicktail chub lived in a relatively unappealing habitat: the marshes, lowlands, and weed-choked backwaters of California's Central Valley. As recently as 1900, the small, minnow-sized thicktail chub was one of the most common fish

in the Sacramento River and San Francisco Bay, and it helped to nourish central California's Native American population. Sadly, this fish was doomed both by overfishing (to service the burgeoning population of San Francisco) and the conversion of its habitat for agriculture; the last attested sighting was in the late 1950s."[11]

These species represent just a small slice of the legacy that our ancestors left behind. Today, far more species are on the brink of extinction. People will inevitably ask: can we survive without thicktail chubs or the ivory-billed woodpecker? On the grand scale, of course humans can endure the loss of these species. We have already shown it is possible.

But what happens when we start to lose species at an alarming rate such as the 1,300-bird species at risk, according to BirdLife International? What happens when there are no more bees to pollinate our crops? What happens when our oceans are bare and there are no more fish to feed a growing population? Just like the game Jenga, if you remove too many blocks the whole structure collapses. Mussolini had it right. No one is looking out for the whole chicken.

Here are two different perspectives, one from the last century and one from this century. Both offer a disturbing trend about the past and future plight of wildlife.

Food, Fashion, Scapegoating and The Origins of Avian Conservation: An Excerpt From "Taking Flight"

Birds are the one type of wildlife that people encounter on an everyday basis, watching their flight and listening to their song. The relationship between humans and birds goes back millennia, with the winged animals serving as a source of veneration, fascination and sustenance.

In Wisconsin and around the Midwest, birds were central to numerous Native American cultures, and were one focus of a nascent movement of naturalists cataloging the world around them. Birds were omnipresent, but over the course of just a few decades at the end of the nineteenth century, millions upon millions were killed in a spree of hunting for food and feathers for stylish hats. As exemplified by the extinction of the passenger pigeon, which had the largest nesting on record in Wisconsin in 1871, commercial markets for game bird meat and plumage in the burgeoning industrial centers of the Great Lakes and Northeast spurred professional hunters to harvest a variety of species up to and past the point of eradication.

Bird populations began to tumble under pressure from market gunners, sport hunters and habitat loss from draining wetlands for farming. Conservation measures first appeared in the Midwest when hunting licenses were mandated late in the nineteenth century. The first states in the region to require licenses were Arkansas and Missouri (in 1875 and 1877), but these applied only to nonresidents. The passage of the Lacey Act of 1900 by Congress was designed to prohibit trade in wildlife and plants that have been illegally taken, possessed or sold.

Then, in 1897, William Hornaday of the New York Zoological Society collected nearly 200 questionnaires from observers around the country and concluded that, nationwide, nearly half of all American birds had perished since 1882. Fifteen years later, in 1912, Hornaday performed another survey, which showed that 25 bird species had become extinct in at least one

Midwestern state where they had once been common. Three – the Carolina parakeet, passenger pigeon, and whooping crane – were entirely gone from the region.

Midwestern hunters killed 2.8 million game birds and waterfowl annually between 1878 and 1918, or 112 million birds in all. But Hornaday's observers suggested that not market gunners but sportsmen and plume collectors were the chief cause of population declines. Assuming sportsmen contributed as much to the slaughter as market hunters did and that plume hunters killed half as much, the total would be more than 250 million birds killed in a single generation in the

Mississippi Flyway.[12]

The 1,300 Bird Species Facing Extinction Signal
Threats to Human Health

Birds are the planet's superheroes, built for survival. The ice of Antarctica doesn't faze them, nor does the heat of the tropics. They thrive in the desert, in swamps, on the open ocean, on sheer rock faces, on treeless tundra, atop airless mountaintops, and burrow into barren soil.

Some fly nonstop for days on end. With just the feathers on their backs, they crisscross the hemisphere, dodging hurricanes and predators along the way, arriving unerringly at a precise spot, year after year.

They have penetrated nearly every ecosystem on Earth and then tailored their own size, habits, and colors to each one, pollinating, dispersing seeds, controlling bugs, cleaning up carrion, and fertilizing plants.

But for all their superhero powers, birds are in trouble. Globally, one in eight – more than 1,300 species – are threatened with extinction, and the status of most of those is deteriorating according to BirdLife International. And many others from the tropics to the poles are in decline.

In North America's breadbasket, populations of grassland birds such as sweet-trilling meadowlarks are in free fall, along with those everywhere else on the planet. Graceful fliers like swifts and swallows that snap up insects on the wing are showing widespread declines in Europe and North America. Colonies of seabirds such as murres and puffins on the North Atlantic are vanishing, and so are shorebirds, including red knots in the Western Hemisphere.

While birds sing, they also speak. Much of their decline is driven by the loss of places to live and breed – their marshes, rivers, forests, and plains – or by diminished food supply. But more and more these days, the birds are telling us about new threats to the environment and potentially to human health in the coded language of biochemistry.

Through analysis of the inner workings of birds' cells,

scientists have been deciphering increasingly urgent signals from ecosystems around the world. Like the fabled canaries that miners once thrust into coal mines to check for poisonous gases, birds provide the starkest clues in the animal kingdom about whether humans, too, may be harmed by toxic substances. And they prophesy what might happen to us as the load of carbon-based, planet-warming gases in the atmosphere and oceans climbs ever higher.[13]

PBS News Hour, September 19, 2019: According to a new study that focused on sheer numbers rather than extinctions, North America's skies are lonelier and quieter as nearly three billion fewer wild birds soar in the air than in 1970. The bird population in the United States and Canada was probably around 10.1 billion nearly half a century ago as opposed to about 7.2 billion birds today. This represents a 29 percent drop across the continent.[14]

Chapter Three

The Robber Barons

"When men are pure, laws are useless; when men are corrupt, laws are broken."

-Benjamin Disraeli –

The expanding America of the post-Civil War era led to the rise of robber barons who demanded a free hand in the marketplace. Their promise was simple. They would benefit the country while enriching themselves. It is a story of an irresistible drive toward monopolies despite any public or governmental objections for these so-called "Captains of Industry" who were determined to transform our nation into a mass production economy. No longer would America be an agrarian society, instead we fulfilled our destiny – with these men who became the leaders of the exploding world-wide Industrial Revolution. It is known as the Gilded Age.

These entrepreneurs ruled our economic system from the end of the Civil War into the twentieth century, and Americans threw themselves into their new roles with a revolutionary zeal never seen before. The names of the leaders of this new economic boom are still familiar today mainly due to their philanthropic efforts and various institutions that bear their names, e.g. Cornelius Vanderbilt, John D. Rockefeller, Andrew Carnegie, J.P. Morgan and Andrew Mellon. They are also called robber barons – ruthlessly powerful U.S. industrialists who became wealthy by exploiting natural resources and corrupting legislators.[1]

Some of these men succeeded by producing a quality product in large quantities at a competitive price, while others used the power of government to outlast their competition. The latter succeeded by receiving subsidies or getting the government to cause harm to their competitors. By 1910, large U. S. companies dominated the world in oil, steel and railroads. In fact, so dominant that in 1911 the Supreme Court famously broke up John Rockefeller's Standard Oil.[2]

> "Until the Civil War there had been little competition among manufacturers. Most companies served the market in their own region, and new companies simply went where they were needed. But after the war the large new industries sold their products across the nation, creating true business competition for the first time in American history.
>
> This competition caused some major problems. When several manufacturers tried to sell the same product to the same market (population of buyers), the result was often a flooding of the market with more goods than consumers could buy. With too much product on the market, manufacturers lowered their prices to draw customers away from competitors. Sometimes they were forced to drop their prices below the cost of producing the goods. Unlike large companies that had strong financial backing, small companies could not survive a period with meager earnings and collapsed when prices fell too low."[3]

During the late 1860s, competing companies in some industries got together to form pools. These were agreements among rivals to share their profits or divide up territories to avoid adverse competition and maintain higher prices.

> "U.S. salt producers were among the first to create a successful pool, when competition had created a chaotic price war. After the formation of the Michigan Salt Association in 1869, the salt companies agreed to divide up their territories and were immediately able to double the price of salt. Other industries soon formed similar

pools. While this stabilized the market for the companies, the lack of competition in the market hurt consumers, who had to pay higher prices."[4]

New modes of transportation played a major role in facilitating the rapid growth of industry with railroads leading the way as the first transcontinental *rail line* was constructed in 1869. This new steel highway improved the lives of millions of city dwellers. By the 1890s, the U.S. was becoming an urban nation, and railroads supplied cities and towns with food, fuel, building materials, and access to markets. The simple presence of railroads could bring an economic prosperity to rural areas resembling that of large cities.

The railroads were owned by powerful men who embodied a new class of citizens – billionaires. They exploited Chinese laborers, destroyed Native American lands, fought with settlers over property rights and were subsidized via land grants. The construction of rail lines led to the fragmentation of ecosystems and habitats by creating physical barriers that prevented wildlife from reaching their usual habitats. For the first time, there was the threat of animal mortality due to collisions and human disturbance. Protecting the environment held no sway with a country anxious to expand westward.[5]

More significant than recognizing the environmental impacts, railroads provide a glimpse into how we feel about business and if political power should be aligned with economic power.

Perhaps no single industrialist of this era better symbolizes the melding of economic power with political influence than Andrew Mellon (1885-1937). Born into a wealthy family from Pittsburgh, Pennsylvania, Mellon established a vast business empire that included everything from banks to aluminum and railroads before transitioning into politics, serving as Secretary of Treasury (1921-1932) under three Presidents – Warren Harding, Calvin Coolidge and Herbert Hoover.[6]

Mellon was the first American to practice supply-side economics. He supported cuts on income tax rates for all groups and over time successfully got the rate cut on the wealthiest Americans, from 73 percent to 25 percent. At the same time, he helped persuade the Federal Reserve Board to lower interest rates in 1921 and 1924. Both these actions led to an economy that grew by leaps and bounds.[7]

As the economy continued to grow, some worried about the dangers posed by the booming market and other speculative ventures. By 1928, this forced the Federal Reserve to begin raising interest rates. Despite efforts to put the brakes on the economy, the higher rates did little to slow it down, leading (in part) to the unprecedented economic catastrophe known as the Great Depression.

The economic lessons from the 1920s remain significant today. It can be argued that our present economy faces the same potential pitfalls following a long period of economic growth. A collapse of a similar proportion will not only be a financial disaster, but the impact will cause added side effects just when we need to make major investments in the future. The potential lack of federal funding will make it more challenging to switch to green energy, to modernize the national electric grid, and to rebuild aging infrastructure such as subways, bridges and highways. Never mind the federal aid that will be needed to respond to weather-related disasters and other unforeseen catastrophes such as the Covid-19 pandemic that crippled the U.S. economy in 2020.

This is the legacy left by the robber barons. Instead of an evenly distributed, well-regulated economy designed for everyone's benefit, a winner-takes-all mindset was planted in the national psyche. How we move forward as a nation largely depends on whether we can embrace living in harmony with nature or continue to let the economy drive our attitudes and policies.

Were these titans of industry national icons or simply robbers? This debate rages on along with misleading attempts to rewrite history and portray the barons as America's most revered heroes. Their ethos stemmed from Sir Francis Bacon who lived in the late 1500s and is credited with developing the scientific method. Bacon believed that nature needed to be conquered and molded into something new by the hand of man. The robber barons enthusiastically embraced this archaic philosophy. They also left an indelible stain on our culture that lingers today. It is called political influence.

Control Over the Political Parties

The major industrialists and bankers firmly established their control over the political system, firmly entrenching the two-party system through which they would control both parties. Thus, "whether Democrats or Republicans won, national policy would not change in any important way." Labor struggles had continued and exacerbated throughout the decades following the Civil War. In 1893, another economic depression took place, and the country was again plunged into social upheaval.

The Supreme Court itself was firmly overtaken by the interests of the new elite. Shortly after the Fourteenth Amendment was added to the Constitution in 1868 to protect newly freed blacks, the Supreme Court began to develop it as a protection for corporations, as corporate lawyers argued that corporations were defined as legal "persons," and therefore they could not have their rights infringed upon as stipulated in the Fourteenth Amendment.[8]

The impact of the Court's preference to protect corporations is still being felt today. This subject will be discussed further in Chapter Sixteen: The Lawyer Economy.

Chapter Four

The Potato Fields Came Calling and the Rise of Suburbia

"Our national flower is the concrete cloverleaf."

-Lewis Munford –

Following the end of WWII, planned communities like Levittown on Long Island, New York sprang up across the country, welcoming returning veterans who were eligible for low interest, government-backed mortgages. Since very little suitable housing had been built during the Great Depression and World War II, the demand for affordable homes grew exponentially.

Located in Nassau County along the Hempstead Turnpike (see Introduction), an area that was once mostly potato fields, Levittown was named after the Levitt family who owned a real estate development company called Levitt & Sons. Built between 1947 and 1951, this planned community is widely regarded as the archetype for postwar suburbs throughout the country and William Levitt, who assumed control of Levitt & Sons in 1954, is considered the father of modern suburbia in the U.S.[1]

"The Levitts' homes were affordable, planted in a picture-perfect, carefully controlled community, and were equipped with futuristic stoves and television sets. The houses were simple, unpretentious, and most importantly to its inhabitants, affordable to both the white and blue-collar worker. And the Levitts took more than the homes themselves into consideration— they designed community streets along curvilinear patterns to create a graceful, un-urban grid-like feel, and directed cars going through the development to the outside of the community so Levittown would not be disturbed by noisy traffic."[2]

During WWII, like most industries during wartime, Levitt & Sons went to work for the U.S., building housing units for the U.S. Navy in Virginia. The invention of low-cost mass building techniques was required to build these units quickly and make a profit for the company. Following the War, the Levitts applied these same techniques to the construction of residential properties. Between 1946 and the early 1960s, they built three communities totaling more than 17,000 homes (in addition to Long Island, similar communities were built in New Jersey and Pennsylvania). At peak production, 30 houses were finished in a day and production barely kept up with demand. In a single day, they once signed 1,400 contracts for their homes.[3]

As the first and one of the largest mass-produced suburbs, Levittown quickly became a symbol of post-war suburbia. The simple, cookie-cutter homes were both affordable and offered what many residents felt to be a congenial community. While critics decried its homogeneity, blandness and racial exclusivity (initially non-whites were prohibited from leasing or buying homes in the development under the claim "it was the custom of the time"), people liked their new Levitt homes. They were glad to be far away from the grime and crowds of the city. They were living the American Dream.[4]

"The suburbs have clearly come to symbolize more than just collections of white picket-fenced houses outside the grimy city environs. Kenneth Jackson wrote in *Crabgrass Frontier*, 'Suburbia...is a manifestation of such fundamental characteristics of American society as conspicuous consumption, a reliance upon the private automobile, upward mobility, the separation of the family nuclear units, the widening division between work and leisure, and the tendency toward racial and economic exclusiveness.' To some, suburbia was a symbol of American can-do; to others, it was a symbol of conformity and exclusion. The story of Levittown captures both the hopeful and darker sides of the rise of the American suburbs."[5]

While this explosion in housing was occurring, Congress passed the Federal Highway Act of 1956 authorizing the construction of 40,000 miles of interstate controlled-access highway to crisscross the nation; the auto industry's lobbying efforts helped to get it approved. President Dwight Eisenhower, who championed the bill and signed it into law, stated: "Together, the united forces of our communication and transportation systems are dynamic elements in the very name we bear – the U.S. Without them, we would be a mere alliance of many separate parts."[6]

The original portion was completed in the early 1990s, although some urban routes were cancelled and never built. Since then, additional routes were added and the system now features over 48,000 miles of highway. In 2006, the cost of construction was estimated at about $425 billion. At the same time, the number of automobiles on the road has increased steadily since 1960. As more people drove cars, it led to a decline in passenger rail.[7]

This new network of roads that linked the nation triggered the rapid growth of suburban communities causing an upsurge in land values as well. As the population swelled, land values in some prime suburban neighborhoods increased as much as 3,000 percent. "Nearly two-thirds of all industrial construction during the 1950s was taking place outside cities; residential construction in the suburbs accounted for an astonishing 75 percent of total construction."[8]

The impacts from the growth and expansion of these new communities are significant. Like rail lines, the construction of inter-continental highways led to the fragmentation of ecosystems by again creating physical barriers that prevented wildlife from reaching their usual habitats. Historian Lewis Mumford predicted that Americans would regret "all the damage to our cities and our countryside this ill-conceived and preposterously unbalanced program will have wrought." No one was listening. Americans fell in love with their vehicles and it would change the shape of the landscape forever. Cars not only replaced rail service but influenced growth patterns within the cities. The old Streetcar lines all converged downtown, radiating outward from the heart of the city. "This centralizing orientation of the city ultimately was lost because of the ubiquity of cars and trucks, which pushed the suburban boundaries outward beyond the reach of the trolleys."[9]

The car was not just a mode of transportation. The interstate system provided access to places that had been hard to get to in the past. People loved that they could drive fast and not worry about traffic lights or intersections. The fact this road network was dependent on public financing in the forms of government road construction, tax subsidies to oil and gasoline producers, favorable treatment to automobile manufacturers, and a variety of public taxing and bonding plans was of little consequence.[10]

While enormous public investment went into accommodating automobiles, much less was devoted to mass transit. In 1945, buses and subways accounted for 35 percent of urban passenger miles; by 1965, they made up only five percent. Highway construction near cities displaced residents and divided neighborhoods, further hastening urban deterioration. These new suburbanites were now tied wholly to the automobile.[11]

Retail businesses soon followed the fragmentary development of suburbia, which led to the development of regional shopping centers. In 1956, the first enclosed, climate-controlled mall opened in Edina, Minnesota. The Southdale Shopping Center featured 72 stores, including two anchor stores, and shoppers had their choice of 5,000 free parking spaces. The developer's vision was to create a center of commerce and social life for local suburban residents. As it fueled suburban growth, the mall became a much-imitated model that offered a fresh approach to consumerism; approximately 1,500 enclosed malls were built in the U.S. between 1956 and 2005.[12] As trucks began to replace railroads as the preferred method of shipping goods, it dramatically changed the way our food was delivered and what we ate. In an article by the Independent Media Institute:

> "This new post-war suburban lifestyle was anchored by the supermarket. Stocked regularly by refrigerated trucks rolling into suburban towns, they made one-stop shopping just a short drive away. 'After the war, the popularity of refrigerators and automobiles for nearly every household kept feeding the [supermarket] model, so much so that free parking became a necessity at every supermarket,' wrote Ashley Ross in *Time Magazine*, adding that the supermarket was such a marvel that in 1957, during a visit with President Eisenhower, Queen Elizabeth and Prince Philip visited a Maryland grocery store for fifteen minutes to see what it was all about."[13]

Heavy industry and manufacturing also crept out along the new highways searching for low-priced land compared to urban centers. As trucking replaced freight trains, industrial parks blossomed around the transportation hubs of suburbia. These parks brought jobs with them making it even "more attractive to move to the 'burbs."[14]

> "We tend to imagine the 1950s as a tranquil decade, but in fact, Americans spent the years moving and searching. They moved physically, from the Northeast to the South and the West— California's population grew by 49 percent during the 1950s, Florida's by 79 percent. They moved from rural areas to cities and from cities to suburbs. By 1960, a third of the country's population lived in the 'burbs. We were also

well on the way to becoming a motorized society. During the 1950s, the number of cars in the U.S. nearly doubled from 39 million to 74 million."[15]

There was nothing wrong with people wanting to move to the suburbs. Our cities were over-crowded and dirty. WWII veterans and their families needed a place to live and prosper. The American way of life was bound to change after the Great Depression and a successful war effort. Upon closer introspection, however, this growth occurred with little regard to how we were fundamentally changing the history of the country. We accepted this new lifestyle with great aplomb and we continue to grow our communities using the same patterns of development.

As with every era, there were critics who recognized the enormous waste of resources that was starting to unfold:

> "Some point to the imaginative cars of the second half of the '50s—with their swooping decorative fins and sparkling chrome accessories—as classic examples of automobile design. Others are more critical of all the waste involved. Cars were becoming more aerodynamic before the 1950s, but with the advent of fins and lavish grilles, most cars of the decade only appeared streamlined. As cars became heavier and their engines more powerful, they required more and more gas to operate. Safety, efficiency and durability were all sacrificed on the altar of automobile fashion."[16]

Another critic, Wright Mills, wrote in *The Power Elite*, that Americans had lost autonomy to a small number of powerful decision-makers in business. Mills, who popularized the term the "New Left" in the U.S., believed power was shifting from the middle class to an elite social class and that the country would retain the character of a war economy even in peacetime to satisfy the elite's self-interests.[17]

As America continued to grow in the 1960s and beyond, some suburbs that grew too fast began to look like the urban areas left behind. People could now drive until they found an area with more affordable homes. This led to the phenomenon of pushing suburbs further and further away from the inner cities eventually causing metropolitan areas to bleed into one another.

> "Ultimately, metropolitan growth morphed into megalopolitan development with urbanization stretching for 200 miles in California from Santa Barbara to San Diego, with Houston, Texas engulfing more than 600 square miles, and with the nation's capital part of an urban matrix extending northward to New York City and southward to Richmond. In the late 1990s, Chicago accounted for only six percent of the land area of its metro region."[18]

The cost of sprawl and the required water lines, sewer lines, and roads created a huge financial burden. Because of the typical spread pattern of suburban housing and the greater distance between homes, public service costs became generally higher. Along with these costs existing infrastructure suffered, as most of the government's money set aside for community improvements went to paying for the new necessities in areas further out from the urban core. As a result, the government, to this day, will often forgo maintenance on previously-built infrastructure.[19]

Suburbanization and the spread of people living outside the city led to other negative impacts on the environment. Buildings, heavy machinery and vehicle traffic resulted in soil compaction and soil degradation. The rich top soil found in many suburban areas – often prime farmland – was stripped and distributed elsewhere. Increases in vehicle mileage and residential energy consumption were also important contributors to the degradation of air quality during the 1960s.

Unlike their fellow city dwellers, suburbanites found something else they loved almost as much as their vehicles – green lawns. This greatly increased water usage in suburban neighborhoods. At the same time, the presence of impervious surfaces – everything from roof tops to driveways and roads – disrupted the normal hydraulic and biogeochemical cycles (a process where chemical elements and simple substances are transferred between living systems and the environment).[20]

Widespread habitat loss wiped out native wildlife as only particularly adapted species could survive in this newly-created fragmented landscape. Often these were nuisance species that are still prevalent today in most suburban areas, e.g. squirrels, rodents and feral cats. Meanwhile, America's traditional wildlife were and are getting pushed to smaller and smaller areas. We now face the possible extinction of many of these iconic species.

Others recognized how the growth of suburbia would threaten nearby coastal areas. Anyone growing up on Long Island knows the beautiful beaches of the south shore. Formed by the glaciers, they stretch all the way from Brooklyn to the East End. Most of this shoreline – which is now Jones Beach and Fire Island – was protected through the inspiration of New York's master builder, Robert Moses. While many of his projects were controversial, he had the foresight to protect these barrier beaches which today are enjoyed by millions including the residents of Levittown. His indelible legacy now faces a new threat – storm damage and sea level rise due to climate change.[21]

The history of suburbia on Long Island revolves around the conversion of agricultural land to development and the long-forgotten farms, never mind the bountiful grasslands that existed before the first settlers arrived – a story that has been repeated a thousand times across the nation. It is not too late to change this pattern of development if we shift our focus away from the continuing march outward to reclaiming our abandoned cities and towns.

Perhaps the greatest social impact of suburbia is traffic congestion, which leads to commuters spending more and more time in their vehicles, as well as it being a major contributor to air pollution. In 2010, the U.S. Census Bureau reported that 76.6 percent of all Americans commuted alone by car; in 2017, this figure was 76.4 percent meaning there has been little change in commuter patterns over that period despite the increase in vehicles on the road. It is also worth noting the percent is higher for most rural states as they are more car dependent.[22]

As for today's suburbs, they have evolved from their earlier roots. The homes have become bigger, more luxuriant and modern. There are more appliances and power tools. "The suburbs themselves have expanded to cover a large majority of residential areas in the U.S.; more than 50 percent of the population reports living in the suburbs, as compared to about 25 percent in 1950. Today, unlike the 1950s, the suburbs are thought by many to be a dead-end destination.[23]

Living in the suburbs has in some ways become more of a mirage. While many Americans still dream of a larger home in the land of picket fences and lawn mowers, a recent study shows many suburbs are more expensive than urban centers. Of the fifteen costliest suburban areas to move to, Philadelphia's suburbs had the largest expense differential costing more than $13,850 per year to reside outside the city center.[24]

> "The deepest suburban money pit surrounds Philadelphia. That's right. Moving away from the city means you'd not only be farther away from juicy cheesesteaks, but you'll also spend over $1,154 per month in extra housing and child care expenses. That sounds like a lose-lose scenario. People looking to raise a family in this area will need to decide what's most important. Having less square footage to call your own in the city might be a downer, but paying $7,402 a year in housing instead of $19,439 a year might sweeten the deal a bit. That's a savings of over

$12,000 annually, available to Philadelphia's dedicated urbanites."[25]

Cities like New York, Chicago and San Francisco did not make the list, no doubt due to their high housing costs (Los Angeles was fifteenth). None the less, escaping urban areas in search of that suburban oasis may not make financial sense and only strengthens the argument to continue investing in the downtown areas of our decaying cities rather than paving over more of the landscape.

Every community is unique in its own way. This include the historic and ethnic neighborhoods in our cities. Groups like Main Street America offer community-based revitalization initiatives that are designed to create more attractive, safer and healthier places to live. Congress needs to earmark the necessary funding and offer tax incentives to support these efforts.[26]

We can make our cities and towns more livable by providing affordable housing and embracing renewable energy sources. Cities of the future will feature vertical gardens and modern rapid transit; our towns will bring shoppers back to main street. The path to a greener future begins from the inside out, not by expanding our footprint to undeveloped areas.

How Many Malls Are There in America?

The shopping mall has become a place of worship for many Americans. There are about 1,000 to 1,100 enclosed malls in the U.S. as of 2014. This number represents only a fraction of the 47,000 shopping centers of all types located in the country. Approximately 40 percent of U.S. malls target high-income shoppers.

A shopping mall is considered a regional mall if it contains two anchor stores, typically large department stores, and if its shoppers come from a 20-mile radius. In the U.S., there are about 350 "super-regional" malls that are even larger, serving shoppers within a 100-mile radius and featuring a minimum of five anchor stores. The largest mall in the U.S. is the Mall of America in Minneapolis, Minnesota. The Mall of America features 4.2 million square feet of shopping space and includes a 7-acre amusement park and a wedding chapel.

Since 2006, not a single new enclosed mall has been built, and many malls have closed or are predicted to do so in the future, as of 2014 (the one exception is the American Dream Mall as described in Chapter Twenty-Nine). One of the key elements in the reported death of the shopping mall is the ease of online shopping. Some estimates predict that fifteen percent of U.S. malls are likely to fail by 2024.[27]

Chapter Five

1980s – The Decade of Greed

"When the last tree has been cut down, the last
fish caught, the last river poisoned, only then
will we realize that one cannot eat money."

-Native American Proverb –

Following the tumultuous 1960s and 1970s, America
experienced a cultural shift. With the election of Ronald
Reagan in 1980, whose presidency spanned most of the
decade, the Republican party reinvented itself. In stark
contrast to the earlier interventionist policies – such as
U.S. involvement in Vietnam – the party turned its sights
on the growth of business and deregulation.

President Reagan's platform was based on cutting
taxes and reducing the size of government. This
naturally led to purging government services including
many of the environmental programs established just a
decade earlier. His actions gave rise to the phrase
"trickle-down **economics,**" which is a theory that states
economic benefits provided to upper income level
earners will benefit all societal members. Their extra
wealth will be put back into the economy, providing
wealth for lower income earners and creating jobs which
in turn grows the economy.

Whether trickle-down policies work is still open to
debate considering the recent tax cuts passed by
Congress in 2018. Reagan is also remembered for ending
the Cold War and, due to his enormous communication
skills, he altered the image of America. This in turn
radically changed how people saw themselves and
individualism became a tenet of the 1980s. Reagan's
appeal also stressed family values and a
conservative Judeo-Christian morality which still
prevails today.[1]

The acquisition of wealth would have a profound effect on how our country moved forward. The environment no longer was a priority as if we had checked that off our list of things to do. Expanding the economy became our measure of success.

This increased interest in economic growth allowed President Reagan to appoint James Watt as his Secretary of the Interior. Watt was far more interested in pro-development activities than protecting our natural resources. He sanctioned the leasing of massive tracts of federal land to coal mining companies, opened large sections of the outer continental shelf to offshore drillers, and supported widespread forestry and ranching activities with little or no emphasis on conservation. Watt once stated, "We will mine more, drill more, cut more timber." In 2008, *Time Magazine* named Watt among the ten worst cabinet members in modern history.[2]

Reagan did not believe his political standing would be damaged by downplaying environmental issues. Instead, the President imagined that he brought "a common-sense view to environmental issues that was widely shared by Americans" and he rarely thought about the environment in political terms.[3] He even went so far as to remove the solar panels that his predecessor Jimmy Carter had installed on the roof of the White House. These actions had a profound and long-lasting effect on U.S. policy.

Reagan rejected proposals to tackle acid rain finding them burdensome to industry and he would not approve budget expenditures by the EPA to address the problem, referring to it as "wasteful government spending." Like today's climate deniers, he questioned the scientific validity of acid rain and he subverted much of the EPA's authority to enforce regulations while questioning their legitimacy as an independent authority. These attacks eventually led to the mass resignation of EPA officials in 1983.[4] It was later discovered that the administration was releasing Superfund grants for cleaning up local toxic waste sites to enhance the election prospects of local officials aligned with the Republican Party.[5]

On another front, a movement that had started in the 1970s suddenly found a friend in the White House. Known as the "Sagebrush Rebellion," this was an effort to force major changes in the control and use of about 500 million acres of federal lands. A broadening of the decades-old state versus federal powers, the Sagebrush Rebels – a coalition of ranchers, sheepherders, miners, and other leaders of the wide-open West – wanted increased jurisdiction of the federally-owned lands in western states to be handed over to state and local authorities to promote economic growth.[6]

Then candidate Ronald Reagan declared himself a sagebrush rebel in an August 1980 speech in Salt Lake City, telling the crowd, "I happen to be one who cheers and supports the Sagebrush Rebellion. Count me in as a rebel." With the appointment of James Watt, the administration was successful in derailing some wilderness designation legislation, but little else was accomplished and the rebellion slowly faded away. However, the struggle persists today under a new name – the "wise use movement" – with organized groups leading the way promoting mineral extraction on federal lands and other pro-growth policies.[7]

This dramatic shift in public sentiment from responsibility for environmental protection has its roots in part due to the failures of the previous Carter Administration. Besides the poor economy, America had just experienced its first energy crisis.

The 1970s was a period when the U.S. and industrial countries faced substantial petroleum shortages – real and perceived – as well as inflated prices. The two worst crises were in 1973 and 1979, the latter a result of the Yom Kippur War and the Iranian Revolution which triggered interruptions in Middle Eastern oil exports. These events led to stagnant economic growth in many countries as oil prices surged.[8]

Upon taking office, Reagan lifted the price controls on oil and natural gas leading to a surge in supply and price reductions. Gasoline and home heating fuels were suddenly in abundance. This was in stark contrast to the earlier gasoline rationing, which limited buying it to every other day depending on the last number of your license plate. Whereas President Carter had told Americans to beat the gas crisis by riding their bicycles to work and to beat the oil shortage by wearing a sweater, President Reagan solved the problem in six months.[9]

The oil crisis of the 1970s revealed that Americans had no appetite for long gas lines and higher fuel prices. They welcomed Reagan's policies and we became more amenable to increasing domestic supplies. These events still reverberate today and remain part of the American psyche as we strive towards energy independence and security.

The 1980s also gave rise to a slew of financial crimes involving Wall Street that are well documented. As noted in Harvard Business Review's assessment of the decade, "Too many people made too much money too quickly or too many talented young people were lured by the glitter and intensity of the financial world at the expense of more quietly rewarding pursuits." Instead of public indignation, a great many Americans shared this fascination with money and the trappings of success.[10]

Takeovers and leveraged buyouts became more prevalent in the 1980s. This had a profound effect on the fabric of American life. Although charitable giving by individuals and corporations jumped dramatically, as pay for executives began to skyrocket, workers' wages stagnated – a trend that is pervasive today. As wages go down as a percent of the economy, it hurts the middle class and widens the divide between the wealthy and less fortunate members of society.[11] In a period of just 35 years, the wealth of the top 400 richest Americans has increased 29-fold since 1982, from 93 billion to 2.7 trillion according to the Forbes 400 in 2017.[12]

Warren Buffet, the billionaire investor and chairman of Berkshire Hathaway, wrote an opinion piece in *Time Magazine* in 2018 explaining what's wrong with America's economic system:

> "During this period, the tsunami of wealth didn't trickle down, it surged upward. The richest 0.1

percent of Americans own as much as the entire bottom 90 percent, and the wealthiest 10 percent own nearly 90 percent of stocks, according to data from DB Global Markets Research and the World Wealth and Income Database."[13]

Here is the reason the accumulation of wealth matters – economics is often the driving force behind political policy making. It explains why some policies are made and others never gain traction. Protecting the environment and dealing with climate greatly affects the bottom line. Corporate America would prefer to pass these costs on to others, i.e. the taxpayer. Just like ignoring infrastructure improvements and the national debt, those bills have now come due.

The 2007 Recession and Beyond

MarketWatch, January 5, 2018: Dubbed the "Decade of Greed," the 1980s was seen by many as one long consumption binge, fostered by the Reagan Administration and characterized by what political pundit Kevin Phillips called "conspicuous opulence." The evidence offered in support of this contention includes casual references to the jump in the sales of luxury automobiles, the number of MBAs, the number of get-rich books, and the number of Wall Street brokers who went to prison.

Renowned economist John Kenneth Galbraith, of course, won't let the decade die. It lives on, he says. How? In the recession. In a recent article titled "The Economic Hangover from a Binge of Greed," the venerable professor says it's time to cut through the excuses: "The present recession is not an autonomous, self-correction economic drama. It is the wholly predictable response to the speculative extravagances and insanities–and specific government policies–of the 1980s." The country's continuing problems could be blamed on a simple five-letter word: Greed.[14]

Chapter Six

The Menace of Coal

"It is difficult to get a man to understand something when his job depends on him not understanding it."

–Upton Sinclair —

America has a love affair with coal. It is the largest domestically-produced source of energy and coal generates a significant chunk of our nation's electricity.[1] While we first began digging for coal in the early 1800s in Virginia and Pennsylvania, its use in the U.S. goes back even further.

According to the web-based Encyclopedia of Economic and Business History:

> "Although coal had served as a major source of energy in Great Britain for centuries, British colonists had little use for North America's massive reserves of coal prior to American independence. With abundant supplies of wood, water and animal fuel, there was little need to use mineral fuel in seventeenth and eighteenth-century America. But as colonial cities along the eastern seaboard grew in population and in prestige, coal began to appear in American forges and furnaces. Most likely this coal was imported from Great Britain, but a small domestic trade developed in the bituminous (soft coal) fields outside of Richmond, Virginia and along the Monongahela River in Pennsylvania."[2]

Development of the coal industry goes hand in hand with the industrial revolution of the 1800s.

As cities along the East Coast grew, anthracite coal – often referred to as "stone" coal, which has the highest carbon content and the fewest impurities – became more plentiful than bituminous coal. The increased scarcity of wood, animal and waterpower only added to the demand.

In 1840, American miners produced 2.5 million tons of coal to serve these growing markets and by 1850 annual production rose to 8.4 million tons. Just prior to the Civil War, it reached twenty million tons for the first time and as the price per ton dropped due to increased production and competition, coal was the preferred energy source for manufacturing.[3]

The outbreak of the Civil War created more demand. Both sides along with the suppliers of military goods depended on coal to meet their energy needs. Railroad companies emerged from the Civil War as the most important purveyors in the nation's coal trade.[4]

By the 1880s, coal became the largest source of energy when it overtook wood. It provided more than half of the nation's energy from the 1880s to the 1940s, and from 1906 to 1920 provided more than three-quarters of US energy. It was not until the 1950s when coal was finally overtaken by petroleum.[5]

When evaluating the environmental impacts of burning coal, it is imperative to examine every part of the process beginning with extraction. The two primary methods are surface and underground mining:

> "Surface mining, including strip mining, open-pit mining and mountaintop removal mining, is a broad category of mining in which soil and rock overlying the mineral deposit (the overburden) are removed, in contrast to underground mining, in which the overlying rock is left in place, and the mineral is removed through shafts or tunnels."[6]

While surface mining is practiced throughout the world, the majority of surface coal occurs in North

America. It achieved wide acceptance throughout the twentieth century, and surface mines now produce most of the coal mined in the U.S. In most forms of surface mining, the top surface is first removed and the mineral removed using huge excavators.[7]

The most controversial type of surface mining is by mountaintop removal where a coal seam lies below the overlying rock – often hundreds of feet. After explosives are used to break up the rock layers, the waste is used to fill the hollows or valleys below creating a much flatter landscape.

Advocates of mountaintop removal point out "that once the areas are reclaimed as mandated by law (per the Surface Mining Control and Reclamation Act of 1977), the technique provides premium flat land suitable for many uses in a region where flat land is rare." They also maintain that the new growth on reclaimed mountaintop mined areas is better able to support populations of game animals as opposed to a diverse array of wildlife.[8]

Critics contend that "mountaintop removal is a disastrous practice that benefits a small number of corporations at the expense of local communities and the environment." An EPA environmental impact statement found that streams near valley fills sometimes may contain higher levels of minerals in the water and decreased aquatic biodiversity. Their findings also estimated that 724 miles of Appalachian streams were buried by valley fills from 1985 to 2001.[9]

Coal from most mountaintop removal activities is burned in power plants in the eastern U.S. One cannot judge the real outcome by simply saying flat land is preferred over mountaintops. Flat lands may not be local to where mountaintop mining occurs, but that does not justify the massive earth disturbances – over one million acres involving some 500 mountains. We cannot pretend to be better stewards of the planet than Mother Nature. But this is only the beginning of the story.

According to a 2010 report in the journal *Science*, mountaintop mining has caused numerous environmental problems which mitigation practices have not successfully addressed. For example, valley fills frequently bury headwater streams causing permanent loss of ecosystems. In addition, the destruction of large tracts of deciduous forests has threatened several endangered species and led to a loss of biodiversity.[10]

You also just do not dig coal out of the ground and send it along. It must be washed to separate out pieces of rock or soil. The more impurities a company can remove from coal, the higher its market value and the lower the transportation costs. And the washing of coal is a messy affair as it must be chemically treated before it is shipped for burning. The byproduct of this process is called coal slurry – a mix of water, coal dust and clay containing toxic heavy metals such as arsenic, mercury, lead and chromium. This slurry is often dumped in open impoundments that are built with mining debris which can become unstable.[11]

For people who live near these slurry ponds, exposure to disturbed streams, airborne toxins and dust puts them at a higher risk for potential health impacts. Published studies have shown the following:

> "A 2011 study found that counties in and near mountaintop mining areas had higher rates of birth defects for five out of six common types. These defect rates were more pronounced in the most recent period studied, suggesting the health effects of mountaintop mining-related air and water contamination may be cumulative. Another 2011 study found the odds for reporting cancer were twice as high in the mountaintop mining environment compared to the non-mining environment in ways not explained by age, sex, smoking, occupational exposure, or family cancer history. Adult rates of mortality, lung cancer, kidney disorders and chronic heart disease are increased."[12]

According to Appalachian Voices, a local watchdog group, while reclamation efforts are required by federal law, coal companies often receive waivers from state agencies with the idea that economic development will occur on the newly flattened land. "In reality, most sites receive little more than a spraying of exotic grass seed, and less than 3 percent of reclaimed mountaintop removal sites are used for economic development." A 2003 EPA impact statement found it may take hundreds of years for a forest to re-establish on the mine site.[13]

In 2006, the U.S. Department of Interior banned mountaintop coal mining from more than 500 miles of ridges in East Tennessee's Cumberland Mountains. This action designated nearly 75,000 acres of mountain ridges as unsuitable for surface mining including mountaintop removal. The National Mining Association called the decision "yet another unwarranted blow to our ability to responsibly utilize this nation's domestic resources."[14]

The coal industry argues that America needs the power and that all types of mining are necessary to meet the demand. Others disagree:

> "If mountaintop removal mining ended tomorrow, not a single American would lose power. Coal mined underground would be the most readily available alternative for utilities in the short term. But, to provide electricity and protect Appalachian communities, Appalachian Voices strongly advocates for investments in renewable energy sources, such as wind and solar, which would easily make up for the 3 percent of electricity currently provided by destroying mountains for coal."[15]

Underground mining causes its own litany of problems. Huge amounts of earth and rock are brought to the surface and these mining wastes can release toxins – mercury, arsenic, fluorine and selenium – when exposed to air and water. The dust generated during the mining process is also hazardous to human health and can lead to black lung disease.[16]

Other issues include what is known as acid mine drainage. This is where sulfuric acid forms and is released into local waterways and can seep into the groundwater. Methane gas is released as well during the mining process and although much of it is captured to be used as fuel, the rest escapes into the atmosphere. Methane, while less prevalent than carbon dioxide (CO_2) in the atmosphere, is a far more dangerous greenhouse gas – twenty times more potent (some estimates put this number much higher, up to 80 times more potent).[17]

Finally, there are the coal-seam mine fires. These can burn for centuries releasing extremely toxic smoke into the atmosphere. Of the hundreds of mine fires in the U.S. burning today, most are found in Pennsylvania including the Centralia mine fire that has been burning beneath the borough of Centralia since 1962. No one knows when or if it will ever burn itself out.[18]

The mining of coal is just the tip of the iceberg when it comes to looking at its impacts on our environment. From the mines, the transport of coal involves big trucks and railroads – both of which contribute to air pollution and carbon emissions. At the other end of the coal cycle, it is burned to create electricity generating huge quantities of ash.

> "The cheapest way for the utilities to dispose of this ash is to mix it with water and dump it into large, often unlined, 'ponds.' As with slurry impoundments, these ash ponds contain toxic materials that can leach into groundwater or seep through cracks in the dams and reach surface water. In addition, many of these ash ponds are above population centers. EPA has identified 25 coal ash dams in the Southeast as 'high hazard' impoundments, meaning that if they fail, there is a high likelihood of fatality."[19]

In December 2008, a dam in Kingston, Tennessee, did fail, spilling over one billion gallons of toxic coal ash – a volume over 100 times larger than the 1989 *Exxon Valdez* oil spill. In addition to destroying several homes, 5.4 million cubic yards of ash poured into two tributaries of the Tennessee River. It was the largest fly ash release in U.S. history.[20]

The impacts of the spill were further intensified when, as part of the clean-up response, much of the coal ash was transported to a landfill in Uniontown, Alabama. A predominantly African American, low-income community, residents worried about the health consequences.[21] This is just one example of environmental injustice where poor people shoulder a larger burden of the effects from exposure due to the improper disposal of hazardous materials.

Back in Kingston, the Tennessee Valley Authority that owned the spill site bought up 180 properties from private landowners. Some folks held out insisting the issue was not money, but they had nowhere else to go. TVA also pledged to convert to dry ash storage, a far safer option.[22] In the aftermath of the spill, Congress held hearings on the spill vowing to classify coal ash as a hazardous material. It never happened thanks in part to opposition from industry groups and some lawmakers.[23]

In 2014, EPA issued its first-ever regulations on coal ash, but declined to designate it as a hazardous waste. The rules also do not apply to power plants that are no longer in operation thereby allowing these existing ponds to remain unregulated. As some states crack down on the storage of coal ash, there is no excuse for EPA's dangerously weak coal ash rule which treats toxic waste loaded with carcinogens like "common household garbage."[24]

> "Companies will also now be required to perform regular inspections of the safety of their coal ash ponds, monitor their groundwater, and share the results of those inspections publicly. But the rule does not allow for any federal enforcement, instead leaving states and citizen lawsuits to ensure that companies are meeting those requirements."[26]

Nowhere is this more evident than in North Carolina where hundreds of residents near Duke Energy's fourteen coal ash storage sites were told in 2015 by state officials their well water was contaminated. Despite legislation passed in 2016 that required Duke Energy to provide permanent replacement water sources to affected residents, many have been surviving on bottled water for over two years. The threat is far from over as marginal progress has been made despite an October 2018 deadline.[26]

Duke Energy has been under the regulatory microscope since 2014 when 9,000 tons of coal ash spilled into the Dan River in Eden, North Carolina. The company later pled guilty to criminal negligence in its handling of coal ash at Eden and elsewhere, which resulted in substantial fines. The EPA then entered into an agreement with Duke to clean up the site.[27]

At the same time, North Carolina's Department of Environment Quality ordered Duke to evacuate the fourteen coal ash sites that were contaminating local water supplies; by 2019, nine of the slurry ponds were still in operation. That April, the State again told Duke to take immediate action to close them. Instead, Duke Energy had a better idea – fight the order in court. In August 2019, the administrative judge presiding over the case ruled the State has the power to order the company to force the closure of the nine remaining ash ponds. Duke plans to appeal the decision and continues threatening to pass the clean-up costs onto their ratepayers.[28]

Coal ash remains the second-largest form of waste generated in the U.S. with an estimated 130 million tons produced in 2014. There are some 1,400 coal-ash impoundments across the nation with the largest one – at 1,300 acres – located in Pennsylvania. Many of these are found in southeastern states such as Georgia, North Carolina and South Carolina, which are more prone to hurricanes. The EPA has found that up to 95 percent are leaking with the most recent spills occurring in North Carolina as the result of Hurricane Florence.[29]

Meanwhile, the Trump Administration continues its efforts to roll back the modest rules that went into effect in 2015. In July 2018, the EPA finalized the first set of revisions to the earlier rules. In a statement, the Agency said:

> "These amendments provide states and utilities much-needed flexibility in the management of coal ash, while ensuring human health and the environment are protected. Our actions mark a significant departure from the one-size-fits-all policies of the past and save tens of millions of dollars in regulatory costs."[30]

The presumption that states will use these new "flexibilities" to improve the management of coal ash impoundments is unlikely. It is rare for a state to have stricter guidelines – California is a notable exception – when it comes to environmental protections. Far more likely, this is code for less regulation.

As states face increasing budget restrictions, environmental enforcement is often one of the first things to be cut, especially when there is an effort to attract industry and increase the tax base – often at the expense of public health and safety. Even if we stopped burning coal today, we would be stuck with hundreds of ash disposal sites for decades to come.

Political interference is nothing new. In 2002, the Bush Administration changed the definition of "fill material" in the Clean Water Act to include toxic mining waste, which allowed coal companies to legally dump the debris into nearby valleys. These "valley fills" have buried more than 2,000 miles of headwater streams and polluted many more.[31] The purpose of the Clean Water Act is to protect water quality for all Americans, not to make exceptions for certain industries that enhance their profits.

The many air pollutants found in coal-burning emissions are also well documented, e.g. sulfur dioxide, nitrogen oxides, particulates, carbon dioxide, and fly ash. The release of these pollutants into the atmosphere contributes to everything from acid rain and smog to respiratory illnesses and lung disease. They are often transported from one state to another; the poor air quality in New England can be traced in part to the burning coal in the Midwest.

Fly ash contains contaminants like mercury, cadmium and arsenic. Whereas fly ash was once released into the air, it is now mostly captured by smokestack scrubbing devices and later stored with bottom ash near power plants or placed in landfills (bottom ash being heavier sinks to the bottom of the boiler). Scrubbers also do not remove carbon dioxide and there are no regulations limiting carbon dioxide emissions in the U.S.[32]

While it is possible to build new plants that burn coal with oxygen and capture the carbon dioxide – as shown by a new plant in Germany – most of the coal plants in the U.S. were built prior to 1990 and retrofitting these plants would be financially prohibitive. With so many aging plants in the U.S., this is our opportunity to switch to new sources of energy.

Instead, the Trump Administration is rolling back President Obama's visionary Clean Power Plan. First proposed by EPA in 2014, the plan was designed to reduce carbon emissions from power plants. In 2017, EPA Administrator Scott Pruitt announced the formal process to repeal the plan. Trump also has the backing of the U.S. Supreme Court which rejected to hear an appeal in October 2018 to keep the Clean Power Plan in place.[33]

So why do we need to use coal? A case can be made that Americans have never wanted to pay the real cost for their energy. Coal is a cheap source of electricity and we ignore the subsidies the coal industry enjoys. Only recently has output started to decline. From 2000 through 2014, U.S. production of coal was consistently producing 1,000 million tons annually. Since then production has slipped ten to twenty percent, although President Trump is trying to boost coal production nd reopen previously closed mines.[34]

One major reason coal has fallen out of favor with some utility companies lies with the onset of hydraulic fracturing – known as "fracking" – which has reduced the cost of natural gas. Utility companies have no trouble swapping one fossil fuel industry for another if it saves money. In addition, they are also under increasing pressure to clean up their emissions and natural gas is a much cleaner fuel compared to coal. The U.S. Energy Information Administration has documented this shift as shown in Figure 1.[35]

Figure 1
Coal is the Most-Used Electricity Generation Source in 18 States; Natural Gas in 16

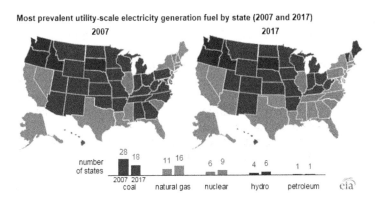

Most prevalent utility-scale electricity generation fuel by state (2007 and 2017)

Source: U.S. Energy Information Administration, Electric Power Monthly

In 2017, despite the decline in coal, the U.S. continued to rely on nuclear energy and plants that burn oil and natural gas for its electricity. At the same time, according to the U.S. Energy Association, the use of renewable energy sources was on the rise.

> "In 2019, U.S. annual energy consumption from renewable sources exceeded coal consumption for the first time since before 1885. This outcome mainly reflects the continued decline in the amount of coal used for electricity generation over the past decade as well as growth in renewable energy, mostly from wind and solar. Compared with 2018, coal

consumption in the U.S. decreased nearly fifteen percent, and total renewable energy consumption grew by one percent."[36]

It has been suggested that natural gas serves as a gateway to sustainable options like wind and solar. The U.S. Energy Department is also working to develop technologies that make coal cleaner and developing carbon capture, utilization and sequestration technologies – a process thatcaptures carbon dioxide emissions and either reuses or stores it.[37]

Developing these technologies is not only expensive – and heavily subsidized by federal tax dollars – but also fails to address the other impacts related to coal; i.e. the mining of coal, its transport and the disposal of coal ash. We need different priorities that focus on renewables. Coal had its run during the two past centuries; it has no place in the new millennium as a major fuel source and its use should be restricted to poorer nations.

The other part of the pro-coal agenda is to protect the jobs of coal miners. By the end of 2016, the coal-mining industry employed approximately 50,000 miners. This was below the previous low of 70,000 in 2003, and the lowest number of U.S. coal miners in at least 125 years.[38]

To put this number in perspective, Arby's employs around 80,000 employees. The country's largest private employer, Walmart, has some U.S. 1.4 million employees – providing 28 times as many jobs as coal mining.[39] Thousands of retail jobs – an estimated 250,000 at department stores alone – have been lost thanks to the success of Amazon and other internet retailers and yet no one is lobbying to keep these jobs.[40] It is called the cost of progress.

To provide potential employment for displaced coal workers, the *Harvard Business Review* discussed retraining them for solar photovoltaic employment to meet the growing demand in the solar industry. Their study found it would cost just five percent of the coal industry's revenue from a single year to provide coal workers with the required training. With the requisite skills, these workers will earn more than their miner counterparts.[41]

The Trump Administration is more interested in revitalizing the coal industry than retraining its miners to be part of the green new economy. Like it or not, the future viability of the coal industry is clear. As the profitability of U.S. coal-fired plants continues to decline, it will be up to the miners and their union to demand better education and training opportunities to ensure a smooth transition.

Of course, protection of jobs is not the driving force behind our dependence on coal. It is the powerful influence of the coal industry and their political alliances that forces our reliance on coal, as well as our own reluctance to do something different that might disrupt our daily lives. If the nation makes a commitment toward sustainable energy and away from fossils fuels, we can solve the ensuing aftereffects like retraining displaced workers. Every day, technology makes advances that can cost someone their job while creating new areas of employment elsewhere.

We cannot lose sight of the real objective – building a sustainable future for our grandchildren. Ending our dependence on coal for generating electricity is the first step toward combatting climate change. Do we have the political courage to do so?

Why Americans Need to Curtail Their Appetite for Electricity

Post Carbon Institute: The precise future is unknown, but the present is certain. Our current energy economy is destructive to nature and dangerous to democratic institutions, community life and human health. It is a toxic system that requires fundamental reform. The political, philosophical, economic and physical barriers to rebuilding the energy economy make the task difficult. But it is achievable.

Americans who have become accustomed to the idea that anyone should be able to use as much energy as they want, whenever they want, for whatever purpose (and it should be cheap!) will face a different reality in an energy-constrained future. In a sane world, we would not blow the tops of mountains in Appalachia to keep coal-burning power plants belching pollution so that office towers can leave the lights on all night. From motorized paper-towel dispensers and illuminated empty parking lots to the worst inefficiencies of suburban sprawl, there are worlds of energy-wasting products, activities, and living arrangements that can and should be abandoned. The sooner citizens voluntarily begin curtailment efforts, the more options remain open to transition toward a more durable, ecologically-sustainable energy system.42

Life and Death in the Coal Mines

Best of NPR, January 24, 2019: Black lung disease was declining in coal country, but then it came roaring back. As the biggest, purest coal deposits were mined-out in Appalachia, miners had to cut through more rock to get to what was left. That kicked up silica dust – which is twenty times more toxic than coal dust alone. By the mid-1990s, federal regulators knew the risks. They were urged to strengthen regulations. They did not do enough, then or since.

Even though more and more coal miners have been getting sick from exposure to silica dust, the federal agency monitoring the disease missed the epidemic. From 2011 to 2016, federal researchers counted nearly 100 cases of advanced black lung. In a 2016 investigation into the resurgence, NPRs Howard Berkes counted more than 2,000.

Federal regulations for silica dust in coal mines have not changed in decades. But after our reporting, Rep. Bobby Scott, D-Va., chair of the House Labor Committee, said he would hold congressional hearings on the black lung epidemic. "Congress has no choice but to step in," he said. 43

To date, Congress has failed to act. Instead, in April 2020 as Covid-19 spread across the nation, the major U.S. coal companies asked the federal government to cut the excise tax they pay to support black-lung miners. Citing the economic costs associated with the pandemic, the coal companies wanted the Labor Department to pick up more of the cost of the 25,000 retired miners supported by the Black Lung Disability Trust Fund. Their request has yet to be approved.[44]

Chapter Seven

1990s – The Decade of Missed Opportunities

"I do not intend that our natural resources shall be exploited by the few against the interests of the many."

- President Teddy Roosevelt -

After twelve years of Republican leadership under Presidents Reagan and Bush, the election of Bill Clinton in 1992 put a new focus on the environment. As the twentieth century was ending, many believed the Clinton Administration would set the tone for the next century.

During his eight years as President, Clinton sought to protect public health by supporting cleaner communities. This was accomplished in part by implementing the toughest standards ever on soot and smog, and strengthening the Safe Drinking Water Act. He signed the Food Quality Protection Act, which limited the use of pesticides in food grown in the U.S., and enabled the EPA to implement broad rules governing clean air and water along with many other pro-conservation measures.[1]

President Clinton also urged the federal government itself to become more environmentally friendly through a series of executive orders that encouraged federal agencies to purchase alternative fuel vehicles and energy-efficient computer equipment. Clinton felt strongly that the federal government had a responsibility to set an example for the rest of the country in terms of environmental policy. The Administration expanded the "Right to Know" law so Americans could learn more about environmental hazards in their communities by doubling the number of chemicals that companies must report.[2]

While the Clinton Administration's attempts to tackle climate change issues were broad in scope, many of his policies were short-lived due to a lack of support from Congress. On October 22, 1997, President Clinton gave a highly anticipated speech at the National Geographic Society outlining the administration's policy on climate change prior to the Kyoto negotiations on the U.N. Framework Convention on Climate Change (UNFCCC).

He said, "Today we have a clear responsibility and a golden opportunity to conquer one of the most important challenges of the 21st century – the challenge of climate change – with an environmentally sound and economically strong strategy, to achieve meaningful reductions in greenhouse gases in the U.S. and throughout the industrialized and the developing world."[3]   A law review by Golden Gate University summarized his record this way:

> "The Clinton Administration created numerous programs designed to reduce greenhouse gas emissions.   It embarked upon innovative voluntary programs with industry, including electric utilities and the transportation and buildings sectors, and established the Climate Change Technology Initiative (CCTI), a $6.3 billion, five-year package of spending and tax incentives designed to stimulate the use of energy efficient technologies in building, industrial processes, vehicles, and power generation."[4]

To stand apart as a world leader in addressing climate change, Clinton committed the U.S. to lowering their greenhouse gas emissions to 1990 levels – which accounted for 36 percent of worldwide emissions – by 2000. In 1993, he then signed an international treaty protecting rare and endangered species that followed a specific timetable to reduce the threat of global warming.[5]

Clinton signed the Kyoto Protocol treaty on behalf of the U.S. in 1997, pledging the country to a non-binding seven percent reduction of greenhouse gas emissions. He claimed that the agreement was "environmentally strong and economically sound," and expressed a desire for greater involvement in the treaty by developing nations.[6]

In his second term, the President announced a new Clean Air Partnership Fund that included tax incentives and investments as well as funding for environmental research of both natural and manmade changes to the climate. He also created incentives in support of clean energy.

> "The Climate Change Technology Initiative provided $4 billion in tax incentives over a five-year period. The tax credits applied to energy efficient homes and building equipment, implementation of solar energy systems, electric and hybrid vehicles, clean energy, and the power industry. It also provided funding for additional research and development on clean technology, especially in the transportation and other sectors."[7]

As for the Kyoto Protocol, it had to be ratified by the U.S. Senate to become formally binding. Unfortunately, there was no political will to do so. Senators and many others feared the required reductions would harm the economy of the U.S. and that the agreement unfairly penalized developed nations. Unless developing countries shared in mitigation commitments, which was not specified in the treaty's language, Senators would not support the agreement and ultimately sealed its fate.[8]

The Byrd–Hagel Resolution – sponsored by Senators Byrd (D-WV) and Chuck Hagel (R-NE) – stated that it was not the sense of the Senate that the U.S. should be a signatory to the Kyoto Protocol. On July 25, 1997, the resolution was passed unanimously with a vote of 95 to

0 and the agreement was never submitted to the Senate floor for ratification thus tarnishing President Clinton's record on climate change.[9]

By 2011, a total of 192 countries eventually signed and ratified the Kyoto Protocol. Even North Korea agreed to the treaty. The countries that did not ratify include Afghanistan, Southern Sudan, Taiwan, and the U.S. Since Southern Sudan did not even become an independent country until 2011, not signing on is understandable and Taiwan's legal status with China presented its own legal problems.[10]

Afghanistan, an active war zone, became the last country to sign on in 2013. This left the U.S. as the only country in the world with no justification for backing out of approving the agreement.[11] As reported by *Science* magazine in 2011:

> "So that leaves the United States as the biggest economy on the planet and the richest nation in history. The only country that is convinced it can afford to say, 'to hell with fighting climate change' at the expense of the 192 other nations with which it shares the Earth."[12]

When Clinton left office at the start of the new millennium, we had failed to meet his proposed target for greenhouse gas emissions. Instead, emissions rose steadily during his eight years in office. Emissions only began to decline in 2007. One major factor was how we generated electricity. As referenced earlier, 2007 was also the year where coal use began to fall as natural gas, nuclear, and hydroelectricity gained market share. Unfortunately, despite these positive developments, greenhouse gas emissions remained too high.

The promise of the Kyoto Protocol, which led to the Paris Agreement, was our best hope to avert an eventual climate disaster. Instead, we kicked that prospect to the curb. By not ratifying the Kyoto Protocol, the U.S. passed on the opportunity to become a world leader in combatting climate change. President Clinton, who worked so hard for its approval, was hopeful his efforts would carry over should Vice President Gore be elected President. That dream died with the election of George W. Bush in 2000.[13]

While Bush did express support for carbon restrictions during his race for the White House in 2000, he would later back away from those positions as President. He opposed the Kyoto treaty because it exempted 80 percent of the world, including China and India, from compliance. He believed this would cause serious harm to the U.S. economy.[14]

> "This policy reversal received a massive wave of criticism that was quickly picked up by the international media. Environmental groups blasted the White House, while almost all world leaders including China expressed their disappointment at Bush's decision."[15]

In response to this criticism, Bush stated: "I was responding to reality, and reality is the nation has got a real problem when it comes to energy." The Tyndall Centre called this "an overstatement used to cover up the big benefactors of this policy reversal, i.e., the U.S. oil and coal industry, which has a powerful lobby with the Administration and conservative Republican congressmen."[16]

Bush, the former Texas oil man, chose a different path where technology was to play a bigger role in cutting pollution and providing incentives for people to cut back, thereby allegedly reducing the intensity of greenhouse gases by eighteen percent over ten years. What really happened paints a much different picture of industry influence and the suppression of regulation.

> "Bush's do-nothing policy on global warming began almost as soon as he took office. By pursuing a carefully orchestrated policy of delay, the White House blocked even the most modest reforms and replaced them with token investments in futuristic solutions like hydrogen cars. 'It's a charade,' said Jeremy Symons, who

represented the EPA on Dick Cheney's energy task force, the industry-studded group that met in secret to craft the administration's energy policy."[17]

The National Environmental Policy Act (NEPA) of 1969 was the first major environmental law in the U.S. and is often called the "Magna Carta" of Federal environmental laws. NEPA is our basic national charter for protection of the environment. It establishes policy, sets goals and provides means for carrying out the policy. The law contains "action-forcing" provisions to make sure that federal agencies act according to the letter and spirit of the Act. It also created the Council on Environmental Quality (CEQ) in the Executive Office of the President to ensure that Federal agencies meet their obligations as required by statute.[18]

To underscore how the Bush Administration's policies protected America's energy industry, we only need to look at how the White House managed the Council. It quickly became Vice President Cheney's shadow EPA, with industry calling the shots. To head up the Council, Cheney installed James Connaughton, a former lobbyist for industrial polluters, who once worked to help General Electric and ARCO skirt responsibility for their Superfund waste sites.[19]

According to testimony taken by the U.S. House of Representatives, the Bush White House pressured American scientists to suppress discussion of global warming:

> "High-quality science was struggling to get out as the Bush administration pressured scientists to tailor their writings on global warming to fit the Bush Administration's skepticism, in some cases at the behest of an ex-oil industry lobbyist. Nearly half of all respondents perceived or personally experienced pressure to eliminate the words 'climate change,' 'global warming' or other similar terms from a variety of communications."[20]

Christine Todd Whitman, who had been appointed by President Bush to lead the EPA, later described the exit of Kyoto as "the equivalent to 'flipping the bird,' frankly, to the rest of theworld."[21] Vice President Cheney's insistence on a new EPA rule easing air pollution controls and allowing power plants to make major alterations without installing costly new pollution controls led to her resignation in 2003. A federal court eventually overturned these changes on the grounds it violated the Clean Air Act.[22]

Following eight years of the Bush Administration's attempts to minimize climate change science, candidate Barack Obama pledged to "make polluters pay for overheating our shared atmosphere, leveraging the power of the market to drive change." He endorsed cutting emissions 80 percent by 2050, as called for by the prevailing science. However, his Administration endured a pattern of obstructionism that persisted for most of his Presidency, derailing any real progress toward reversing the policies of the previous Administration.[23]

When the Democrats controlled Congress during his first two years, Obama secured federal funding for renewable energy, sparking renewed interest in wind and solar power. While he was a strong proponent of vehicle fuel efficiency, his administration also pursued an energy policy that made the U.S. the world's leading producer of oil and gas. While the country viewed energy security as a good thing, it did little to reduce our reliance on fossil fuels.[24]

One clear victory for the President occurred in 2014 when the U.S. and China signed a joint statement committing both countries to cutting emissions. Since the Kyoto talks, it was always a bone of contention that China's commitments to reduce emissions were voluntary under the treaty. Obama planned to achieve our reductions through his Clean Power Plan, which focused on reducing emissions 32 percent below 2005 levels by 2030 from coal-burning power plants.[25]

Republicans immediately assailed the plan as an attack on coal that would lead to higher energy costs for Americans, a message that candidate Trump championed in his 2016 Presidential race. More than two dozen states, industry representatives and others sued the EPA when the plan came out, claiming that it went far beyond what existing law allowed. One of those states was Oklahoma, where Scott Pruitt, the Attorney General, had previously sued the EPA multiple times over environmental regulations. The U.S. Supreme Court consequently ordered the EPA to halt enforcement of the plan until the case was settled.[26]

Following his election in 2016, President Trump then appointed Pruitt as head of the EPA while making it clear that the U.S. had no intention of meeting the commitments his predecessor had made to curb planet-warming carbon dioxide pollution. He then directed the EPA to withdraw and rewrite the Clean Power Plan rule. After Pruitt approved the final proposal that would lead to the repeal of the Clean Power Plan, the U.S. Supreme Court issued a 5-4 ruling in 2018 blocking any attempt to appeal the Trump Administration's decision to overturn the Clean Power Plan.[27]

Withdrawing the U.S. from the Paris Agreement was another top priority for the Trump Administration. In 2015, the nations of the world met in Paris to draft a new climate agreement within the United Nations Framework Convention on Climate Change (UNFCCC). The goal of the Paris Agreement – a critical breakthrough – is to keep the increase in global average temperature from 1.5° to 2°C above pre-industrial levels starting in 2020. Each country must determine, plan, and regularly report on their progress. As of November 2018, 195 UNFCCC members have signed the agreement.[28]

Many have criticized the agreement claiming it does not go far enough in reducing emissions and it is full of promises with no binding enforcement mechanism. None the less, when Obama left office in January 2017, the U.S. was committed to fulfilling its responsibility to reduce emissions. That position quickly changed once President Trump took office.[29]

> "In a televised announcement from the White House Rose Garden on June 1, 2017, Trump said, 'In order to fulfill my solemn duty to protect the United States and its citizens, the United States will withdraw from the Paris climate accord,' adding 'The bottom line is that the Paris accord is very unfair at the highest level to the United States.' He claimed that the agreement, if implemented, would cost the United States $3 trillion in lost GDP and 6.5 million jobs. He added that it would undermine our economy, hamstring our workers, and effectively decapitate our coal industry."[30]

In his withdrawal speech, President Trump stated, "I was elected to represent the citizens of Pittsburgh, not Paris." The incumbent Mayor of Pittsburgh, Bill Peduto, acknowledged on Twitter with a reminder that his city had supported Hillary Clinton for president, wrote: "As the Mayor of Pittsburgh, I can assure you that we will follow the guidelines of the Paris Agreement for our people, our economy and future."[31]

In an immediate response to the withdrawal, the governors of California, New York and Washington founded the United States Climate Alliance, pledging to uphold the Paris Agreement within their borders. By the evening of June 1, 2017, eight other states had declared their desire to join the Alliance.[32]

On August 4, 2017, the Trump Administration delivered an official notice to the United Nations that the U.S. intends to withdraw from the Paris Agreement as soon as it is legally eligible to do so. Under the terms of the agreement, the earliest possible effective withdrawal date for the U.S. is November 4, 2019. We are the only nation in the world to make this request; it will become official on

November 4, 2020 – a day after the presidential election.[33]

While celebrated by some members of the Republican Party and the coal industry, there was an outcry of dismay from businesses, political leaders, environmentalists, and scientists from the U.S. and abroad. Even corporate America disagreed with the decision as Exxon, Chevron, Shell Oil, Goldman Sachs, General Motors, Google, Apple and Facebook reaffirmed their support for the Paris Agreement. Elon Musk of Tesla and SpaceX resigned from the two presidential councils that he served on stating, "Climate change is real. Leaving Paris is not good for America or the world." Robert Iger, CEO of The Walt Disney Company, did the same.[34]

Scrapping the Clean Power Plan and pulling out of the Paris Agreement are major setbacks towards a move to better energy choices. This has not stopped many states from moving ahead with their plans to reduce carbon emissions. The President cannot put a hold on technology and innovation in the search for cleaner energy. But his actions have left the world in a state of flux. It is now the U.S. against the rest of the world.

Of course, implementing the strict limits as outlined under the Paris Agreement will not be easy as the world witnessed in late 2018. In Paris, ironically, there were violent and destructive "climate riots" in large part to protest the French government's plan to raise the tax on fuel beginning in 2019. The tax increase is designed to persuade French drivers to switch from diesel-fueled cars to less polluting models to help combat climate change. Because of the riots – the most violent in Paris since 1968 – the government was forced to put the measure on hold.[35]

Are the Paris riots a harbinger of things to come? Is it too late to do anything? Of course not; it is never too late to work towards a better planet. But as we race past the tipping point – a point when a global climate changes from one given stable state to a potentially less stable state – it will be more difficult and costly to adapt to a much different world. Many species will not be able to survive the cataclysmic changes.

"I Don't Believe It": Trump Rejects U.S. Government Climate Report

The New York Times, November 26, 2018 – President Trump had a clear message Monday when asked about the core conclusion of a scientific report issued by his own Administration: that climate change will batter the nation's economy. "I don't believe it," he said. The report, Volume II of the Fourth National Climate Assessment, is the work of 13 federal agencies and 300 leading scientists. It states unequivocally that climate change is happening, is human-caused and will get worse if we do not take immediate action.

Mr. Trump then laid responsibility for cleaning the atmosphere on other countries like China and Japan: "Right now we're at the cleanest we've ever been, and that's very important to me. But if we're clean but every other place on Earth is dirty, that's not so good. So, I want clean air. I want clean water. Very important."

The remarks fit a pattern, and not just for their bluntness. In almost two years since taking office, President Trump has denied the scientific reality of climate change and taken aggressive steps that will increase emissions of heat-trapping greenhouse gases — despite unequivocal scientific evidence that those pollutants are warming the planet to dangerous levels.

"Since virtually the first day the administration came into office, they have systematically worked to reverse policies in place to reduce greenhouse gas emissions," said Robert N. Stavins, a professor of environmental economics at Harvard. "But this report, which is mandated by law, shows that greenhouse gas emissions are going to have profound effects on the United States in this century."[36]

Chapter Eight
How We Are Still Getting It All Wrong

"The earth was created with the assistance of the sun and it should be left as it was. I never said the land was mine to do with it as I chose. The only one with that right is the one who made it."

- Chief Joseph of the Nezperce –

The journal *Scientific American* released a special edition (*Crossroads for Planet Earth*, September 2005) that outlined the critical environmental and economic issues facing the world today. The way we respond to these challenges – climate change, disparity between the rich and poor, the emergence of new diseases, shortages of food and fresh drinking water, and the ever-increasing demand for energy from a growing population base – will determine our future.[1]

Many believe a new way of thinking is required to create a sustainable world. "The emerging bridge between the sciences that tell us how the universe works, and the spiritual traditions that give knowledge meaning in our lives, plays a vital role in the new thinking required to head off the darkest possibilities of our future."[2]

Unfortunately, our actions have failed to meet the challenge. Take tar sands for example, one of the most carbon-intensive fossil fuels found on earth – a fuel that the U.S. currently relies on to make us energy independent.

Tar sands – also known as oil sands – are a mixture of predominately sand, clay, water and bitumen. Like bituminous coal, bitumen is more of a black, tarry substance that burns with a bright flame. And just like coal it is made of hydrocarbons that is used to produce gasoline and other petroleum products. Compared to gasoline refined from conventional oil, a gallon of tar sands gasoline produces up to fifteen percent more carbon dioxide emissions. Its use runs counter to our goal of reducing U.S. emissions.[3]

The largest oil sands deposits are found in Canada and Venezuela, with lesser deposits in Kazakhstan and Russia. The only U.S. deposits are mostly concentrated in eastern Utah. There is more oil contained in these deposits than in all the reserves of conventional oil worldwide.

Canada's deposits are primarily in the provinces of Alberta and Saskatchewan. What is most striking is if only 30 percent of this oil was extracted, it could supply the entire needs of North America for over 100 years at 2002 consumption levels. If it was only that simple.[4]

The mining of tar sands also requires huge amounts of water – almost three times the quantity compared to conventional oil. Much of this water is polluted by harmful toxic substances and later stored in ponds which can cover an area nearly as large as Manhattan Island. When in-situ mining is used, the wastewater is stored in the same well the bitumen is extracted posing a risk to groundwater.[6]

Since Alberta is not near any major population's centers, transporting crude bitumen involves a complex network of feeder pipelines that feed into two main collection points. In recent years, lack of access to markets and limited export capacity have forced the oil sands producers to propose the construction of new transmission pipelines. Several of these projects have stalled due to the regulatory process, both by the Canadian and American governments. The most controversial of these projects is the Keystone Pipeline.[7]

"The Keystone Pipeline System is an oil pipeline system in Canada and the United States, commissioned in 2010 and now owned solely by TransCanada Corporation. It runs from the

Western Canadian Sedimentary Basin in Alberta to refineries in Illinois and Texas, and also to oil tank farms and an oil pipeline distribution center in Cushing, Oklahoma. The pipeline became well-known when a planned fourth phase, Keystone XL, attracted opposition from environmentalists and became a symbol of the battle over climate change and fossil fuels."[8]

Environmental groups have also expressed concern over the potential for oil spills along the pipeline's originally planned route that would cross the Sandhills – the large wetland ecosystem in Nebraska – and the Ogallala Aquifer, one of the largest reserves of fresh water in the world.

As opposition grew for laying the pipeline there, TransCanada agreed to change the route. The project is also a threat to the boreal forest of Canada, which represents about one-third of the circumpolar boreal forest that rings the Northern Hemisphere.[9]

The legal, political, economic and social issues surrounding Keystone are multi-faceted and, for many environmentalists, the project represents a line in the sand that must not be crossed if we are to finally reduce our dependence on oil. In 2015, following years of protests, President Obama temporarily delayed permitting of Keystone XL. When Donald Trump took office in January 2017, he acted quickly to try to push the permitting process through to allow for the pipeline's completion. He was unable to do so because the project was still in litigation. An additional environmental review has been ordered by a federal judge.[10]

Due to increased production in North America and the regulatory delays preventing new pipeline capacity, crude oil is now being transported in growing amounts by rail, raising fears about potential spills. The worst spill to date occurred on July 6, 2013, in the eastern township of Lac-Mégantic, Quebec. An unattended 74 car freight train carrying Bakken Formation crude oil – a large contiguous deposit of oil and gas located in North Dakota and Montana as well as several Canadian provinces – rolled down an embankment into the town. The resulting explosion left 42 confirmed dead and more than 30 buildings destroyed. All but three of the remaining downtown buildings were later demolished due to petroleum contamination.[11]

The advancement of hydraulic fracturing and horizontal drilling technologies have also caused a boom in natural gas production. Fracking is a hotly debated political and environmental issue. Proponents claim it is a safe source of clean energy and argue that natural gas is a "bridge" fuel to the future emitting half as much CO_2 as coal. Driven by price, many large utility companies have already switched from coal to natural gas, but swapping one fossil fuel for another does not necessarily translate to a reduction in emissions. A recent study in the *Environmental Research Letters*, a peer-reviewed scientific journal, found the following:

> "Increased use of natural gas has been widely credited with having reduced U.S. carbon dioxide emissions in recent years. But a new study states that between 2013 and 2055 the use of natural gas could only reduce cumulative emissions from the electricity sector by no more than nine percent – a reduction the authors say will have an insignificant impact on climate. In some scenarios, the researchers found that use of natural gas would actually boost emissions from the power sector by up to 5 percent."[12]

According to the study, this new reliance on natural gas will discourage the development of "carbon-free renewable energy." To achieve lower emissions, this also assumes the natural gas industry captures all the methane gas that is released during the process. A 2014 study published in the journal *Science* study found that methane emissions were likely 50 percent higher than previous government estimates and suggested far more monitoring of drill sites is required. Methane is a main component of natural gas and a far more potent greenhouse gas.[13]

Hydraulic fracking results in other environmental impacts that are often minimized by the industry. Like tar sands, the process requires huge amounts of water. During the drilling process, water is pumped into the well along with hundreds of additives and chemicals. Once the oil and gas start flowing, the resulting wastewater contains radioactive material, heavy metals, hydrocarbons and other toxins. The polluted wastewater is then stored in pits, injected into deep underground wells, or transported to a wastewater treatment facility. None of these options is ideal and wastewater that leaks into the soil is a threat to underlying water supplies. Fracking wells release numerous dangerous compounds into the air as well, including benzene – a known carcinogen.[14]

Central Oklahoma has also seen a recent rise in earthquakes. Scientists are now studying the link between hydraulic fracking and these geological disturbances. "From 1975 to 2008, the U.S. Geological Survey found that central Oklahoma experienced one to three 3.0-magntitude earthquakes annually; that number jumped to an average of 40 per year from 2009 to 2013."[15] A 2016 study found the chances of a damaging earthquake occurring in parts of Oklahoma and other nearby states is just as likely as in quake-prone California.[16]

America's fracking boom is not about to end anytime soon. "The Marcellus Shale region in Appalachian Basin is particularly attractive to gas drillers because it is a rich supply of natural gas — some call it 'the Saudi Arabia of natural gas' or 'Frackistan' — and because many of the region's rural communities are economically depressed and eager to attract an energy industry that enjoys handsome profits."[17]

How do we regulate this rapidly-expanding industry? George W. Bush and his prior Administration were more interested in promoting the industry than regulating it. At the forefront of this effort was his Vice President.

"The energy company Halliburton had been on the forefront of new fracking technology since the beginning, pulling in $1.5 billion a year during the fracking boom. Former Halliburton CEO Dick Cheney, who left his post when he was tapped for Vice President by Bush, was instrumental in crafting energy legislation rife with industry loopholes. When Congress passed the Energy Policy Act of 2005, it exempted fracking from safety regulations stemming from the Safe Drinking Water Act."[18]

Known as the FRAC Act, Congressional Democrats have tried several times since 2009 to pass legislation to close these loopholes without success. Instead, EPA conducted a five-year study with little cooperation from the energy companies that found fracking activities "have the potential to impact drinking water resources."[19]

In 2015, President Obama proposed standards for fracking on federal lands that included several basic protections such as wastewater being stored in aboveground tanks rather than in pits. The process was designed to strike a reasonable balance between energy exploration and public safety. At the end of 2017 and in line with his agenda to slash regulations, President Trump ordered the Interior Department to scrap the rules that had not yet been implemented.[20]

To make matters worse, the federal government allows companies operating offshore to dump unlimited amounts of wastewater into the Gulf of Mexico. Federal documents reveal that in 2014 alone, more than 75 billion gallons of wastewater were dumped in the Gulf. A byproduct of the drilling process, the discharge is laden with dangerous chemicals and is a threat to marine species. Most of this oil and gas drilling activity, which is federally permitted, takes place off the coasts of Texas, Louisiana, Mississippi and Alabama.

Numerous environmental groups are now suing the Trump Administration claiming that EPA's permit that allows fracking wastewater dumping violates the Clean Water Act and the National Environmental Policy Act. An attorney for one of the groups said, "The EPA is supposed to protect water quality, not give oil companies free rein to use our oceans as their garbage disposal."[22]

With little federal oversight, it has been left to the states to regulate the industry. A few states – most notably New York and Maryland – have banned fracking while others have enacted some limited restrictions. Local regulations are sometimes enacted, but state law can intervene and override any standards not deemed suitable.

Finding new ways to drill for oil and gas is not necessarily a bad thing. It has helped drive down the price of energy for consumers and made the country more energy independent. But like any endeavor, finding new sources of energy should not come at the expense of the environment. We need to implement and enforce federal standards that are applicable on both land and water. There are always tradeoffs, but the role of government is to maintain a balance between protecting the environment and private interests.

We live in a nation that generates a disproportionate share of the world's carbon emissions. The energy industry must be held responsible for cutting emissions from their own operations and doing everything possible to protect our air and water. It will take federal leadership to make this happen. Ultimately, we must wean ourselves off dirtier sources of energy like coal and tar sands. As noted by President Theodore Roosevelt, "the rights of the public to the nation's natural resources outweigh private rights." There are several ways we can accomplish this, which will be discussed later.

How to Steal Defeat From the Jaws of Victory
Part One – The Victory

The National Academies of Science, Engineering, and Medicine: One of the most impressive fuel efficiency successes in modern memory is the result of the federal Corporate Average Fuel Economy (CAFE) standards established in 1975. They stipulated that the average fuel economy for new cars and sport utility vehicles (SUVs) would be 25 miles per gallon (mpg) by model year 1985; an average for light trucks of 20.7 mpg. Automakers complied, dramatically improving the fuel economy of the nation's light-duty vehicle fleet, reducing dependence on imported oil, improving the nation's balance of trade, and reducing carbon dioxide emissions.

In December 2007, Congress passed an updated CAFE law mandating that new cars, SUVs, and light trucks together average 35 mpg by 2020, an increase of 40 percent from the previous 25 mpg average. As of 2014, manufacturers were meeting standards of 34.2 mpg for passenger cars and 26.2 mpg for light trucks.

The most recent federal efficiency standards finalized in 2012 during the Obama Administration are projected to increase fuel economy of 54.5 mpg for cars and light-duty trucks by model year 2025, while also reducing CO_2 emissions. According to the National Highway Traffic Safety Administration, the 2012 standards and other current federal programs are expected to save drivers about $1.7 trillion at the gas pump and reduce U.S. oil consumption by twelve billion barrels.[23]

How to Steal Defeat From the Jaws of Victory
Part Two – The Defeat

NBC News, March 16, 2017: President Trump said he was ordering the EPA to reopen a mid-term review of Corporate Average Fuel Economy, or CAFE, standards that would require the industry to deliver a fleet average of at least 54.5 mpg by 2025. Many — though not all — manufacturers have warned they cannot meet that target without raising vehicle prices beyond what consumers could afford, something Ford CEO Mark Fields in January told the president could cost one million automotive jobs.

The announcement that the government would review both the mileage target and timing was less of a radical development than many had expected, with some industry observers questioning whether the new administration might slash the numbers immediately or, perhaps, repeal CAFE entirely as part of Trump's promise to reduce government regulations.

Another prospect is that the administration may revoke the waiver that allows California to set its own emissions standards. The state has used that rule to demand automakers start rolling out large numbers of zero-emissions vehicles, such as the hydrogen-powered models from Honda, Toyota and Hyundai, as well as battery cars like the Tesla Model S and Chevrolet Bolt EV. A dozen states have now copied the California mandate.

"My administration will work tirelessly to eliminate the industry-killing regulations," Trump said, his new EPA chief Pruitt adding his assertion that "these standards are costly for automakers and the American people."

Not surprisingly, automakers praised the Wednesday announcement, though the president's action also was roundly condemned by those who said it would condemn Americans to deal with dirtier air, a warming global climate and be a boondoggle for energy companies.[24]

The Acting EPA Director and Former Coal Attorney and Lobbyist Eases Rules to Prop Up the Coal Industry

Associated Press, December 6, 2018: The Environmental Protection Agency acted again today to ease rules on the sagging U.S. coal industry, this time scaling back what would have been a tough control on climate-changing emissions from any new coal plants.

The latest Trump Administration targeting of the Obama Administration efforts to slow climate change comes in the wake of multiplying warnings from the Agency's scientists and others about the accelerating pace of global warming.

In a ceremony today at the Agency, acting EPA administrator Andrew Wheeler signed a proposal to dismantle a 2015 rule that any new coal power plants include cutting-edge techniques to capture the carbon dioxide from their smokestack.

Wheeler called the Obama rules "excessive burdens" for the coal industry. Asked about the harm that coal plant emissions do people and the environment, Wheeler responded, "Having cheap electricity helps human health."[25]

Big Insurance is Climate's Quiet Killer

Rolling Stone Magazine, April 20, 2020: The role of big insurers behind the Keystone pipeline cannot be overlooked. Climate and social justice advocates have long worked to connect the dots between flows of big money and the main players propping up the fossil fuel economy. Surprisingly, one of the biggest culprits guilty of accelerating the climate crisis is an often-overlooked part of our daily lives: Big Insurance.

Liberty Mutual is providing insurance to fossil fuel infrastructure giant TC Energy to enable construction of the dangerous Keystone XL (KXL) pipeline, which would carry extracted tar sands oil from Alberta, Canada to the U.S. Already, Liberty Mutual has provided a 15.6 million bond to cover the risks related to the construction of KXL through South Dakota.[26]

CNN, November 1, 2019: Just as environmentalists and the local Indigenous Environmental Network feared, in late October 2019, Keystone 1 Pipeline sprung a leak. About 9,120 barrels of oil spilled into a nearby wetland and the company managing the pipeline has no idea what caused the leak.[27]

Chapter Nine

Population Dynamics:
Why Does Everyone Have to Live So
Close Together

**"No civilization has survived the ongoing
destruction of its natural support systems."**

- Lester Brown –

The term anthropogenic refers to impacts to the
environment from human activity. In the context of
climate change, it more specifically relates to pollution
emissions and the issue of too many people. The ethics
of over population are complex. Wealthier nations emit
far more emissions per capita but tend to have lower
population growth rates; their offspring will also require
more energy and other natural resources than a child
living in an impoverished country.

When wealth is not equally shared amongst the
general population, it becomes increasingly difficult to
solve society's most vexing issues; poverty must be
overcome before you can build environmental
awareness and the will to do things differently. If the
rich horde their resources and the rest of the population
is just trying to survive, it is difficult to build consensus
to confront a common problem such as climate change.

In nature, population control is part of life's natural
cycle. There are often animal die-offs where one or
more species may crash and burn. Take lemmings – a
short-tailed mole – whose populations fluctuate widely
based on predators, food, climate and other factors.
Under ideal conditions, the local population can increase
ten-fold. Once their food supply is exhausted, they must
move on or face starvation. While all animals must deal
with population limits, it is worth noting that lemmings

do not commit mass suicide. This misconception stems from a Disney documentary in the 1950s where a lemming migration was staged plunging off a cliff.[1]

Humans are now able to avoid this natural type of population control. Thanks to modern medicine, pandemics like the deadly Black Plague can usually be avoided although there is still wide-spread starvation and disease in the world. It also not out the realm of possibility that some new super bug could emerge that kills millions of people. The Covid-19 outbreak that began in 2019 provided a preview of what can happen as the result of a world-wide pandemic.

Assuming the U.S. population will not fluctuate like that of lemmings, we need to examine the real impacts of too many people in a defined area. At some point, public services become overwhelmed and the population is not sustainable. Humans like to think we control our own destiny, but we are not exempt from the basic ecological principles that govern all life systems.

Hart's Location – the smallest town in New Hampshire and the first in the nation to vote during a Presidential election – has a population of 43 and does not have to worry much about crime, commuter traffic or what to do with their garbage. Located in the middle of the White Mountains, their biggest concern is colliding with a moose at night on the highway.

Whereas New York City, the most populous city in the U.S., has a population over 8,600,000 and the issues listed above are all massive problems – except for hitting a moose. The rest of America fits somewhere in between these two locations and the environmental concerns our cities and towns face range in large part with their size. A farming community in Iowa is much different than Los Angeles although how we grow corn in Iowa to feed people in California matters a great deal as everything is connected.

Therefore, we need to take a hard look at our population numbers and any discussion on this subject begins with one man. Thomas Robert Malthus (1766 to 1834) was an English scholar influential in the fields of political economy and demography. It would be fair to say he was our first real environmentalist. Failure to embrace his views means forsaking any attempt to create a sustainable world.

> "In his 1798 book *An Essay on the Principle of Population,* Malthus observed that an increase in a nation's food production improved the well-being of the populace, but the improvement was temporary because it led to population growth, which in turn restored the original per capita production level. In other words, mankind had a propensity to utilize abundance for population growth rather than retaining a high standard of living."[2]

Much has changed in the world since Malthus released his book, especially if one looks at the technological advances in agriculture and health care that have allowed our population to expand exponentially. But that does not mean we can continue to grow as we have in the past. The growth rate – which is driven by birth rates, life expectancy and migration – may have slowed down in the U.S., but we continue to add people in large numbers. Here is a look at how our population has grown since 1800 and the shift from a rural to urban society.[3]

Figure 2
U.S. Population From 1800 to 2000

Year	Population	Percent Rural	Percent Urban
1800	5,308,500	93.9	6.1
1850	23,191,900	84.6	15.4
1900	76,212,200	60.4	39.6
1950	151,325,800	36.0	64.0

2000   291,421,906   19.0   81.0

Source: U.S. Census data (population numbers rounded to nearest one hundredth)

According to the U.S. Census Bureau's population clock, the estimated 2018 U.S. population is 327,160,000. This means we have doubled our population over the past 68 years. It is projected that our population will continue to grow by about ten million every decade. Shortly after 2050, we will likely pass 400,000,000 people.[4]

America has always been about expansion. It is embedded in our psyche that our resources are endless and that we can achieve anything as a country. If we look at our population density – a raw gauge to measure a population's disbursement across the land – it gives us a clearer picture of how population relates to its resources.

As reported by the 2010 U.S. Census, our population density stood at approximately 87.4 people per square mile. At first glance, this is not a large number and it is much higher in a lot of other countries. Bangladesh, with a population of over 160,000,000, is often considered the most densely populated country with more than 2,750 people per square mile. As one of the world's poorest countries, it has an unsustainable population that will be severely impacted by sea level rise.[5]

Population size and density are the two critical factors in determining one of the most basic principles of ecology known as "carrying capacity" – the maximum population size of the species that the environment can sustain indefinitely, given the food, habitat, water and other necessities available in the environment. It is worth noting that about 90 percent of the world's population inhabit just ten percent of the land.[6]

As an example of carrying capacity, the population density of New York City is some 27,000 people per square mile – almost ten times that of Bangladesh.[7] How does the densest large city in the country sustain itself and provide the requisite public services?

The city's food is imported from all over the world and its potable water comes from upstate reservoirs. Electrical power is provided by Consolidated Edison through a grid that covers over 660 square miles in the city and nearby Westchester County. Here is how the system works:

> "There are about 200 networks that operate independently to balance and regulate the flow of electricity in dense areas. Manhattan alone has 39 networks. In all, there are 129,935 miles of cables snaking underground and overhead, enough to reach more than halfway to the moon. Con Ed spends millions of dollars a year to open utility holes and dig into streets crowded with gas mains, fiber-optic cables, steam pipes and subway lines to make repairs and upgrades to its vast underground network. Partly as a result, its customers pay among the highest electricity rates in the country."[8]

The city also faces a nightmare of challenges related to waste management. As the most populous city in the world's most wasteful country, New York generates over fourteen million tons of trash each year – more than any other city in the world. At the center of the Northeast megalopolis, easily accessible locations for disposing of garbage are in short supply.[9]

> "To deal with these challenges, New York relies on a complex waste-management ecosystem encompassing: 2 city agencies, 3 modes of transport (trucks, trains, and barges), 1,688 city collection trucks, an additional 248 private waste hauling companies, and a diverse network of temporary and permanent facilities across a vast landscape."[10]

Up to the 1950s, most of New York's trash was dumped in the ocean. The city then established the Fresh

Kills Landfill on Staten Island, which opened in 1948 and was named for its location along the banks of the Fresh Kills estuary. It soon became the largest landfill in the world until its closure in 2001. At the peak of its operation in 1986, Fresh Kills received 29,000 tons of residential waste per day. While reclamation efforts are underway, its four mounds still dominate the landscape.[11]

Today, disposing of the city's non-recyclable waste – nearly 7,000 tons daily – is a complex process of moving it from one place to the next. First it is brought to transfer stations spread throughout the city and then eventually loaded onto barges or trains that travel up to 600 miles before the final stop, usually a landfill for about 80 percent of the tonnage. The rest will end up at a waste-to-energy plant, where it will be incinerated and converted into energy – a practice that produces its own environmental problems (see Chapter Twenty-Two).[12]

The source of New York City's drinking water is supplied by a network of nineteen reservoirs and three controlled lakes. The 1,972 square-mile watershed provides about 1.3 billion gallons of safe drinking water to over nine million city and surrounding county residents making it the largest unfiltered water supply in the U.S.[13]

Used water goes into New York City's extensive wastewater treatment system – a vast network of over 6,000 miles of sewer pipes, 135,000 sewer catch basins, and almost 500 outfalls for the discharge of combined sewer overflows (CSOs) and stormwater. This wastewater is then collected by 93 pumping stations and transported to fourteen wastewater treatment plants located throughout the five boroughs. Every day 1.4 billion gallons of treated effluent is released in the city's numerous waterways. The problem is when it rains, raw sewage bypasses treatment plants and flows directly into the waterways.[14]

According to the New York City Department of Environmental Protection, "even a relatively small amount of stormwater – one-twentieth of an inch of rainfall – can overwhelm New York's aging sewer system and trigger the Combined Sewer Overflow (CSO) system, which discharges the rainwater and raw sewage (along with many other pollutants) into the many CSO outfalls dotting the edges of the city." Due to the presence of fecal coliform, these overflows are the single largest source of pathogens in the New York Harbor system.[15]

The environmental challenges posed in treating large amounts of wastewater are not unique to New York City. EPA has listed nearly 860 municipalities across the U.S. that have combined sewer overflows. To address the issue, New York City is currently spending several billion dollars to construct retention tanks to capture the overflows.[16]

While these public expenditures are important, they are not done in isolation. New York City has many infrastructure needs including an antiquated subway system and constant budget shortfalls. In 2016, the city ranked last among the nation's twenty largest cities in terms of its "taxpayer burden." While the city has taken steps to move up the list, its financial struggles are far from over.[17]

None of these facts should startle anyone. The city is the center of a metropolitan area – known as the Tri-State Area – that is largest in the world by urban landmass. At 4,495 square miles, the region includes Long Island, the Mid and Lower Hudson Valley, the five largest cities in New Jersey including Newark, and six of the seven largest cities in Connecticut. As of July 1, 2015, the U.S. Census Bureau estimated the population of the New York City metropolitan area at 23,723,696, an increase of 647,032 from 2010.[18]

Even as the city's population is relatively stable, the Tri-State Area continues to grow putting further strain on local resources. This raises the question, has New York City and the greater metropolitan area reached its carrying capacity? Just importantly, is the region capable of dealing effectively with climate change? When put in this context, there are serious issues that lie ahead and we can no longer ignore the fact that population and climate change are linked.

While the highest natural point in Manhattan is 265 feet above sea level, most of the city's five boroughs are closer to three to six feet above sea level. With sea level rise, New York City faces an increased risk of hurricane storm surges as happened in 2012 when Hurricane Sandy came ashore. As the largest Atlantic hurricane on record when measured in diameter, it affected 24 states from Florida to Maine. Sandy's storm surge flooded New York's streets, tunnels and subway lines, never mind its path of destruction all along the Eastern Seaboard.[19]

More extreme and destructive weather events along with a rising sea will only increase the vulnerability of critical infrastructure. While the City has undertaken a detailed facility risk assessment to identify which wastewater infrastructure may be most at risk, implementing an effective adaptation strategy will require millions if not billions of dollars in improvements. With federal revenue sharing on the decline, it will be that much more difficult to come up with the needed funding.

Sea level rise will also cause widespread flooding in Manhattan, starting with Wall Street. A potential influx of "climate refugees" will put enormous strain on city and local services. Since the city does not grow its own food, disruptions in the U.S. food chain due to other climate-related events could lead to food shortages. Eventually, short of a very high seawall, America's financial hub will either be forced to relocate to higher ground or abandon the city entirely. Long Island is also at high risk for flooding which could lead to large evacuations.

Hunts Point, Bronx, a low-income residential neighborhood mostly of Hispanic descent, is across the East River from Manhattan. It is also the home of Hunts Point Produce Market, the largest of its kind in the entire world. Set on 113 acres and with more than one million square feet of space, the market serves the daily needs of 2,500 grocers. Because it is in such a heavily populated area, the site is vulnerable to breakdowns in the transportation network that services the borough. Had Sandy's fury surged in a different direction, the market would have been demolished causing a major disruption in the region's food supply.[20]

New York City represents potentially the worst-case scenario when looking at the impending climate crisis and its impacts. Less populated areas will have more options to relocate.   This is not to undermine the difficulty associated with relocation, but to recognize its scale. (See Figure 3 below for a list of the U.S. cities most vulnerable to coastal flooding.)

New York City can invest billions of dollars and make their mass transit system the most advanced in the world, but the trains cannot run if they are underwater. They can increase their recycling program and turn all their trash into energy, but if the garbage trucks cannot traverse flooded streets it will not matter. New York City could one day be like Venice, Italy – partly submerged. The difference is the people there learned how to travel by boat a long time ago.

These U.S. Cities Are Most Vulnerable to Major Coastal Flooding and Sea Level Rise

In late October 2012, Hurricane Sandy took a sharp left turn into the coasts of New Jersey and New York, leading to 157 deaths, 51 square miles of flooding in New York City alone, and an estimated $50 plus billion in damage. Risks to America's coastal cities for Sandy-like flooding remain as shown in the below figure.

Climate Central, an independent organization of leading scientists and journalists researching and reporting the facts about our changing climate, on the five-year anniversary of the storm ranked U.S. cities with populations greater than 20,000 that are most vulnerable to major coastal floods based on the total population within the FEMA 100-year floodplain as shown.[21]

The report also indicated those cities most at risk in the year 2050 based on estimated sea rise projections (Figure 3). Although there was some shuffling of where cities placed, New York continued to be first and Florida continued to have the most cities at risk – 22 out of the top 25.[22]

Figure 3

Cities Most Vulnerable to Coastal Flooding Today

Top 25 cities and their populations at risk (in thousands) within FEMA's 100-year coastal floodplain

1. New York	245	
2. Miami	126	
3. Pembroke Pines, Fla.	116	
4. Coral Springs, Fla.	115	
5. Miramar, Fla.	93	
6. St. Petersburg, Fla.	88	
7. Davie, Fla.	87	
8. Fort Lauderdale, Fla.	85	
9. Miami Beach, Fla	85	
10. Hialeah, Fla	76	
11. Sunrise, Fla.	74	
12. Pompano Beach, Fla.	73	
13. Hollywood, Fla	69	
14. Lauderhill, Fla.	66	
15. Charleston, S.C.	64	
16. Cape Coral, Fla.	59	
17. Tamarac, Fla.	58	
18. Margate, Fla.	50	
19. Tampa, Fla.	50	
20. Fountainebleau, Fla.	48	
21. Miami Gardens, Fla.	44	
22. Country Club, Fla.	43	
23. Atlantic City, N.J.	37	
24. North Lauderdale, Fla.	37	
25. Kendale Lakes, Fla.	37	

Source: Figure adapted from Climate Central; climatecentral.org; October 25, 2017

Chapter Ten
Paradise No More

"The world has always been fragile. Just ask the dinosaurs."

- Michael Shannon -

The scientific community has long known about the dangers associated with climate change. While the first scholarly analysis goes back to 1896, it was not until 1988 that people began to listen. Along with an unusually hot summer in the U.S., Congressional testimony by Dr. James Hansen of the Goddard Space Institute received a lot of attention. "It is time to stop waffling and understand the greenhouse effect is here," warned Dr. Hansen.[1]

Now 30 years later, Americans are still undecided if climate change is real or not. Less than half of us believe it is due to human activity while just as many adults believe either the recent warming is due to natural causes or not occurring at all. Despite over-whelming scientific evidence to the contrary, we have failed to convince a skeptical public that climate change is the most significant issue facing our nation and the world.

This data comes from an extensive survey conducted in 2016 by the Pew Research Center. The good news is that most Americans understand that climate change leads to real problems as shown in the figure below[2] Reconciling these poll numbers seems to suggest that while we cannot agree on the causes of climate change, enough Americans – greater than 75 percent – perceive that at some point in time, significant impacts will occur. As extreme weather events continue to intensify, that "point in time" is getting closer by the day.

Many Americans expect harms from climate change

% of U.S. adults who say it is_____ that each of these will occur due to global climate change

	Very likely	Fairly likely	Not too likely	Not at all likely
Harm to animal wildlife and their habitats	43	36	15	5
Storms become more severe	42	36	15	6
Damage to forests and plant life	42	35	16	6
More droughts and water shortages	42	34	17	6
Rising sea levels erode beaches and shorelines	41	35	17	6

Note: Respondents who did not give an answer are not shown.
Source: Survey conducted May 10-June 6, 2016.
"The Politics of Climate"

PEW RESEARCH CENTER

Source: Pew Research Center, Public Views on Climate Change and Climate Scientists, October 4, 2016

The survey further showed that "a narrow majority of Americans anticipate new technological solutions to problems connected with climate change." Technology can solve a lot of problems, but tinkering with the world's climate is not something that has ever happened before and it is questionable we will discover those solutions in time.[3]

In combatting climate change, part of the challenge is describing the science behind it. Most Americans are accustomed to a wide range of seasonal temperatures. During July, the average temperature in New York City is 85 degrees F, while in January it is 40 degrees F – a difference of 45 degrees.[4] For people living in the desert, temperatures ranges are even more severe.

This large variation makes it difficult for most Americans to understand why scientists are so alarmed about a worldwide temperature increase of only 2.7 degrees F. While seasonal temperature ranges are spread out across the globe, heating the entire planet just a few degrees will matter a great deal. The 144 countries participating in the 2016 Paris Agreement agreed that the world should limit the global increase to 2.7 degrees F to avoid massive climate disruption.[5]

Consider these recent temperature records that have occurred in the lower U.S. since 1901. Through 2017, five of the hottest years on record have occurred since 2006; eight of the hottest ten years since 1998.[6] And the trend shows temperatures are continuing to rise further as the U.S. is having its warmest consecutive 24, 36 and 48 months on record, with more than 33,000 record highs set in each of the last three years. Record lows are also being set at a slower pace.[7]

In 2017, Live Science, a science news website based in Utah, noted the following:

> "Right now, the world is about 2.1 degrees F warmer than it was during preindustrial times. The 144 countries participating in the 2016 Paris Agreement announced that the world should limit the global increase in this century to 2.7 degrees F. To put this number in perspective, just about 9 degrees F separates the modern world from the last ice age when sea levels were about 350 feet lower than they are today."[8]

Since 2000, sea levels have risen almost three inches globally and continue to rise on an average of 1/8 inch each year – the highest level it has been in the last 2,800 years. The current best estimates predict that sea level will rise six and a half feet by the year 2100. This is based on the world's "business as usual" approach to reducing carbon emissions. But there are many other factors involved. In simple terms, once the ice sheets begin to disappear there is more open water to absorb additional heat and the process speeds up. While 2100 seems like light-years away, we really have no idea how high sea level will rise.[9]

Southern Florida's low topography makes it a region highly susceptible to coastal flooding. Of the total of 4.2 million U.S. citizens who live at an elevation of four feet or less, 2.4 million of them live in south Florida. In the state's most populous city – Miami – the average elevation is around six feet above mean sea level and even lower towards the coast, i.e. Miami Beach.[10]

Because of its unique geology – the entire area is built on a dome of porous limestone – many residences and businesses are already dealing with rising seawater that bubbles up through drains and pipes. Never mind the threat of hurricanes and the resulting storm surge, the incremental increase in sea level rise has put the city at risk. Frequent flooding is one thing, but threats to the Biscayne Aquifer – their main source of drinking water – is a far greater problem. Residents fear they will not be able to flush their toilets or access fresh water and could lose their federally-sponsored flood insurance; the latter was established by Congress in 1968 to protect property owners unable to obtain coverage from private insurers. Tax revenues will then drop and public services like police and fire could become limited or non-existent.[11]

Meanwhile, residents along Florida's southwest coast are dealing with a far more visible problem that threatens the usually thriving tourist industry – massive algal blooms. The so-called red tide outbreak in 2018 was the worst since 2006, blanketing beaches in dead fish. Affecting both lakes and coastal waters, these aggressive outgrowths are the result of higher water temperatures, pollution, and stagnant water and can last for many months at a time. The risk to humans includes eye and respiratory irritation while sea turtles, manatees, birds and dolphins are more likely to suffer the same fate as the dead fish.[12]

Long term, if sea level were to rise by six feet or more, the entire southern half of the state would become submerged. The Keys would disappear and the low-lying Everglades would be flooded by seawater and form a broad, shallow open sea. This would prove to be catastrophic for the 2.4 million people who currently live there. Meanwhile, construction continues as if this paradise will last forever.[13]

As top Florida officials like past Governor and now U.S. Senator Rick Scott remain climate deniers, more enlightened citizens are being proactive. In 2010, Broward, Miami-Dade, Palm Beach, and Monroe Counties united to form the Southeast Florida Regional Climate Change Compact as a way to coordinate mitigation and adaptation activities across county lines on a regional scale.[14]

Local Florida officials are not the only ones worried about the rising sea. Located at the southern end of Virginia's Chesapeake Bay, a U.S. Naval shipyard started building ships in the late 1700s during the American Revolution. Today, the shipyard faces a much greater threat than the British Navy. In the past 10 years, Norfolk Naval Shipyard has suffered nine major floods that have damaged the dry docks used to help maintain the nation's nuclear-powered submarines and aircraft carriers.[15]

Sea level in Norfolk has risen 1.5 feet in the past century, twice the global average, in part because the coastline is sinking. In response, the Navy has been forced to erect temporary flood walls and uses thousands of sandbags to protect the dry docks. A more permanent barrier is part of a 20-year, $21 billion plan to modernize Norfolk's shipyard as well as Navy shipyards in Maine, Washington and Hawaii. As of 2018, Congress has failed to appropriate the funding. More than 75 other essential U.S. military installations are also estimated to be at risk.[16]

> "A decade ago, in 2008, the Navy commissioned the National Research Council to study the risks climate change poses to its ability to respond to these crises and keep the country safe. The report found that 56 Naval facilities worth a combined $100 billion would be threatened if sea level rose about three feet. The report warned that the Navy needed to begin protecting the most vulnerable facilities

immediately, and had only 10 to 20 years to begin work on the rest. Seven years later, there has been little progress."[17]

The Norfolk Navy Yard engineers are not the only ones worried about coastal flooding in and around Chesapeake Bay. The 450 residents of the tiny island of Tangier in the middle of the Bay are living on borrowed time. The island, first discovered in 1608, is losing roughly fifteen feet of coastline per year. With barely a square mile of land left, its residents face an uncertain future.[18]

The year 2018 also involved other catastrophic climate-related events that were a threat to human life and safety. In May, roaring flash floods struck Maryland's Ellicott City. Located west of Baltimore, the City had already been traumatized two years earlier by destructive flash flooding. Many of the downtown buildings that had recently been rebuilt were severely damaged for a second time. Both storms were termed historic 1,000-year floods.[19]

Afterwards, it was determined that 5.5 inches of rain had fallen in two separate downpours over a three-hour period, including an astonishing 1.84 inches of rain during the highest 30-minute interval causing water levels to rise 60 inches in under 25 minutes.[20]

In September, Hurricane Florence was one of the wettest tropical cyclones on record dropping just shy of 36 inches on Elizabethtown, North Carolina and nearly 24 inches in the Port of Wilmington – a city with a population that exceeds 100,000. This led to widespread flooding which affected local infrastructure and the state's agricultural industry.

The North Carolina Department of Agriculture estimated 3.4 million chickens and turkeys plus 5,500 hogs died in flooded farms as piles of stored manure were carried away by the swollen rivers.[21] From one hog-waste lagoon that overflowed, it is estimated that 2.2 million gallons of fecal sludge rife with pathogens were released into local waterways.[22]

After a power outage at a treatment plant, floodwaters also led to the release of about five million gallons of partially-treated wastewater in the Cape Fear River as well as 2,000 cubic yards of coal ash from a power station near Wilmington.[23] As reported in *U.S.A. Today*:

> "For a troubling glimpse into a future where storms bloated by climate change not only cause widespread destruction but also rinse poisons into drinking water, look no further than the aerial footage of gray muck flowing from a flooded coal ash dump into the Cape Fear River.
> The ash problem is a reminder that coal is doubly destructive when it comes to the environment. Burning it is a potent source of heat-trapping greenhouse gases, and the resulting powdery residue is a mix of toxic metals. Duke Energy, a North Carolina power company, is slowly shifting away from burning coal to generate electricity. But it is left with decades-old coal ash basins dangerously close to waterways."[24]

As of December 2018, Wilmington is still dealing with the aftereffects of Hurricane Florence that kicked off an unusually wet stretch of months for the Southeast. Following a recent bout of rain storms in mid-December, many of the same communities that were hit hard by Florence are once again experiencing widespread flooding. These recent storms pushed the city's yearly rainfall total to 100 inches of rain with more storms predicted before December 2018 ends; normal annual rainfall is less than 58 inches.[25]

Of course, Florence was not the only hurricane to cause major damage in 2018. In October, Michael devastated the Florida Panhandle. With winds of 155 miles per hour, it was the third strongest storm in recorded history to hit the U.S. Few coastal building codes are designed to withstand winds of this magnitude. According to a study by NOAA, scientists are increasingly confident of the links between global warming and hurricanes, and that the warming waters of the Gulf of Mexico helped fuel the storm.[26]

Unlike the East Coast, California's precipitation is more seasonal meaning it is drier in the summer and wetter in the winter. In 2018 after a hotter and drier summer than normal, California was left with an abundance of fire fuel.[27] While the number of California wildfires have been declining over the past 40 years, annual changes in weather patterns can lead to favorable conditions that allow fires to burn faster and hotter. The amount of grass in a region, which serves as source of fuel, appears to be a major factor.[28]

The Camp Fire in Northern California that occurred on November 8, 2018, grew to over 100,000 acres in less than 48 hours as it was whipped into a frenzy by strong winds. It claimed nearly three times as many lives as any other wildfire in the state's history and the 18,000 plus buildings that were destroyed exceeds the state's previous seven worst wildfires combined; the final death toll has yet to be determined. By the time the fire was mostly contained it had consumed over 150,000 acres – almost 240 square miles – as well as the entire community of Paradise.[29]

In southern California, the same conditions resulted in a raging inferno in the hills north of Los Angeles known as the Woolsey Fire. Burning over 95,000 acres, the fire destroyed 1,643 structures including the homes of celebrities living in Malibu on the coast. While California Governor Jerry Brown called the fire "the new abnormal," President Trump blamed it on poor forest management and threatened to cut disaster funding even though 60 percent of the forests are managed by the federal government; California only manages three percent of the forest lands and the rest is in private hands.[30]

The wildfires returned in 2019 burning near 200,000 acres and, for the first time ever, California was forced to issue an "extreme warning." There were 6,190 separate fires that burned some 200,000 acres; the Kincade Fire north of San Francisco was the largest burning nearly 80,000 acres. And once again, President Trump blamed the state for its poor forest management as the cause, ignoring the changing weather patterns prevalent across the state.[31]

Most of the fires occurred in developed areas and other mixed habitats and were not "forest fires." Three of the blazes occurred near Los Angeles and the W1 Fire in northern California is mostly high desert grasses and juniper. While development patterns play an important role in wildfires, climate change remains as the primary driver of these destructive blazes.

Other climate-related events are happening that are not nearly as dramatic as hurricanes and wildfires. The Pando ancient forest in Utah – a gigantic region of 40,000 aspen trees that are all clones with identical compositions – is dying according to scientists. The vast expanse of trees is connected by an underground root system and the forest is considered the largest single living thing in the word.[32]

Thought to be around 80,000 years old, the Pando is now under enormous stress due to an extended drought, fire suppression, human development and the encroachment of hungry deer – all factors due to human interference, from climate change to the elimination of predators. As climate change worsens and humans continue to cut trees, the future of the forest is in doubt.[33]

The mighty Columbia River in the Pacific Northwest is synonymous with salmon. At one time, as many as 30 million salmon returned to the river each year and for thousands of years, Native Americans harvested its bounty. The construction of hundreds of dams starting in the late 1800s, as well as pollution and over-fishing have greatly reduced this number.[34]

Average summer water temperatures in the Columbia River have steadily increased over the past 60 years to the detriment of the salmon who need cool water. Once the water temperature exceeds 68 degrees F, adult salmon are unable to make the journey to spawn, dying from stress and disease. Some 50 years ago, temperatures were too hot for migration only a week or two during the very peak of the summer. Now the river frequently remains above this life-threatening temperature for up to months, a condition that is predicted to get worse.[35]

Forests and fish are not the only lifeforms that dislike the heat. Humans are also feeling the health effects. In addition to heat stroke, extreme heat is linked with sleep loss, kidney stones, low birth weight, violence and suicide. Rising temperatures and carbon dioxide levels are increasing the length of pollen season, which affects people with allergies. The smoke from wildfires can lead to respiratory disorders and can exacerbate medical conditions such as asthma and heart disease.[36]

By studying ecology, we learn how all living things are connected; the same is true with environmental conditions shaped by climate change. Lyme disease is a bacterial illness spread by ticks that bite humans. Tick habitat and populations are influenced by many factors, including climate. The rate of reported cases of Lyme disease in the U.S. has approximately doubled since 1991; ticks also are spreading other harmful diseases. Due to warmer temperatures throughout the year, ticks are now active in all four seasons across many parts of the U.S.[37] Possibly the greatest threat to humans is the correlation between pollution levels and climate change on pregnancies.

> "Higher temperatures caused by climate change and increased air pollution have raised a woman's risk of giving birth to premature, underweight or stillborn children – and hurt African-American babies most. That's the finding of a June 2020 published study in a respected medical journal, which reviewed data from 57 studies collectively analyzing nearly 33 million births in the U.S."[38]

In the previously cited Pew survey, perhaps the most disturbing conclusion is our skepticism towards climate scientists. "No more than a third of the public gives scientists who study climate high marks for their understanding of climate change; even fewer say climate scientists understand the best ways to address climate change." And, while Americans believe information from climate scientists more than they trust that from other groups, only 39 percent of Americans have "a lot" of trust in information from our best experts on the subject.[39]

As America's confidence erodes in our political institutions, justice system and science in general, it is no wonder the trust placed in our climate scientists fares no better. The first so-called "Climategate" occurred in 2009 when several British scientists were correctly accused of manipulating their data. Climate deniers immediately seized upon this incident to claim that all scientists have been untruthful about global warming from the beginning.[40]

A similar episode occurred in 2012 involving Peter Gleick, a prominent U.S. scientist, when he fraudulently obtained internal documents from the Heartland Institute – a group that questions the link between human activities and climate change. The documents allegedly detailed Hartland's strategy to influence school curricula by questioning current scientific evidence on global warming. Gleick later apologized for his underhanded tactics.

These instances of improper behavior do not negate the fact that the planet is warming. Every profession has its miscreants. Since 2009, reams of data and photographic evidence documenting the melting of the world's glaciers and ice sheets has been collected. Instead, climate deniers are asking you to believe there is a vast world conspiracy by scientists and political activists pushing their own agenda while corporate America continues to make billions of dollars from the burning of fossil fuels.

These extreme events – increased coastal flooding, more damaging hurricanes and larger wildfires – are exactly what scientists have been warning about for years. If they can be accused of any miscalculation, the ice caps are melting faster than predicted leading to more severe consequences. As for Americans who mistrust climate science, they are ignoring the basic principles of chemistry and physics that dictate the planet will warm in response to an increase of atmospheric greenhouse gases. And it is not scientists who will lead the nation out of this crisis. We simply need to wean ourselves off fossil fuels.

Will Future Generations Despise Us for Our Lack of Urgency?

PoliticusUSA, October 6, 2016: In some distant future human beings will reflect negatively on the autumn of 2016 and the waning months of summer, but it will not be because of anything happening in America's bizarre political landscape. It will be because the Earth's climate exceeded the "*tipping point*" never to return to normal in any currently living human being's lifetime. In fact, according to climate scientists, what was considered "*safe*" and normal may never return and the dreadful tipping point signals a permanent condition in human terms.

Scientists have carefully monitored atmospheric carbon dioxide for decades and the overriding consensus has always been that exceeding 400 parts per million (ppm) is the tipping point for the Earth's climate. What designates the autumn of 2016 as a serious milestone is that typically atmospheric carbon dioxide is at its lowest point in the fall; this year the value failed to drop below 400 parts per million.

According to *Scientific American* and a report from the Scripps Institute of Oceanography, "The concentration of carbon dioxide in the atmosphere has stayed above the 400 parts per million throughout the entire year up to this point. That all but ensures that 2016 will be the year that carbon dioxide officially passed the symbolic 400 parts per million mark, never to return below it in our lifetimes." This alarming fact should have been the lead story on every news outlet. It means that our climate may never return to the same weather patterns experienced prior to the Industrial Revolution.[41]

Security Risk Posed by Climate Change

Reuters, March 19, 2019: The historic flooding that devastated Nebraska last week has also submerged one third of an Air Force base, offering a further illustration of the threat posed to national security by climate change.

Flooding at Offutt Air Force Base forced the evacuation of eight planes, including one of four Boeing-made E4-B planes that are supposed to act as an aerial command center if ground bases are destroyed in an emergency such as a nuclear attack. Waters inundated 30 buildings at the base.

Offutt Base also houses Strategic Command, which oversees the nation's nuclear weapons, but its headquarters was not impacted by the floods. The incident comes as the Trump Administration is considering forming a panel headed by climate denier William Happer to determine if climate change poses a national security threat. In January, the Pentagon found that climate change currently poses a threat to military bases. Former military and intelligence leaders have written to President Donald Trump urging him not to challenge those findings.[42]

Chapter Eleven
Where Has All the Water Gone?

"Do unto those downstream as you would have those upstream do unto you."

- Wendell Berry -

Great civilizations have collapsed due to drought and lack of access to fresh water. Over 4,000 years ago, the Akkadian Empire in Mesopotamia ended during a 100-year drought. China's Ming Dynasty – one of the greatest eras of organized government and social stability in human history – suffered a similar fate. The Maya civilization of Mexico, at the peak of their cultural development in the ninth century, experienced an extended drought that killed millions of people due to famine and lack of water.[1]

Around 1150, the Ancestral Puebloan culture in the Southwest U.S. suffered through a 300-year period of diminished precipitation called the "Great Drought." "This drought has often been cited as a primary cause of the collapse of the ancestral Puebloan (formally called Anasazi) civilization in the Southwest U.S., and abandonment of places like the Cliff Palace at Mesa Verde National Park in Colorado." The same drought also affected other mound-building Native American civilizations throughout the U.S. leading to their eventual disappearance.[2]

Will the U.S. Southwest be the next "great civilization" to collapse due to a lack of fresh water?

Phoenix, Arizona is now the fifth largest city in the U.S. In 1950, its population was 160,818. At the turn of the century, its population was 1,326,997. By 2017, that number had grown to 1,626,078 – legal residents.[3] As the metro-area continues to grow, it is also very likely that Phoenix will become hotter than it is today.

A recent report by the National Climate Assessment showed that almost every U.S. city will experience a temperature increase for both summer and winter averages by 2050, noting that in some places it will be so hot it will be "dangerous to go outside." According to Climate Central, future average summer daytime temperatures in some regions can best be compared to the Middle East. Phoenix, for example, will be like Kuwait is today – a scorching 112 degrees F.[4]

Phoenix is naturally hot because of its geography, but the "urban heat effect" plays a role as well. Sprawling development means more heat-absorbing surfaces and less natural vegetation. This has caused temperatures, particularly overnight lows, to increase. As a result, the city no longer cools down at night like in the past. The hotter it gets, the greater the need for air conditioning which generates more waste heat just like the internal combustion engine.[5]

Intense heat is not the only problem facing the residents of Phoenix and the State of Arizona. A decade-long drought – the longest in the state's 110-year long observational record – means it could run out of water in the foreseeable future.[6]

The state gets its water from three main sources – groundwater (43%), the Colorado River (36%) and other surface water sources (19%); effluent or reclaimed water accounts for the remaining amount (2%). Groundwater comes from underground aquifers that have existed for millions of years. It is now being pumped out faster than it is being replenished – a predicament made more acute by the extended drought.[7]

The Colorado River flows through five states and is responsible for carving out the magnificent Grand Canyon. This once mighty river used to flow into the Gulf of California after reaching its delta in Mexico – something it has only done five times since 1983. Now tamed by seven or more dams, it is the largest source of surface water in the U.S. The river serves the needs of 25 million people who have a voracious appetite for water.[8]

Water from the Colorado River is shared by seven states and Mexico. Rights to use the water are quantified by a string of legal authorities known as the "Law of the River." Instead of the traditional "first-come-first-serve" doctrine practiced by the early prospectors and farmers, Arizona is guaranteed a minimum annual amount.[9]

Arizona's farms are the biggest user of water at 69 percent. The rest is for municipal and industrial use.[10] There also are some 300 golf courses in the state. But Arizona may soon begin to run out of water as reported by *The New York Times*:

> "The mere prospect of a shortage in Arizona cities, now raised publicly for the first time, is but a proxy for the rising concern among many experts over a longer-term water crisis across the entire Southwest. States along the lower Colorado River use much more water than flows into Lake Mead in an average year, a deficit that upstream states shouldered for decades by opening their reservoir sluices to release more water.
>
> But the drought has all but ended that practice, and Lake Mead has begun a sharp decline; the principal upstream reservoir, Lake Powell, now holds only 42 percent of its capacity, and Lake Mead about 45 percent. If upstream states continue to be unable to make up the shortage, Lake Mead, whose surface is now about 1,085 feet above sea level, will drop to 1,000 feet by 2020. Under present conditions, that would cut off most of Las Vegas's water supply and much of Arizona's. Phoenix gets about half its water from Lake Mead, and Tucson nearly all its supply."[11]

Since that story first appeared in 2014, little has changed. When one lives in the desert, it is important to know what is happening in the mountains. Much of the water that drains to Lake Powell comes from the snowpack of the Rocky Mountains. For the last few years, precipitation rates have been on target. The 2016-

17 winter season was exceptional and the 2017-18 and 2019-20 seasons were saved by several late spring storms. But weather patterns are never predictable and water levels in both Lakes Mead and Powell remain dangerously low. Living on the brink of a major water shortage benefits no one.[12]

As surface water sources dry up, groundwater becomes the resource of choice. However, it takes more electricity to pump it out of the ground than it does transporting surface water. As we continue to rely on fossil fuels, more electricity means more greenhouse emissions creating a vicious cycle – more arid conditions lead to a greater reliance on groundwater just as there is less to take.[13]

While Arizonians struggle with water conservation measures and water reclamation efforts expand, where would people go if their water was suddenly shut-off? Much of the Southwest faces the same dilemma, although the captivating water fountains in Las Vegas belie a potential disaster exists. When it comes to wasting water, no one does it better than Vegas – a city that gets nearly 90 percent of its water from Lake Mead.[14]

> "There is no two-mile stretch of ground in the United States that has such a density of water features, water attractions, and sheer water exuberance. Las Vegas, which can invest something as routine as breakfast with outlandish extravagance, has taken our most unassuming substance and unleashed it as the embodiment of glamour, mystery, power, and allure. In a way that only Las Vegas can, it has created a whole new category – ostentatious water.
>
> It is all the more remarkable because Las Vegas is the driest city in the United States – indeed, it is not even a contest. Of the 280 cities in the United States with a population of at least 100,000 people, Las Vegas is No. 280 in

precipitation and No. 280 in number of days it rains each year."[15]

As the population of Las Vegas nearly tripled between 1990 and 2009, it is also one of the top ten visited cities in the U.S. receiving upwards of 42 million visitors a year. In addition to the casinos – and despite the searing temperatures – visitors also frequent the more than 50 golf courses in and around the city.[16]

While golf courses live by mandated water allowances, the average homeowner faces no such restrictions and growing grass is an obsession. According to the Southern Nevada Water Authority (SNWA), 60 percent of the water use in Las Vegas is used outdoors – everything from watering lawns and gardens to filling swimming pools and washing cars. Since homeowners account for almost half of the water use, 30 percent of the water taken from Lake Mead evaporates into the desert air.[17]

Aggressive conservation measures implemented by SNWA have helped the city and surrounding communities reduce its per capita water use by 36 percent between 2002 and 2017, even as the population increased by nearly 660,000 residents. These measures include seasonal watering restrictions, a water smart landscape rebate program, and pool covers. Las Vegas has also implemented a four-tier pricing system based on the amount of water usage.[18]   While reducing water consumption is now serious business in Las Vegas, there is still a long way to go. If America's gambling capital was to go dry, it would have a severe state-wide economic impact.

Phoenix and Las Vegas are not the only U.S. cities facing major water shortages. Both Miami's and Houston's main aquifers are at risk due to rising sea levels and saltwater seepage. In the 1980s, Los Angeles suffered a major crisis when the city was forced to stop using 40 percent of its drinking water due to industrial runoff contamination. Like Las Vegas, it must now rely on importing large amounts of its water from the Colorado River.[19]

"California's State Water Project (SWP) is the largest water system ever designed and maintained by a state government in the U.S., accounting for 30 percent of Southern California's water supply. The system consists of 34 water storage facilities (reservoirs and lakes), 20 pumping plants, 4 pumping-generating plants, 5 hydroelectric power plants, and 700 miles of open canal and pipeline. It supplies water to 25 million Californians and over 750,000 acres of farmland. SWP water grows approximately 45 percent of the fruits and vegetables produced in the U.S.

The SWP isn't the only aqueduct system LA uses to get water. The 242-mile Colorado River Aqueduct has been delivering water to Southern California for over 70 years. As it flows south, the Colorado river eventually flows into Lake Havasu in Arizona. That lake is where the aqueduct starts. From Havasu, it runs west across the desert and into the east side of the Santa Ana mountains. Upon reaching Southern California, the water goes to several management companies who take the responsibility of making sure it gets to consumers."[20]

The Imperial Valley in Southern California represents a marvel of modern engineering, irrigating the desert to become one of our most productive agricultural regions with an annual crop production of over one billion dollars. With its history going back as far as the California Gold Rush in 1849, agriculture is now the largest industry in the valley accounting for nearly half of all employment.[21]

Wholly dependent on the Colorado River via the All-American Canal for its water, the irrigation of the thousands of acres in production comes with an environmental cost – south of the canal the river, for most of the year, no longer flows above ground to

Mexico.[22]   Perhaps that is why they call it the "All-American" Canal as our neighbor to the south no longer gets to enjoy and utilize the river.

Taking water from a foreign country is one thing, but states are also squabbling over water rights. As Mark Twain said, "Whiskey is for dinking, water is for fighting over." We need to look no further than the Southeastern U.S. to see how a shortage of water can lead to water wars.

> "For nearly 30 years, Georgia, Alabama, and Florida have fought over the use of water in the Apalachicola-Chattahoochee-Flint River Basin (ACF), which is heavily influenced by the U.S. Army Corps of Engineers' operation of Lake Lanier's Buford Dam. Lanier lies within the Chattahoochee River's headwaters, just north of Atlanta.
>
> The Corps built Lanier in the 1950s with clear Congressional authorization for flood control, navigation, and hydropower.   Over time, however, Lanier has become the primary source of drinking water for metro-Atlanta, and Alabama and Florida have argued that Georgia withdraws too much and is not sharing the water fairly. All three states have turned to the courts to try to resolve the conflict."[23]

Atlanta endured a major drought from 2007 through 2008 and now ongoing legal disputes with Alabama and Florida over water releases from Lake Lanier jeopardize the area's future water supply. Part of the legal dispute centered around the survival of several endangered river mussels.   The Tri-State Water Wars began when Alabama sued the U.S. Army Corps of Engineers over the allocation of water held in Lake Lanier.[24] The group Sustain Atlanta describes the growing conflict as follows:

> "When a federal agency decides to divert water from power-generating activities, which are highly important to residents of Alabama, to

drinking water activities, which are highly import to residents of metro-Atlanta, a conflict is naturally going to occur. This one decision in 1989 by the Corps set off a string of lawsuits revolving around key federal environmental and administrative law statutes and principles, relatively ancient concepts of basic water rights, and even cartographic and boundary-drawing disputes.

While we can label the Army Corp's decision as the catalyst, the conflict over how to allocate water in the Apalachicola-Chattahoochee-Flint River Basin (ACF Basin) between Georgia, Florida, and Alabama was always going to be a problem.   It was a time bomb waiting to explode."[25]

During the height of the drought in 2008, Georgia made an audacious attempt to move the state's border with Tennessee 1.1 miles north. Citing a flawed 1818 land survey, the legislature passed a bill to claim part of the Tennessee River by moving the border to the middle of the river in the northwest corner of the state. The Mayor of Chattanooga – the Tennessee city that lies on the border with Georgia – responded by sending a truckload of bottled water to Atlanta. Proving Mark Twain was on to something, the Mayor said, "Today they come for our river. Tomorrow they come for our Jack Daniels."[26]

While states have absolutely no authority to change their boundary lines, Georgia's attempt to do just that exemplifies the steps one will go to keep the water flowing. Meanwhile, the state is involved in a number of other lawsuits that continue to make their way through the legal system. As illustrated below, waterways do not care about boundary lines but decisions in one state can have drastic impacts on another.

Figure 5 – Major Drainage for Two Major Rivers in Georgia*

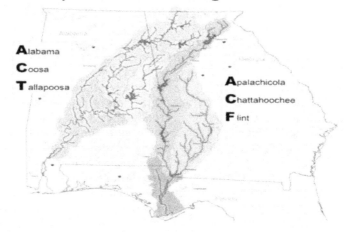

Alabama
Coosa
Tallapoosa

Apalachicola
Chattahoochee
Flint

Source: Saporta Report, May 21, 2018

*Three federal lawsuits are pending over the management of dams by the U.S. Army Corps of Engineers in two river basins that begin in Georgia: the Apalachicola-Chattahoochee-Flint River Basin and the Alabama-Coosa-Tallapoosa River Basin.[27]

The legal shenanigans over water rights in Georgia and neighboring states is what happens when a place exceeds its sustainable population level. Atlanta is not like Las Vegas or even Las Angeles. It has plenty of water available or at least it did at one time. But as the city grew, it continued to rely on one major source for most of its water – Lake Lanier. This shared resource is used for many purposes besides drinking water– everything from cooling waters for a nuclear plant in Alabama to keeping the oyster beds in Apalachicola Bay, Florida alive and healthy. Alabama is also the only state of the three without a general water plan.[28]

In 2016, Atlanta was the ninth largest metropolitan area in the U.S. with over 5,850,000 people. The area's population in 1990 was slightly less than three million, meaning in a span of just 28 years the population doubled.[29] And projections for 2040 predict the area will add an additional 2.5 million people.   As Atlanta continues to grow, it faces an uncertain future when it comes to providing enough water for everyone.[30]

Finding new water sources is not an easy task for any city and taking water from one place and delivering it to another always comes with lots of consequences. For Atlanta to continue its economic growth, the city will need to improve conservation measures and efficiency practices.   To their credit, they have taken some important steps such as doubling water rates and making infrastructure improvements. Atlanteans will also need to deal with a problem they share with other parts of the country – outdated lifestyle choices.

As people have left downtown for the suburbs, they have come to expect athletic fields, golf courses, outdoor pools, wide open green spaces and expansive lawns. All these things require water and, while many places are learning to use recycled water for such purposes, natural landscapes need little or no additional watering.

The Augusta National Golf Club in Georgia – home of the annual Masters Golf Tournament – is arguably America's most famous golf course. To host such a prestigious tournament requires a course that is meticulously maintained. This includes watering the grass that lines the fairways and especially the greens.

Turf requires anywhere from 25 to 60 inches of water annually depending on many factors. A course in the desert will need a lot more water than where it rains more frequently, just as a course in Georgia will need more water than one in the Northeast. Most of this water is also required during the summer months when rainfall is lowest and evaporation rates highest. Unlike trees and shrubs, turf grasses have little capacity to store water and withstand long periods of no rainfall.[31]

There are now approximately 16,000 courses in the U.S. – about half the total in all the world – and if one laid them out together, they would be as large as the State of Delaware. That is almost 2,000 square miles of golf courses using lots of water. Estimates of how much water a golf course needs per day range from 100,000 gallons to as high as one million in the desert.[32]

Our love affair with beautiful green grass does not end there. Americans have the same obsession about their lawns. Until the late eighteenth century, most rural homeowners had a patch of packed dirt outside the front door or a small garden that contained a mix of flowers, herbs and vegetables. Lawns were not practical and were seen strictly as a luxury for wealthy landowners who could afford grounds keepers to maintain the grass with hand tools.

That all changed with the invention of the rotary mower and garden hose. Since then, green, weed-free lawns are common today and millions of Americans spend billions of dollars on landscaping companies to cut and maintain their grass. According to a 2000 Gallup survey, over 26 million US households hired a professional landscaping company. That little patch of green has become a big business.[33]

While the average American family home uses more than 300 gallons of water daily, most of our water supply is used to make energy, manufacture products and grow food. The energy and agricultural sectors together are responsible for over 75 percent of the water used in this country. As we continue to increase our population, there is increased competition for water resources. In a 2014 U.S. Government Accountability Office report, 40 states said they expected to have water shortages over the next ten years not related to drought.[34]

This leads into water rights and water policy which are both complicated and convoluted. The U.S. has always thought of itself as water rich, but in fact we may be approaching what is known as "peak water" – a term that describes the finite amount of available fresh water. As we enter a period where peak water is a thing of the past, we need to think differently about our supply of potable water – "the delivery of water-related services matched to the user's needs and resource availability."[35]

Thanks to an increased public awareness of the importance of clean water, there has been an emphasis on conservation. As a result, along with other efficiency improvements, our per capita water use has been declining. These advances have been partially offset by new contaminants in public water supplies, aging and decaying potable water infrastructure, and climate change including pronounced droughts in certain regions of the country.[36]

The absolute necessity for fresh, clean water can never be overstated. As we continue to divert river water for ourselves, we are putting the health of entire ecosystems at risk. If we contaminate our water supply with pollutants or extract too much groundwater, new sources of water must be found. We must also protect the other components of the water cycle, especially wetlands that help to prevent flooding and purify the surface water through natural filtration.

We need to look no further than California to better understand what can happen when competing uses for water results in conflict. The California Water Resources Control Board wants to restore the Sacramento-San Joaquin River Delta – the West Coast's largest estuary. As thirsty cities and farms have squeezed the rivers that nourish the delta, the health of the estuary is at risk. Under the proposed plan, water withdrawals would be restricted from several of the rivers that are part of the water supply to San Francisco and the region. The Tuolumne is one of those rivers.[37]

San Francisco has long cherished its water supply and since the early 1900s has maintained its rights to water that begins its westward journey to the Pacific in the Sierra Mountains. Under this plan, the city would be forced to limit its draw from the Tuolumne. City leaders have called the restrictions unthinkable as they fear the unprecedented water cutbacks will adversely impact Bay Area residents and businesses. The stalemate demands choosing between a healthy natural ecosystem or meeting the needs of the public. As reported by the *San Francisco Chronicle* in 2018, the choice will become even more difficult during years of drought.

> "The central question of debate is whether the state's push for the environment has gone too

far, threatening commerce not only in California's farm belt, but also in its urban centers where the growth of technology, housing and retail is on the line. State officials acknowledge the plan will cause a decline in farm production — an average of 2.5 percent annually — in the region irrigated by the rivers, where lots of alfalfa, almonds and peaches are grown. Local leaders expect a bigger hit. 'Our whole economy is predicated on agriculture,' said Vito Chiesa, a walnut grower and Stanislaus County supervisor. 'You take away our one strong suit, and you've sent us into a downward spiral (that) I don't know how we get out of'."[38]

This leaves central California totally dependent on future weather patterns to meet its competing needs for water – an unenviable position as climate change may wreak havoc on previous precipitation rates. Our older cities face a much different problem – aging infrastructure. According to the American Society of Civil Engineers, about 14-18 percent of water treated in the U.S. is wasted through aging and damaged infrastructure, as well as faulty meters. Chicago, for example, wastes about 22 billion gallons of treated water a year, enough to serve 700,000 individual needs for a whole year.[39]

Since we are doing little to combat climate change and even less to restrain population growth, how do we deal with the growing water crisis? Water utilities have always focused on supplying water no matter how much demand and this needs to change. We cannot simply increase supply at the old price levels.

We can start by changing how we feel about paying for water. On a global scale, Americans pay considerably less for water than people in most other developed nations – the average is about $1.50 per 1,000 gallons. While we have no problem paying $2.50 or more for a sixteen-ounce bottle of water, people complain loudly when their water bills go up. Since there are eight pints in a gallon, we will pay the equivalent of $20.00 for a gallon of bottled water opposed to a penny for what comes out of the tap – a 2,000 times price differential. It makes no sense and when our tap water is so cheap, there is little incentive to conserve.[40]

The first documented case of bottled water being sold was in Boston in the 1760s, when a local bottling company sold mineral water for 'therapeutic' uses. At 12.8 billion gallons, or 39 gallons per person, Americans today drink more bottled water than milk, soda or beer. For many people, they believe bottled water is safer to drink although tap water is typically tested more often for quality and contamination. The EPA is responsible for conducting these tests and the Trump Administration's efforts to cut their funding could further jeopardize public health; a recent study shows that bottled water may also contribute to the deterioration of teeth because of its low pH.[41]

Making bottled water is also an extensive, resource-heavy process. Some of it comes from faraway lands and is then shipped overseas and finally transported by trucks to markets across the U.S., only to be refrigerated at your local convenience store – all energy-intensive activities.

Americans purchase up to 50 billion plastic water bottles each year – that's an average of over 150 bottles per person. To make all these bottles requires millions of barrels of crude oil. It is calculated that at least 50 million plastic bottles are thrown away – meaning not recycled – every day in the U.S. "Laid end to end, these bottles would stretch from San Francisco to New York city and back again."[42]

There are a few – but not many – legitimate reasons for preferring bottled water. It is easy to transport and if one lives near a place where the water is contaminated, bottled water may be their only option. Just ask the folks of Flint, Michigan where cost-cutting measures implemented by the State led to tainted drinking water that contained lead and other toxins. However, residential water coolers are a far better option than purchasing cases of water as the jugs are refilled meaning no plastic is thrown away.

When our political leaders talk about the need to invest in infrastructure the bias is always toward airports, roads and bridges – the things that promote commerce. Improving our transportation system is critically important, but modernizing existing water infrastructure should be an equally high priority. Unlike the past when the federal government subsidized large water conveyance projects, the emphasis now needs to be on upgrading existing infrastructure. Cities and towns seeking to build new infrastructure need to pass that cost on to the user and not the taxpayer, which will limit growth in areas not already developed.

Irrespective of federal investments, it is ultimately the responsibility of states and individual communities to solve their own water shortages. Higher water prices are inevitable to ensure a reliable and safe supply. Conservation and the recycling of grey water – wastewater absent of fecal contamination generated in households or buildings – will need to be part of the equation.

Imposing summer restriction to manage shortages will also become more common. Many communities have already implemented extensive water conservation programs. One such example can be found in Flagstaff, Arizona, where they offer everything from free rain barrels to a commercial rebate program. With the help of a dedicated staff of eight employees, Flagstaff has chosen to conserve and protect their limited water resources for future generations.[43]

On the other hand, development goes on unabated in some parts of the State. In Benson near Tucson, the U.S. Army Corps of Engineers has permitted a huge master-planned sprawl development for 70,000 people. "The Villages at Vigneto would transform 12,167 acres of largely undeveloped habitat into 28,000 residences, 3 million square feet of commercial space, four golf courses, fountains, lakes and a resort."[44]

The proposed development would draw groundwater from the San Pedro River ecosystem – a desert oasis that supports millions of migratory songbirds and other wildlife. The affected area includes a critical marsh within the San Pedro Riparian National Conservation Area. Hydrologic studies have shown the level of water needed would suck the marsh dry and irreversibly damage the riparian zone. Areas like this have been set aside for one reason – to protect our most critically-valuable places. Development that threatens these areas should not be permitted. In early 2019, several conservation groups filed suit against the Army Corps and its project.[45]

The good citizens fighting this project probably never heard of Owens Lake, a mostly dry water body on the eastern side of the Sierra Nevada in Inyo County, California. The lake once held large amounts of water until 1913 when much of the Owens River was diverted into the Los Angeles Aqueduct, causing it to wither away some thirteen years later. While some of the flow of the river has been restored returning water to the lake, it has long been considered the largest single source of dust pollution in the U.S.[46]

As a society, we must determine how our water is best allocated and utilized. Do we want to grow lettuce and broccoli or build more golf courses and water parks? When people are given clear guidelines, they will invent creative solutions.

Some will turn to technology to solve the problem, such as converting salt water to fresh by building desalination plants. But is this feasible? The ability to do something does not mean the marketplace will accept it. The process is costly and the users will have to pay the price instead of relying on federal subsidizes. These funds are needed elsewhere. It is time that communities take responsibility for creating an adequate water supply without causing harm to others.

Water is one of our most important natural resources and one of the easiest to conserve. Despite recent conservation efforts at the municipal level, wasteful water practices persist. Inefficient appliances in older homes are commonplace even in places where water is scarce.[47] We need more communities to implement the measures adopted in Flagstaff, Arizona. Absent of local leadership, a simple Google search will provide numerous ways to conserve water in the home. Once Americans learn the true value of potable water, they will demand stricter regulations to preserve our limited water supplies.

Is America On the Brink of a Mega-Drought?

The decade-long Dust Bowl drought that plagued big parts of the country during the Great Depression will pale in comparison to the mega-drought many climatologists are predicting – the likes of which have not been seen since the Medieval period. Several civilizations are thought to have been dramatically affected by these past droughts including the Maya and the Anasazi.

By looking at what caused the 14 megadroughts the region has experienced between 800-1600 A.D., researchers discovered the climatic conditions present then are fast approaching now, indicating megadroughts will happen again. Climatologists predict there is an 80 percent chance it will occur sometime between 2050 and 2099 if greenhouse emissions continue.

The drought would prompt dust storms and wipe out trees and agriculture from California to Iowa; the Southwest will likely be hit the hardest.[48]

Chapter Twelve
When the Cupboard is Bare

"Ethanol is the energy equivalent of methadone – a palliative, not a cure."

- Deutsche Bank analyst -

In Colonial America, agriculture was the primary livelihood for 90 percent of the population with the singular purpose of providing enough food for one's family. Rapid population growth and the expansion of the frontier necessitated clearing the land to create new farms. In the first half of the 1800s, Southern plantations grew cotton to be shipped overseas using primarily slave labor. As America entered the Industrial Revolution, there was a need to feed the masses migrating to the city, creating lucrative domestic markets for America's farmers.[1]

Today, there are over two million farms in the U.S. with an average of around 440 acres each. In terms of the number of farms, Texas leads the country by a wide margin – 240,000 followed by Missouri with 97,300. Iowa, Oklahoma and California round out the top five. Since the turn of the century, the number of acres in agriculture has been steadily dropping from 945 million to 910 million in 2017.[2]

Agricultural land is generally defined as non-federal land that includes a diverse array of land cover/use types: cropland, pastureland, rangeland, and woodland associated with farms. Farmers and ranchers use an additional 158 million acres of federal land for grazing. The total proportion of land mass of the lower 48 states dedicated to agriculture is 55 percent.[3]

A major threat to our food security is the loss of agricultural land to development. According to the

American Farmland Trust, "between 1992 and 2012, the U.S. converted about 31 million acres of agricultural land to development – nearly double the amount previously reported." This is equivalent to all the agricultural land in Iowa. Development disproportionately occurred on agricultural land compared to other land types; nearly 11 million of the acres lost was land best suited for agriculture.[4]

The taking of agricultural land to accommodate the spreading suburbs is nothing new. Most farms are ideally suited for development – flat land that is easy to build on. The rich top soil is often sold off for additional profit. The only real wealth of many farmers is the land itself and as development drives up land prices, the opportunity to sell becomes more and more attractive. As local farming communities disappear, the remaining few farmers may have no choice but to sell as the local agricultural services they depend on close shop as well.

America's farmers are also aging. According to the U.S. Labor Department, the average age of farmers and ranchers is 58. Three decades ago, the average was 50.5 years.[5] Since fewer young people are showing an interest in agriculture, the challenge will be to ensure there are enough farmers in the future to meet our food needs. Some will say we can always import our food from elsewhere. We import a myriad of other essential raw materials and finished products; food is just another commodity to be traded across world markets as humans have been doing for centuries. The Independent Media Institute, a think tank based in California, posted the following description about our food system in 2018:

> "Today, advancements in technology and infrastructure have helped make exporting and importing foods and fresh produce big business. Improved transportation methods and storage technologies have made shipping perishables easier, while international trade agreements have reduced tariffs on imports. In addition, low wages, lowered production costs due to increased scale of production, and the monopoly

of agribusiness has created cheap labor markets across the food system.

Furthermore, in the U.S., many staple foods simply can't be domestically produced on a scale to satisfy the standard American diet. According to the USDA, more than 95 percent of coffee, cocoa, spices, fish and shellfish products that Americans consume is imported. The growth of personal wealth has also played a key role in the growing demand. 'As high U.S. incomes drive consumption,' the Agency notes, 'the volume of U.S. agricultural imports has increased by four percent annually, on average, since 2000'."[6]

Unfortunately, there is a huge environmental cost associated with shipping food around the world. "All those trucks, trains, ships and planes are emitting carbon dioxide into the atmosphere while logging thousands of 'food miles' – the distance a food product travels from the farmer or producer to the supermarket and, finally, to your dinner table."[7]

Consumers today have an expectation that all kinds of produce will be available at their local market year-round and have no tolerance for seasonal disruptions. Just a short time ago all our iceberg lettuce was grown domestically, but in the period from 1998 to 2012 domestic production shrank to a mere five percent. From 1999 to 2014, the market share (based on volume) of all imported fruits and vegetables to the U.S. increased from 35 percent to 50 percent.[8]

Strawberries offer a perfect example of how our food habits have changed. As the cultivation of this popular fruit moves to Mexico, Central and South America during the winter months – the source of most imported fruit and vegetables – U.S. consumers are willing to pay a premium price to have berries flown in from overseas. This leaves a huge carbon footprint, not to mention, possible health risks as many other countries have much weaker environmental regulations than we enjoy in the U.S.[9]

While most of the strawberries in the U.S. are grown in California, they are grown in every state. Fresh, local strawberries will be in season at some point during the year but that is no longer good enough. The thought of 'sacrificing' for the good of the planet never crosses the mind of the average consumer. Even the food we buy often has an aspect of its production and delivery tied to climate change, which is why people are overwhelmed by the real sacrifice required to create an ethos of sustainability.

Of course, Americans are not the only ones desirous of certain foods. Maine lobstermen have found a whole new market for their product in Asia. A decade ago, no one was shipping live Maine lobsters to China. Now business is booming and growing exponentially with sales nearly tripling in 2016 from just a year earlier. Since lobsters must be shipped alive, they cannot go by container ship but are flown on commercial jets.[10] Sending lobsters to Asia may be good for lobstermen, but it is bad for the environment due to the amount of energy required.

If giving up strawberries in January would solve the problem, life would be simple. But the problems with our food supply run much deeper.

> "The modern food supply has been hijacked by an amalgamation of both government and private industry, which increasingly controls what people eat and how they eat it. The crux of this largely state-controlled food supply is an industrial system of monoculture that generates high profits for the fat cats, but that also pollutes both land and food."[11]

These radical changes in our food supply have all occurred in the post WWII era. Today, one can go into any supermarket and all one sees is an abundance of food. But do not look closely at the ingredients label. Most of our packaged food is manufactured by large multinational corporations and the ingredients often come from crops that are heavily sprayed with pesticides. These poisons can then wind up in the final product that appears on your grocer's shelf. [12]

Not only our packaged food, but our fruits and vegetables – both domestically grown and imported – are likely sprayed with chemicals that threaten public health and harm the environment. Arsenic is a naturally occurring element that is used in fertilizer and pesticides. High exposures to the inorganic form of arsenic have been linked to cancer. The Food and Drug Administration (FDA) has been measuring total arsenic concentrations in foods, including rice and juices, since 1991 and has set acceptable exposure standards. Unlike the countries of the European Union, the U.S. has no ban on arsenic in our food.[13]

The food industry also relies heavily on genetically modified organisms (GMOs), the result of chemical-based agriculture, which are sold by large chemical companies like Monsanto. Soybeans are the most heavily genetically modified food in the U.S., followed by corn. Using chemicals to taint our food supply is not limited to crops. Animal feed is made using GMOs and cows are often given a bovine growth hormone to increase milk production – a practice banned by the European Union and a few other countries.[14] The Non-Gmo Project in the State of Washington is focused on the spread of genetically modified organisms. Their website states:

> "More than 80 percent of all genetically-modified crops grown worldwide have been engineered for herbicide tolerance. As a result, the use of toxic herbicides, such as Roundup, has increased fifteenfold since GMOs were first introduced. In March 2015, the World Health Organization determined that the herbicide glyphosate (the key ingredient in Roundup) is 'probably carcinogenic to humans.'
>
> Genetically modified crops also are responsible for the emergence of 'superweeds' and 'superbugs,' which can only be killed with ever more toxic poisons such as 2,4-D (a major

ingredient in Agent Orange). The long-term impacts of these GMOs are unknown. Once released into the environment, these novel organisms cannot be recalled."[15]

Whenever one attacks an unwanted organism using the same method every time, the survivors that have mutated and survived become "superweeds" and "superbugs." Eventually, one needs to resort to a more powerful weapon. This evolutionary process is called resistance, a phenomenon well-known to scientists. Just another unsustainable practice that is threatening our future food supply for a growing population.

Many have argued that GMOs have allowed farmers to increase yields, but that does not mean the food being grown is good for us. There is some evidence that the rise in Celiac disease – an autoimmune disease related to eating gluten – is due to GMOs and the use of glyphosate. While controversial and still unproven, the fact remains no one really knows the impact GMOs have on our health. The one thing we can count on is that the large chemical agriculture business will continue to dominate our food supply.[16]

Yields of corn have increased from less than two dozen bushels per acre back in 1920 to 180 bushels in 2005. Modern science created adaptable hybrid seeds that can greatly increase yields by allowing the corn stalks to be grown closer together. We have literally modified corn to tolerate the equivalent of "city life" by making them genetically identical. They keep coming out with seeds that offer greater yields but it costs more, so the large corporations make more money and not the farmer, as the increased productivity is neutralized by the higher seed prices.[17]

Industrial farming has other far-reaching effects. Any method of agriculture impacts the environment, but industrial farming is in a class by itself. The Union of Concerned Scientists, a science advocacy group based in Massachusetts, describes industrial farming as:

"At the core of industrial food production is monoculture – the practice of growing single crops intensively on a very large scale such as corn and wheat. Monoculture farming relies heavily on chemical inputs such as synthetic fertilizers and pesticides. The fertilizers are needed because growing the same plant (and nothing else) in the same place year after year quickly depletes the nutrients that the plant relies on, and these nutrients must be replenished. The pesticides are needed because monoculture fields are highly attractive to certain weeds and insect pests.

Much of industrial monoculture's harvest goes to feed livestock in concentrated animal feeding operations, or CAFOs, where they are fed a high-calorie, grain-based diet, often supplemented with antibiotics and hormones, to maximize their weight gain. Their waste is concentrated and becomes an environmental problem, not the convenient source of fertilizer that manure can be for more diverse, less massively-scaled farms."[18]

Breeding crops to increase the size and yield can have the unintended effect of decreasing the nutrient value of the produce. Bigger vegetables do not always mean more nutrients. Studies have shown significant decreases in the vitamin, mineral and protein in 43 common vegetables and fruits since 1950 when the USDA first began tracking nutrient content.[19]

Industrial agriculture also threatens America's traditional social fabric. Family farms and small towns are dying because of centralized industrial agriculture. Up to 80 percent of the beef sold in the U.S. is produced by just four companies – Tyson, Cargill, JBS and National Beef. Cargill Meat Solutions is just one of 75 businesses under Cargill Inc., the largest privately-held corporation in the U.S. Cargill also runs the biggest flour-milling company in the world and is a leading corn syrup and soybean processor.[20]

With contract chicken farms raising an average of 500,000 birds a year, they are wholly tied to the industrial agriculture companies who provide the chicks, slaughter them when ready and then process the meat for shipment to your supermarket.[21] In part, larger farms are the result of rising construction costs and the need to comply with environmental regulations. Farmers must be efficient or companies like Perdue and Tyson will not buy from them, just part of the same vicious cycle – more people, more demand, bigger agricultural operations, good-bye family farm.[22]

Maryland produces over 300 million chickens a year worth nearly a billion dollars, making it a big business with more chicken houses on the drawing board. For residents who live near these large chicken farms, the stench can be overwhelming. Many of these farms are located on Maryland's Eastern Shore and the manure runoff contributes to the pollution of Chesapeake Bay.[23]

> "For decades, the historic Chesapeake Bay watershed has been polluted by excess levels of nitrogen and phosphorus from manure that runs off industrial farm operations. These factory farms have been choking the bay with excess pollutants, causing algae blooms that consume oxygen and create 'dead zones' where fish and shellfish cannot survive. A U.S. Geological Survey report released last year pointed specifically to the Eastern Shore for levels of nitrogen in the region's waters that are among the highest in the nation."[24]

It is estimated that at least 228,000 tons of excess – meaning it cannot be used on site – manure is produced by those 300 million chickens. And who pays to clean-up the Bay when this excess manure is washing into the local waterways – the Maryland taxpayer. As of 2016, Marylanders had spent over 750 million dollars on Chesapeake's restoration. The contractors who raise the chickens are also at the mercy of the big chicken companies, as the waste is their problem.[25]

Legislation was introduced in 2016 called the Poultry Litter Management Act. If passed, it would require the chicken companies to pick up the excess manure from the contract growers and dispose of it in a way not harmful to the environment. This would make corporate America clean-up after themselves and make them pay for the cost of keeping our waterways clean. As of 2018, no final action has been taken on the bill. With climate change and the potential for more intense storms, the problem may only get worse.[26]

Biofuels present another side of the corporate farming world. U.S. prairies across the Great Plains have been converted into farmland to grow corn – not for food, but for fuel. Biofuels also illustrate how fixing one problem can lead to new ones.

The demand for ethanol produced from field corn was spurred by the discovery that the gasoline additive methyl tertiary butyl ether (MTBE) was contaminating groundwater. The result of amendments to the Clean Air Act in 1992, MTBE was used in gasoline to reduce carbon monoxide emissions. A decade later when the dangers associated with MBTE were fully exposed, many states banned its use. This opened the door for ethanol, its primary substitute.[27]

The steep growth after 2005 in ethanol consumption was driven by federal legislation aimed to reduce oil consumption and enhance energy security. Federal legislation passed in 2007 during the Bush Administration required the use of advanced biofuels, defined as renewable fuels that reduce greenhouse gas emissions by at least 50 percent.[28]

> "The total amount of biofuels used in the U.S. is required to be at least an amount stated in the legislation. The total target volume increases to 36 billion US gallons by 2022, from 4.7 billion gallons (18,000,000 m3) mandated in 2007. The Energy Independence and Security Act further specifies that 21 billion gallons of the 2022 total must be derived from non-cornstarch products (e.g. sugar, biodiesel, or cellulose)."[29]

Historically, most U.S. ethanol has come from corn and the required electricity for many of the ethanol distilleries emanated from coal.   Growing corn to be turned into ethanol also required large amounts of arable land that could be used for crops.[30]   "Plowing into untouched grassland releases carbon dioxide that has been locked in the soil. It increases erosion and requires farmers to use fertilizers and other industrial chemicals. In turn, that destroys native plants and wipes out wildlife habitats." [31]

Planting corn to make fuel is not sustainable. Its use was initially promoted to reduce our dependence on foreign oil. While other bioethanol fuels made from sugar fermentation – such as sugar cane – offer a lower carbon footprint, their availability in the U.S. is limited. A much better choice is biodiesel fuels especially when made from recycled vegetable oils or fats.

The advantages of biodiesel are significant. It is a natural and renewable domestic, clean-burning fuel alternative for diesel engines. It can be used to run cars, buses and other modes of transportation or mixed with home heating oil. Biofuel is the only alternate fuel approved by EPA that meets the criteria of the Clean Air Act and California's strict air quality requirements.[32]

The technologies around biofuels and biomass are changing rapidly.   At one end of the spectrum, ExxonMobil is researching how to produce synthetic algae biofuels.   Then there is a small Boston-based company called Xyleco that is converting biomass to a material that contains sugars, which can be used to make fuel. Since this technology uses non-food sources, it offers a superior alternative to using food crops.[33] Further research should be focused on using waste products or easily renewable sources and not things like palm oil, which is often grown on plantations that were once rain forests and is better suited for use in food products and cosmetics.

The decline of bee populations is another problem facing modern agriculture that could also be related to GMOs due to the increased dependence on pesticides.

Known as colony collapse disorder, it is a phenomenon that befalls the hive when the worker bees fly away never to return, leaving the queen and a few nurse bees behind. While not an uncommon occurrence, there was a dramatic increase in the number of colonies affected as the rate doubled over the next six years beginning in 2006.[34]

Farmers are understandably worried as bees – along with other insects – pollinate a wide variety of our most important crops. While many of our essential staple foods crops like corn, wheat, rice and soybeans are wind pollinated, bees help pollinate more than 90 flowering crops, representing about a third of the U.S. food supply.[35]   As the bee die-off continues to puzzle scientists, a class of chemicals used in pesticides called neonicotinoids were thought to be the primary cause. Other potential triggers include a new virus transmitted by a mite that targets the bee's immune system. The disease spreads quickly from bee to bee leading to the collapse of the colony.[36]

A fourth factor has recently emerged – Electro-Magnetic Frequencies (EMFs). Many flying animals use energetic frequencies and magnetics as tools for orientation and navigation.   Honeybees contain magnetic crystals in their fat body cells and now EMFs may be interfering with the natural biological rhythms that allow bees to swarm.[37]

The die-off has not discouraged the chemical companies from producing more pesticides. Dow AgroSciences, an agricultural chemical company, has applied to the EPA to allow for use of the pesticide known as sulfoxaflor on rice, avocados, residential ornamentals and at tree farms. Sulfoxaflor, which attacks the central nervous system of insects, is designed in part to replace neonicotinoid pesticides, which multiple studies have linked to bee colony collapse; this is the same nerve-agent class of pesticides German chemical giant Bayer provides to seed companies to coat corn and soybean seeds to kill pests.[38]

Unfortunately, sulfoxaflor has also been shown to harm bees. In a recent study, the sulfoxaflor colonies had a 54 percent reduction in natural offspring compared to control colonies. Although EPA had already ruled the pesticide "very highly toxic" to bees, it allowed for its limited use in 2013. A court decision over-turned that approval, but under "emergency exemptions" it was sprayed on an estimated 17.5 million acres of farmland; full approval was given in 2019.[39]

Switching one pesticide for another will do little to bring the hives back and the only "emergency" should be to save the nation's beehives. In the meantime, food researchers are trying to alter nature by producing hybrids that are human pollinated. A far better option is the effort by farmers, ranchers and others working with the USDA to protect bee populations. A farmer in New Mexico is creating "pollinator highways" by planting perennial grasses and flowers to attract bees.[40]

If the overuse of pesticides is not enough to scare the average consumer, foodborne illnesses are a far more immediate concern. The Center for Disease Control (CDC) estimates that each year roughly 1 in 6 Americans – around 48 million people – get sick, 128,000 are hospitalized and 3,000 succumb to foodborne diseases. There are 31 known pathogens as well as other "unspecified agents" that cause illness and 46 percent of these cases are from leafy vegetables and other produce.[41]

> "Perhaps the most notable outbreak of 2018 involved romaine lettuce contaminated with a strain of E. coli bacteria known as E. coli O157:H7. The outbreak, which began in March and ended in June, killed five people and sickened more than 200 others in 36 states, making it the largest U.S. E. coli outbreak in over a decade, according to the FDA. The contaminated lettuce was tied to the Yuma growing region of Arizona, and at one point, health officials advised consumers to avoid all romaine from this region."[42]

These outbreaks have led to greater interest in buying locally-grown food or from growers through community-supported agriculture. Doing so increases the odds of getting whole, unprocessed vegetables, fruits and products grown by small, local farmers as opposed to corporate farms that focus on supply only and have far more detrimental effects on our environment. Consumers are also buying more organically-grown food products.

Between 2008 and 2014, local food sales in the U.S. more than doubled. There is even a word now for people who prefer locally produced food – "locavore." In 2007, it was named "Word of the Year" by Oxford American Dictionary. However, when it comes to reducing our carbon footprint, buying local does not make a significant difference. While fresh fruits transported by air are energy-intensive, it is estimated that the distribution of most foods to your grocer contributes less than four percent of the greenhouse gas emissions of food consumed.[44]

Eating local produce and meats is more about food safety and promoting environmental stewardship. Local farms also contribute to a community's food security. Future disruptions in our food supply due to climate change, drought, or transportation issues are unknown. Therefore, understanding one can still feed a family thanks to the local farmer can be uplifting.

The U.S. food industry is designed to provide American families with unhealthy calories in the form of high-fructose corn syrup, added fats and other highly-subsidized food crops. Federal crop subsidies began in the 1920s when a quarter of the population worked on farms; today, these subsidies support corporate farms while the small, diversified farmers are left to survive on their own. Look no further than Wisconsin to see what is happening to the average dairy farmer in this largely agrarian state.

Once the largest milk producing state, it has now slipped to second behind California. In 2018, there were 8,304 dairy farms supplying milk, a reduction of 1,100 dairies over the past two years. With wholesale milk prices half of what they were in 2014, farmers lose money on every gallon produced. While the state continues to make the most cheese in the nation, the future of its dairy industry is in doubt.[45]

With all the varied issues facing California and its agricultural sector, do we really want to rely on them to provide our milk? If we can subsidize large commodity crops like corn, we should subsidize our dairy farmers so they too can become profitable. A report commissioned by the dairy farmers of Canada showed that the U.S. government direct and indirect subsidies to the dairy sector in 2015 only provided a 73 percent return.[46]

For the average American family, what is more important: to provide milk at an affordable price or soda sweetened with high-fructose corn syrup? These are the kind of choices that rarely cross the mind of the average supermarket shopper as we have failed to connect people to the land and to the reality of where our food comes from.

It is time for all Americans to learn more about their food supply; to understand that it takes far more water and energy to grow meat than it does to raise fruits and vegetables. How many of us know that ruminants – think cows and sheep – generate methane gas through their normal digestive process and expelled through burping and flatulence or that the hamburger from our local fast-food chain may have come from a cattle ranch that was carved from the rain forest? According to the Yale School of Forestry and Environmental Studies, "Cattle ranching is the largest driver of deforestation in the Amazon region, accounting for 80 percent of current deforestation rates."[47]

The fact is Americans love their meat and only three percent of us are vegans or follow a strict vegetarian diet. The average American now eats over 200 pounds of beef, pork and/or chicken a year (or more than 3.7 pounds a week), up from roughly 184 pounds in 2012. As shown in the below figure, the poundage we consume has been on the rise since 2014. The popularity of one meat over the other is mostly driven by price, but any choice has its environmental impact.[48]

Figure 6

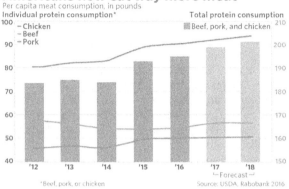

Americans now eat way more meat
Per capita meat consumption, in pounds

Our love of meat does not mean that everyone wants a processing plant in their backyard. Just ask the good folks of Nickerson, Nebraska. When Georgia-based Lincoln Premium Poultry wanted to process 1.6 million chickens a week for warehouse chain Costco, the 400 residents of Nickerson said no way. While deep-rooted agricultural communities around the country are seeking new economic opportunities, they are not willing to give up their way of life and forever alter the town's rural character.[49]

There also may be no better example of industrial farming than how cattle are now raised in the U.S. In the plains of western Kansas in places like Garden City, America's feedlots first began to appear in the early 1950s. Feedlots are where endless bushels of corn are converted into steaks.[50]

Known as Concentrated Animal Feeding Operations (CAFOs), cattle are now raised in pens and not on the open range. As we subsidized the growing of corn, farmers could no longer afford to compete with these factory farms. Of course, cattle are superbly adapted through evolution to feed on grass but have been reduced to eating corn for one simple reason – it is more profitable. The only way to meet the growing demand for fresh beef was to move away from the natural relationship between animals and the landscape.

While beef cattle are raised by ranchers from an early age feeding on grass, they are being bred to tolerate corn and are soon shipped to the feedlots to fatten up. Unlike the pasture, CAFOs have led to a host of environmental and health problems ranging from polluted water and toxic wastes to deadly pathogens. The use of growth hormones and antibiotics to deal with health problems related to the animal's cramped quarters is just another part of the story that is the antithesis of how we should be raising our food.[51]

With almost one hundred million acres of land dedicated to corn production, it is time to rethink our dependence on this single crop that is not being grown to feed people. Almost all the corn grown in the U.S. is used for animal feed or to make ethanol and high-fructose corn syrup. This has led some people to seek out alternatives such as natural sweeteners. For those who prefer grass-fed beef, it is important to consider all beef production has a large carbon footprint and requires a high use of water compared to other food sources.

> "The average Iowa cornfield has the potential to deliver more than 15 million calories per acre each year (enough to sustain 14 people per acre, with a 3,000 calorie-per-day diet, if we ate all of the corn ourselves), but with the current allocation of corn for ethanol and animal production, we end up with an estimated 3 million calories of food per acre per year, mainly as dairy and meat products, enough to sustain only three people per acre. That is lower than the average delivery of food calories from farms in Bangladesh, Egypt and Vietnam."[52]

No discussion of contemporary farming in the U.S. would be complete without discussing climate change. In 1988, following one of the worst droughts in the nation's history to hit Midwestern farmers, scientists first warned that global warming may affect the future viability of American farming. This was 30 years ago and yet we are still debating whether climate change is real or not.[53]

The world's climate zones that cover vast regions are changing with potentially dangerous implications.

> "The word 'tropical' usually suggests rainforests, colorful birds, and lush, dripping foliage, but the majority of our planet's middle region is actually quite dry. About a decade ago, scientists first noticed that this dry belt seemed to be getting bigger. The dry edges of the tropics are expanding as the subtropics push both north and south, bringing ever-drier weather to places such as the Mediterranean."[54]

This alteration in climatic zones impacts the U.S. as well. Just as the Mediterranean is likely to experience drier weather, this will affect the southern U.S. stretching across the entire country from Florida to California. The 100th meridian is also on the move. Scientist and explorer John Wesley Powell first noticed in the 1870s that the 100th meridian – which runs from Mexico to Manitoba, Canada through the middle of North Dakota down through the middle of Texas – split the nation in half. More rain falls east of the 100th meridian making the land better suited for rain-loving crops like corn, while the lands to the west are drier making them more ideal for growing wheat.[55]

While rainfall has not changed much in the northern plains, hotter temperatures are increasing the rate of evaporation from the soil and drying things out. As a result, the line between the drier and wetter halves of the country has moved about 140 miles eastward since 1980. If this trend continues, it will have a significant impact; rich agricultural states like Iowa could soon become a lot drier. This same trend is pushing what is known as Tornado Alley hundreds of miles to the east as evidenced by the increase in the number of tornados in eastern states like Alabama and Tennessee.[56]

Climate skeptics will say look at the bright side, we will experience longer growing seasons. If only the laws of nature were that simple. Drought will cause crops to dry up and die, and pests can overwinter with warmer temperatures putting crops at greater risk. Erratic weather patterns can cause intense storm events that flood crops and erode the soil. If plants bloom too early due to warmer temperatures, a late spring freeze can kill them. Our ecosystems are incredibly complex and by changing entire climate zones, we have no idea if plants will be able to adapt.

We do not want to overcome these challenges by using more water, fertilizers or pesticides. Fertilizers are a source of nitrous oxide, the most potent greenhouse gas behind carbon dioxide and methane. It also destroys stratospheric ozone, which protects the planet from harmful ultraviolet rays.

If you do not think Americans are spoiled when it comes to food choices, consider the recent efforts by Walmart and Whole Foods to sell slightly blemished fruits and vegetables at a discount. Not enough consumers bought these "ugly misfits" and instead continued to purchase the more expensive perfect looking produce. Trashing food because it is dented or not the right size, shape or color is wasteful. "The two chains and others quietly ended their tests, suggesting dented apples and undersized potatoes may not be all that appealing in stores where better-looking fruits and vegetables are on display."[57]

We need a new way of thinking about our food systems, from growing crops to disposing of food waste. Importing Kobe beef from Japan and sending our lobsters back to Asia is not sustainable. We need to look at our food habits and diet, including eating less meat. It is also eco-friendlier to buy fruits and vegetables that are seasonal and locally grown.

Organic food products may be healthier, but it does not mean they were grown sustainably. Lab-grown meat is on the rise, but the process requires lots of energy;

plant-based meat requires ingredients that have their own environmental impacts. Food and water go hand in hand along with energy use and must be addressed collectively. We are on a path toward food shortages and higher prices – a future no one wants for their children and grandchildren. Food does not originate in a supermarket, something a large segment of our society has forgotten.

And before you think your local supermarket has your best interests at heart consider the real reason grocers in most cases mist their produce with water. Unaware shoppers think shiny vegetables sprayed with water will remain fresh longer; some stores even pipe in thunderstorm sound effects to complete the deception. To highlight our ignorance about food, water adds lots of weight to the vegetables and, at the checkout, we pay by the pound. These produce showers are just another gimmick used by supermarket chains to take your money.[58] The practice can also cause produce to spoil more quickly. We will know society has become more enlightened about our food supply and delivery system when shoppers are seen across the country rigorously shaking their kale and broccoli in the produce aisle.

How Much Food is Wasted?

October 28, 2015: According to Fast Forward, a California-based group that fights hunger and food waste, figuring out how much food ends up in the trash is tricky, and the data that we have on national food waste is, at best, an estimate. However, several different studies have put food waste between 30-40 percent, so it is safe to say that something around 1/3 to 2/5 of our national food supply is never eaten. That number is even higher for highly perishable food groups like fruits and vegetables.

It is tempting to point fingers at restaurants, but the reality is that food waste occurs at every point along the food production chain. A lot of food is lost in distribution and in grocery stores. In addition, according to a 2015 study by the National Resources Defense

Council, twenty percent of all fruits and vegetables grown never even leave the farm.

Why are we throwing away six billion pounds of food every month? Three of the biggest reasons are: 1) cosmetic standards demand that fruits and vegetables be free of blemishes, bruises, spots or wrinkles; 2) overstocking and over-purchasing; and 3) confusion about sell-by and expiration dates. Whether it is ugly or not quite fresh, the food that we are throwing away is, for the most part, perfectly edible and tasty.[59]

Four Major Crops In The Crosshairs Of Climate Change

NPR's The Salt, October 25, 2018: Climate change is already here and our food, so dependent on rain and suitable temperatures, sits right in its path. The plants that nourish us will not disappear entirely, but they may have to move to higher and cooler latitudes. Some places may find it harder to grow anything at all, because there is not enough water. Wheat is one of those crops which will suffer from hotter temperatures. Over time, we may need to import more of our wheat from Canada. Here are three other foods grown in the U.S. that will see the impact:

Despite Georgia's claim to be the Peach State, California is the country's biggest peach producer. Farmers there grow about half of the country's fresh peaches, and most of the fruit that is canned or processed in other ways. Many fruit trees, including peaches, have a peculiar requirement. If they don't experience enough chill during wintertime, they get confused and don't bloom properly. No bloom, no harvest.

The peach trees currently grown in California's Central Valley require about 700 "chilling hours" during the winter. But scientists are predicting that by the end of the century, only 10 percent of the valley will reliably see that much chilling. And even if plant breeders create peach varieties that need less chilling, there's another problem: Peach trees also yield less fruit when it gets too hot in summertime.

Nothing says Iowa quite like fields of corn. Climate models, though, see a different future. Scientists are predicting that a warming climate will bring several changes, most of them bad for growing corn. Rain will come less often, and when it comes, the storms will be more intense – neither of which is helpful for a crop that demands frequent rains, but doesn't do a good job of preventing soil erosion. In addition, corn suffers when it gets too hot — especially when it's too hot at night.

Add it all up, and one study estimates that corn yields in Iowa will fall substantially, anywhere from 15 percent to an astounding 50 percent. Like wheat, we will need more corn from Canada.

What will replace corn on Iowa's fertile land? According to one study, by the end of the century this part of the Midwest will be more suited for growing cotton, soybeans, grass and forests.

California, the biggest single source of America's fresh vegetables and nuts, and the primary source of almonds for the entire world, is a dramatic illustration of how subtle shifts in climate can have huge effects. Also, there will be more variation from year to year; wet years will be wetter, and dry years will be even dryer.

Both trends increase the chances that from time to time, farmers will face catastrophic shortages of water. And that's especially bad for tree crops, of which almonds are the biggest, because losing an orchard results in a greater financial loss than losing a single crop of, say, tomatoes. California's farmers may be forced to reduce the amount of land devoted to orchards, since there is a chance that they will not survive a major drought.[60]

Chapter Thirteen
Our Waterways, Estuaries and Oceans in Peril

"We cannot win this battle to save species and environments without forging an emotional bond between ourselves and nature as well – for we will not fight to save what we do not love."

- Stephen Jay Gould -

Mankind has always been attracted to the sea. Yet, despite enjoying its riches, we seem to be more interested in exploring space even though oceans dominate the Earth's surface. Many coastal benefits arc easy to recognize, such as a source of food and recreation. But the ocean and associated coastal resources are so much more. Our lack of understanding of how coastal ecosystems function has led to the abuse and destruction of these valuable resources.

In addition to fisheries, many other products of economic value derive from the ocean. This includes ingredients used in pharmaceuticals, food supplements and cosmetics. Phytoplankton – those tiny plant organisms that permeate the world's oceans – produce oxygen in every breath they take. In fact, scientists believe phytoplankton produce at least half of the world's oxygen supply and the figure could be much higher, perhaps as much as 85 percent.[1]

Our estuaries and marshes absorb storm waters protecting the upland from flooding. Much of the white sand we enjoy when visiting a tropical paradise originates from living coral reefs offshore.[2] Coral reefs also provide shoreline protection. The total economic value of coral reef services under our nation's jurisdictions has an estimated annual value of nearly three and a half billion dollars.[3]

Perhaps most important, oceans play a critical role in regulating climate. The steadily increasing volume of carbon dioxide emissions is not only raising water temperatures around the globe, but increasing ocean acidity which could have far-reaching effects on life in the ocean and the entire planet.

On average, the oceans absorb about a quarter of the carbon dioxide released from the burning of fossil fuels and other sources such as burning fires and decay. The transformation of carbon dioxide in salt water involves a complex chemical reaction. The result is our oceans are becoming more acidic and producing less calcium carbonate, critical to the formation of shells. Scientific measurements show, since the beginning of the Industrial Revolution, ocean acidity has increased by 30 percent. Scientists believe the pH range of seawater – a measurement of acidity – is now, after one million years, becoming unstable.[4]

This increased acidity is detrimental to the growth of coral reefs, clams, mussels, oysters and many forms of phytoplankton and zooplankton. The harmful effects have been likened to a marine version of osteoporosis. If the water becomes too acidic, the fragile shells of a coral reef could begin to dissolve. Since denser, colder waters absorb carbon dioxide at a faster rate, ocean acidification may be heightened in the polar regions.[5]

Protecting the world's oceans and reducing carbon emissions has major implications for the U.S. Compared to much of the world, we are blessed with incredible coastal resources "from sea to shining sea." The coast embodies our national identity as a country with unlimited resources, and it is where a majority of Americans live today. According to NOAA:

> "While U.S. counties located directly on the shoreline constitute less than ten percent of the total land area (excluding Alaska), they account for 39 percent of the total population. From 1970 to 2010, the population of these counties increased by almost 40 percent and are projected to increase by an additional ten

million people by 2020. Coastal areas are substantially more crowded than the rest of the U.S. In fact, the population density of coastal shoreline counties is over six times greater than the corresponding inland counties and this trend is expected to continue in the future."[6]

But are we loving our coasts to death? The unending development of this fragile resource is fundamentally changing natural coastal ecosystems. In addition to people flocking to the coast to live, much of this development is centered around tourism. Coastal tourism accounts for up to 85 percent of all tourism revenue in the U.S. This results in the alteration of water flows, new sources of water pollution, poor air quality and habitat loss – both on the land and in the water – putting entire ecosystems are at risk.[7]

These impacts are most pronounced on barrier islands and along beaches. Barrier islands are the first defense against storm surge; they can also be an ideal location to build a summer cottage. One such place is Plum Island off the coast from Newburyport, Massachusetts. Created during the last Ice Age, most of the island is a wildlife refuge, but the southern portion has been heavily developed. In recent years, several powerful winter storms have washed away entire buildings.[8]

The situation was made more complicated by the installation of two long jetties that were designed to manipulate the flow of the Merrimack River. The mouth of the river is located at the northern tip of the island and the jetties have changed the pattern of sand deposition resulting in substantial beach loss. In other words, the island is washing away and now the Army Corps of Engineers wants to dredge sand from Portsmouth Harbor in New Hampshire and bring it down to Plum Island. There is just one problem – there is no money available to complete the project.[9]

Some homeowners have built seawalls to keep the rising waters at bay. At best, this is a short-term fix. With more intense storms and sea level rise, the forces of nature will prevail. Family cottages and seasonal homes passed down from one generation to the next will more than likely be destroyed sometime during this century. But Plum Island is just the beginning. With some 1,500 miles of coastline in Massachusetts, there are 681 barrier beaches at risk. People will continue to build seawalls and other hard structures to prevent further erosion, but the seawater must go somewhere. One person's seawall will become someone else's problem.[10]

The coastal City of Myrtle Beach in South Carolina is a man-made barrier island created by the construction of the Intracoastal Waterway along the East Coast and is in the center of a large, continuous 60-mile stretch of beach known as the Grand Strand. In 2016, The Myrtle Beach metropolitan area had an estimated population in 2016 of 449,495, an increase of over 72,200 in just six years.[12] The 2018 census estimates it is the second fastest-growing metropolitan area in the country. Because of its subtropical climate and extensive beaches, the area also attracts an estimated 14 million annual visitors. Nearly 100 golf courses in the area provide a big part of the attraction.[13]

The one thing missing from this vacation paradise is large, natural sand dunes. They used to be there but were flattened by Hurricane Hazel in 1954, the worst hurricane to ever hit Myrtle Beach. While there are still dunes along the beachfront, the only large "sand dunes" left are a resort hotel of the same name with two fourteen-story towers. Like Plum Island, Myrtle Beach has been lucky when it comes to hurricanes. The last storm to cause significant damage was Hurricane Hugo in 1989.[14]

Myrtle Beach does have a problem with beach erosion retreating at a rate of up to one foot per year. Barrier beaches are dynamic terrains that are constantly being altered by ocean currents. To compensate for this loss, the state replenishes the beach sand every seven years or so with sediment dredged from the sea bottom. Most consider this money well spent considering the economic value of the area.[15]

But what happens if Myrtle Beach does receive a direct hit from a hurricane? Instead of serving as a barrier against a storm surge, development has put the entire area at risk with the potential for huge financial losses. Low-lying areas are also susceptible to coastal flooding due to sea level rise. Our love of the sea drives these kinds of economic decisions and, of course, Myrtle Beach is not unique. Similar beach developments line almost the entire East Coast.

When it comes to erosion, the Mississippi River delta basin best demonstrates what happens when man interferes with natural water flows. The basin encompasses more than 500,000 acres consisting mainly of marshes and coastal wetlands along the southern coast of Louisiana. The Mississippi stretches some 2,320 miles from its source in northern Minnesota – Lake Itasca – and flows south past New Orleans into the Gulf of Mexico. Draining the entire mid-section of the U.S. from the Appalachian Mountains to the Rockies, the river system transports half a billion tons of sediment each year.[16]

> "For the past 100 million years, redeposited sediment has gradually increased the size of the Mississippi River delta, but over the past several decades, the coast of southern Louisiana has been losing rather than gaining land. This is due to a combination of physical factors (such as hurricanes, tidal erosion and sea level rise) and human factors (such as dams trapping sediment and flood control systems) which prevent the buildup of deposited sediment."[17]

Flooding in the Midwest causes runoff tainted with fertilizer that flows into the Mississippi River which eventually winds up in the Gulf of Mexico. This influx of nutrients consisting of high levels of nitrogen and phosphorus triggers blooms of algae that then die and decompose. The result every summer is a hypoxic "dead zone" – an area where there is not enough oxygen for fish and other marine life to survive.

Since 1985, NOAA has been studying the effects of hypoxia in the Gulf and, in 2017, the dead zone covered 8,776 square miles, an area the size of New Jersey. This was the largest dead zone ever recorded in the Gulf, partly the result of torrential rains in the Midwest which washed away large amounts of nutrients like phosphorus and nitrogen, essential ingredients in algal blooms.[18]

What is the cause of this runoff? It should come as no surprise that agriculture is responsible for the large amounts of fertilizer being used to grow crops like corn. It is, as noted, the same corn that is grown to produce ethanol and later mixed with our gasoline. The resource-intensive meat industry shares a lot of the blame, not only for its dependence on feed corn but also for the toxins from manure that exacerbates a growing problem.[19]

> "A new report by Mighty, an environmental group chaired by former congressman Henry Waxman, analyzed supply chains of agribusiness and pollution trends and found that a 'highly industrialized and centralized factory farm system' was resulting in vast tracts of native grassland in the Midwest being converted into soy and corn to feed livestock. Stripped soils can wash away in the rain, bringing fertilizers into waterways.
>
> Arkansas-based Tyson Foods is identified by the report as a 'dominant' influence in the pollution, due to its market strength in chicken, beef and pork products. Tyson, which supplies the likes of McDonald's and Walmart, slaughters 35 million chickens and 125,000 head of cattle every week, requiring five million acres of corn a year for feed. This consumption resulted in Tyson generating 55 million tons of manure last year."[20]

When we start to make the connections between land use and food, we realize how all parts of the environment are connected. Our current food supply system is not sustainable and this recent study further highlights the challenge we face with adding more people to the general population.

Unlike Myrtle Beach, New Orleans and the surrounding area know all about damaging hurricanes. On August 29, 2005, the center of Hurricane Katrina passed southeast of New Orleans causing over 50 breaches of levees and floodwalls. With some parts of the city under 15 feet of water, 80 percent of New Orleans was flooded. As mandated in the Flood Control Act of 1965, responsibility for the design and construction of the city's levees belongs to the Army Corps of Engineers, with the Orleans Levee Board responsible for their maintenance. Many consider the failure of the levees as the worst engineering disaster in the history of the U.S.[21]

Katrina's destruction was not limited to New Orleans and the coastal area of Louisiana. Besides also causing damage in the Gulf states of Florida, Alabama and Mississippi, the storm continued to wreak havoc all the way north to Vermont. In all, the storm resulted in between 1,200 and 1,800 deaths as well as damages exceeding $125,000,000,000, tying it with Hurricane Harvey in 2017 as the most expensive in U.S. history.[22]

The harm to Louisiana and other Gulf states does not end with Hurricane Katrina. On April 10, 2010, the largest marine oil spill in the history of the petroleum industry began in the Gulf in Mexico. Known as the Deepwater Horizon oil spill, the British Petroleum operated Macondo oil well had a blowout that took five months to seal. Although the well has been declared "effectively dead," oil slicks due to leakage continued to appear for several years. In the end, the U.S. government estimated the total discharge at 4.9 million barrels – 210 million US gallons – released into the Gulf.[23]

The health and environmental impacts from the Deepwater spill are well documented, as are the many missteps in attempts to seal the well and capture the spilled oil. One of the oil dispersants used to divert oil from the shoreline was Corexit. Its use was "purely experimental." A 2011 analysis showed that the dispersant could contain cancer-causing agents, hazardous toxins and endocrine-disrupting chemicals.[24] Nearly ten years later, offshore oil and gas drilling continues to pose a threat to our marine ecosystems.

Until Deepwater occurred, the most famous and largest oil spill in U.S. history was the *Exxon Valdez*. On March 24, 1989, the tanker became grounded on Bligh Reef in Alaska's Prince William Sound, rupturing its hull and spilling nearly eleven million gallons of crude oil. Multiple factors contributed to the disaster, with the blame falling entirely on Exxon Shipping Company. The spilled oil eventually covered 1,300 miles of coastline and 11,000 square miles of ocean water.[25]

Prior to the spill, Prince William Sound was a remote, scenic and highly biologically productive water body. Because of the harsh Alaska winters, most of the beach clean-up occurred over four consecutive summers. At its peak, over 10,000 workers using boats, planes and helicopters did their best to clean the oily shores. Despite this effort, not all the beaches were cleaned and some beaches still show signs of oil. The wave action from winter storms may have done more to disperse the oil than the cleaning efforts.[26]

> "As for wildlife, no one knows for sure how many animals died because of the spill. The carcasses of more than 35,000 birds and 1,000 sea otters were found after the spill, but since most carcasses sink, this is no doubt only a small fraction of the actual death toll. The best estimates are: 250,000 seabirds, 2,800 sea otters, 300 harbor seals, 250 bald eagles, up to 22 killer whales, and billions of salmon and herring eggs."[27]

Over 90 percent of the world's sea otters live in coastal Alaska, ranging from Kodiak Island through the western Aleutian Islands. The Valdez spill devastated the sea otter population in Prince William Sound. Although few were saved by rescue efforts, much knowledge was gained about how to successfully rehabilitate oiled sea otters. A 2006 report from the Exxon Valdez Oil Spill Trustee Council named the sea otter as one of several species still being affected by the lingering oil in the area. As of 2006, there are an estimated 73,000 sea otters in Alaska.[28]

In addition to the catastrophic environmental damage, over 32,000 fishermen saw their income crash due to the spill. Many native communities in Alaska continue to meet most of their dietary needs through hunting, fishing and foraging; these natives were gravely affected by the spill as it decimated traditional seaweed harvest, clamming and fishing zones that are vital to the natives of the area.[29]

As an aftermath of the spill, Exxon was sued for damages including the death of sea otters. An Anchorage jury awarded $287 million for actual damages and $5 billion for punitive damages, which was immediately appealed by Exxon claiming the spill was an "accident" and they had spent an estimated $2 billion cleaning up the spill and a further $1 billion to settle related civil and criminal charges.[30] They went so far as to blame the U.S. Coast Guard for the accident and the State of Alaska for interfering with their clean-up efforts. After a whole succession of appeals in the lower courts, the Supreme Court ruled in 2008 that the damages should be no more than $507.5 million. Most of this money was used to support fisheries. After all its legal fenagling, Exxon paid out over 1.5 billion in damages in addition to the clean-up costs.   There is no public accounting of their legal fees.[31]

One of the most interesting aspects of the settlement is the value placed on sea otters. It was determined the value of a dead otter was $89,000. In an article for *USA Today*, author Terrie Williams asked how does one place a value on an otter's life? Since their population once numbered over 300,000, using the figure determined by the courts over time it comes to over $26 billion.[32]

In response to the spill, Congress passed the Oil Pollution Act of 1990 (OPA). The legislation included a clause "that prohibits any vessel that, after March 22,

1989, has caused an oil spill of more than 1 million U.S. gallons in any marine area from operating in Prince William Sound." Its purpose was to minimize the potential of future oil spills in the Sound. This restriction was also unsuccessfully challenged in court by Exxon.[33] The OPA also called for phasing-in the double-hull design for oil tankers. The U.S. Coast Guard believes this design could have lessened the impact of the spill by more than half. Congress enacted legislation requiring all tankers to be double-hulled as of 2015.[34] Other far-reaching measures dealing with preparedness and liability compensation were also addressed in the legislation. While we will never know the true damage caused by the spill, it forced us to carefully think through the viability of drilling for oil and shipping it in fragile environments like Prince William Sound, a controversy that continues today.

Luckily, massive oil spills are a rare occurrence. A far greater threat to our coastal waterways is nutrient pollution. Earlier we learned about the millions of chickens being raised in the Chesapeake watershed, but that is not the only factor leading to degradation of our nation's largest estuary and the third largest in the world. According to the EPA:

> "The Chesapeake Bay watershed encompasses the entire District of Columbia, as well as parts of six states: Delaware, Maryland, New York, Pennsylvania, Virginia and West Virginia. Nitrogen and phosphorus loadings to the Chesapeake are a regional water quality concern.
>
> Nitrogen and phosphorus have always been a part of the Chesapeake Bay ecosystem, but have increased to excessive levels over the last few decades. Prior to substantial human activity in the region, most nitrogen and phosphorus were absorbed or retained by natural forest and wetland vegetation. However, the activities of over 13.6 million people in thewatershed have

overwhelmed the Chesapeake Bay with excess amounts of nutrients.

Nitrogen and phosphorus come from a wide range of point and nonpoint sources, including sewage treatment plants, industrial facilities, animal operations, agricultural fields, golf courses, lawns, and the atmosphere. As forests and wetlands have been replaced by farms, cities, and suburbs to accommodate a growing population, nitrogen and phosphorus pollution to the Chesapeake Bay has greatly increased."[35]

Historically, Chesapeake Bay was well known for its seafood. In the middle of the twentieth century, the Bay supported 9,000 full-time watermen who plied its waters for blue crabs, clams and oysters. Important fish species include rockfish – the regional name for striped bass – and menhaden which is rendered into oil and fish meal for dietary supplements and feed for livestock and aquaculture. Poor water quality along with over-harvesting and invasive species has led to a drastic reduction in these high-value species.[36]

In May 2009, President Obama issued an Executive Order designating Chesapeake Bay as a national treasure and calling on the federal government to lead an effort to restore its once abundant natural resources. This action resulted in action plans with measurable goals; a year later, EPA released what they called a "pollution diet" for the Bay.

"Section 303(d) of the Clean Water Act authorizes EPA to assist states, territories and authorized tribes in listing impaired waters and developing Total Maximum Daily Loads (TMDLs) for these waterbodies. A TMDL establishes the maximum amount of a pollutant allowed in a waterbody and serves as the starting point or planning tool for restoring water quality."[38]

The purpose of the TMDL is to limit the amount of nitrogen, phosphorus and sediment pollution discharged into the Chesapeake Bay and its tributaries. The goal is to restore habitats that support critical species on the decline. In part, this is accomplished by protecting local watersheds and public outreach programs. One method to measure success is to track the acreage classified as "dead zones" or hypoxic low-oxygen zones. NOAA has the responsibility for estimating their size. The models used are based on seasonal predictions around the start and end of summer.[39]

Of course, nutrient pollution is hardly the only issue facing the Chesapeake. Climate change exacerbates many of the Bay's existing problems. We know that warmer waters lead to a decrease in dissolved oxygen furthering the effects of algal blooms and dead zones. Rising sea levels threaten to inundate thousands of acres of environmentally critical wetlands. As in so many other places, population growth increases the pressures on the ecosystem. While some progress is being made, its future has yet to be decided. A recent report on the health of the Bay by the Chesapeake Bay Foundation gave it a D+ grade.[40]

> "Experts agree that the science-based Chesapeake Clean Water Blueprint is our last chance to save the Bay. Since the Blueprint's beginning in 2010, the Bay has been improving. But as this year's *State of the Bay* shows, progress is never a straight line. Simply put, the Bay suffered a massive assault in 2018. Extraordinary weather flushed enormous amounts of nitrogen, phosphorous, and debris – mostly from Pennsylvania, but also from other regions – off our lands and into the Bay. As a result, the *State of the Bay* score fell one point to a 33. In other words, a D+."[41]

Another critical ecosystem when we talk about fisheries is the Gulf of Maine. The Great Bay estuary that was highlighted in Chapter One is part of this incredible ecosystem whose boundary stretches from the tip of Cape Cod north to the Canadian provinces of New Brunswick and Nova Scotia. Its cold waters, extreme tidal mixing, and diverse bottom make the Gulf one of the most productive marine environments in the North Atlantic.[42]

Once the home to millions of cod, the Gulf provides suitable habitat for many diverse species, most notably haddock, Atlantic herring and the American lobster. The highly endangered North American right whale migrates through the Gulf, traveling from its feeding grounds in the Labrador Sea to the coastal waters of Georgia and Florida to bear calves. There are about 400 individuals still in existence; the number of breeding females is estimated as closer to 100.

Vessel strikes and entanglement in fixed fishing gear are the greatest threat to their survival.[43]

Climate change is also impacting the whales' feeding habitats. As the waters of the Gulf of Maine heat up, the whales must move further north from their usual feeding grounds. Right whales feed on zooplankton, specifically copepods, and now must travel to spots where the appropriate food can be found, putting even greater stress on their shrinking population.[44]

The near collapse of a once thriving cod industry is best described by a term used in the social sciences. It is called a "tragedy of the commons" and describes a situation where a shared resource – in this case the Gulf of Maine – is exploited for the short-term economic interests of a few individuals to the detriment of the long-term common good of all users.[45]

> "InxAugust (2014), scientists declared that the abundance of Gulf of Maine cod was at an all-time low. Scientists estimated that the population was at a mere *3-4 percent of a* sustainable abundance level. They also found very few young cod in the population, which means recovery of the population is not going to occur anytime soon."[46]

To protect the severely depleted population, NOAA declared a short-term moratorium on the taking of cod. Fishery managers moved to restrict commercial and recreational fishing in the areas where the highest concentrations of cod catch had occurred in recent years. They also restricted fishing in cod spawning areas. In places where cod fishing could occur, a 200-pound limit per fishing trip was implemented.[47]

The cod catch in U.S. waters has dropped dramatically in the face of the meager quotas allowed by the federal government; numbers have fallen from more than 18 million pounds in 2011 to about a million pounds in 2016. In Maine where cod is sacred, fish landings have dropped from 21 million pounds in 1991 to a record low of less than 170,000 pounds in 2016. In a period of just five years this dramatic drop has led many to question if cod fishing in New England is a thing of the past. We now import most of our cod from Norway, Iceland and Russia.[48]

Cod are groundfish that live near the ocean bottom. This means if one can only take a certain poundage of cod, they must stop fishing for other desirable fish species like haddock and halibut once that quota is reached. This puts pressure on fishermen trying to make a living and has led to distrust between them and the scientists and managers trying to protect cod stocks. Cod need safe places to feed, grow and reproduce if they are going to have any chance of a resurgence, but they now face a new threat – the rapid warming of the Gulf due to climate change. Years of overfishing complicated by a changing environment where phytoplankton reproduction rates are declining make recovery efforts that much more difficult if not impossible.[49]

The tragedy of the commons that occurred in the Gulf of Maine is not unique to this region. Salmon populations in the Northwest have also been greatly reduced due to human impacts. In 2000, the University of Oregon conducted an intensive study of the factors that caused the decline of salmon in the Columbia River Basin. While dams play a major factor in the ability of salmon to migrate, there are many other causes that negatively affect salmon populations such as overfishing, logging, agriculture, climate change and population growth. [50]

The Oregon study then matches potential problems and how each risk factor plays a role. What is significant is the number of issues the study identifies that could potentially impact salmon – thirteen in total. As the saying goes, a chain is only as strong as its weakest link, and any single threat can have a dramatic impact on any given population; it is how our natural world operates and why understanding how as best we can it all ties together is imperative in saving a species from extinction.[51]

Today, many of our major rivers, estuaries and oceans are depleted of abundant fish stocks. In the Great Lakes which is a shared resource between the U.S. and Canada, algal blooms and chemical pollution are the major threats to fish. In the past decade, massive toxic algal blooms have reappeared in Lakes Erie, Ontario and Huron; increased inputs of phosphorous from agriculture and urban areas are mostly to blame. In 2014, an algal bloom in Lake Erie caused the City of Toledo, Ohio to shut off the water supply to its nearly 500,000 residents due to toxins found in a water treatment plant. It was several days before the tap water was safe to drink again.[52] According to the National Research Council:

> "Reproductive and developmental abnormalities have also been observed in several populations of fish exposed to effluents from sewage treatment plants and paper mills of the Great Lakes. Effects observed include intersexes in trout exposed to sewage-treatment-plant effluent; increased egg and fry mortality in trout and salmon; thyroid enlargement in salmon; and changes in plasma sex-steroid concentrations, decreased egg and gonad size, and delayed sexual maturity in white suckers exposed to effluents from paper mills along Lake Superior."[53]

The thyroid enlargement in salmon is thought to be caused by exposure to polychlorinated biphenyls. Commonly known as PCBs, this organic chlorine compound was once widely deployed in numerous industrial applications including coolants and insulating fluids. Known as a legacy organic pollutant that persists in the environment for decades, PCBs were banned by the U.S. in late 1970s. Like methylmercury, many PCB compounds bioaccumulate rapidly through food chains, resulting in toxic effects, and can lead to restrictions on fish consumption by humans. [54]

The Great Lakes were not the only waterways heavily polluted with PCBs. Perhaps the most documented example is the Hudson River in New York. Over a period of 30 years from 1947 to 1977, General Electric (GE) dumped an estimated 1.3 million pounds of PCBs into the river from two of their capacitor manufacturing plants. The pollutant is found in the river's sediments from north of Albany down to New York Harbor.

Below is a timeline of the discovery of PCBs in the Hudson and GE's response:[55]

> **1970** – Journalist Bob Boyle has 5 striped bass from the Hudson River near Verplanck tested for pollutants. The results show abnormally high levels of PCBs. Boyle shares findings with the NY State fisheries director; the findings are suppressed.

> **1977** – PCBs are banned in the U.S. and Hudson River levels decline significantly once GE stops active dumping.

> **1983** – EPA classifies the 200-mile stretch of the Hudson River from Hudson Falls to the Battery in New York City as a Superfund site under the Superfund law.

1985 – The State of New York closes commercial striped bass fisheries in New York Harbor and waters off western Long Island.

2001 – GE files a lawsuit challenging the constitutionality of the Superfund law. A federal judge throws out the suit in 2003. GE appeals and, in 2004, a federal Court of Appeals reverses the ruling and sends the case back to the district court for a hearing on the merits of GE's claim.

2006 – After battling for two decades to avoid the cleanup project, GE agrees to begin testing for PCB hotspots in the Hudson and contract with environmental specialists to dredge contaminated sediments from the river.

2008 – EPA accepts GE's plan to remove a third less contaminated river sediment than they agreed to remove.

In the case of the *Exxon Valdez*, Exxon tried to blame others for the spill and then fought the judgment against them. GE chose a similar path, arguing the law that protects all American citizens from hazardous materials was unconstitutional. In both cases, the courts ruled against them although the penalties could have been much worse. However, these assaults on our most valued waterways, while horrific, only scratch the surface. One of the most undeniable examples of neglect involves the Cuyahoga River; in 1969, its story was front page news.

"On June 22, 1969, oil and debris on the surface of the Cuyahoga River – which flows into Lake Erie – in Cleveland, Ohio burst into flames and burned for 25 minutes. The burning river quickly became national news. *Time Magazine* published an article headlined 'The Price of Optimism,' complete with a spectacular photo of the river aflame. Randy Newman wrote a song about the famous fire called *Burn On*. And decades later, environmental leaders remembered the fire as an emblematic cause of the burgeoning environmental movement. 'I will never forget a photograph of flames, fire, shooting right out of the water in downtown Cleveland,' President Clinton's EPA administrator Carol Browner said years later. 'It was the summer of 1969 and the Cuyahoga River was burning'."[56]

For at least 100 years before 1969, industrial river fires were a normal part of American life. After the Ohio fire, it was possible to purchase a Cuyahoga River Fire Department t-shirt as a symbol of how bad things had gotten. However, as sometimes happens when documenting an historic event, the famous photograph that appeared in *Time* was not taken in 1969.

"It was of a far more serious fire in 1952 that burned for three days and caused $1.5 million in damage. In fact, the Cuyahoga had caught fire on at least a dozen occasions since 1868. Most of those earlier fires were much more devastating than the 1969 blaze. A fire on the Cuyahoga in 1912 killed five people. A fire in 1936 burned for five days. The 1969 fire, by contrast, lasted just under 30 minutes, caused only $50,000 in damage, and injured no one. The reason *Time* had to use the photograph of the 1952 fire is that the 1969 fire was out before anyone could snap a picture of it."[57]

The history of the Cuyahoga River is one of persistent exploitation. In 1881, the mayor of Cleveland called the Cuyahoga "an open sewer." The river was so flammable that if a steamboat captain dumped glowing coals from his boat's boiler, the river was burst into flames. When the city acted to build a sewer system it was not fires or protecting the environment that forced them to do so. It was to prevent more cholera outbreaks.[58]

This is a common theme in our history as a developing country. It is okay to neglect the environment and wipe out an entire species, but we will take corrective action once public health is at risk. Unfortunately, this degree of concern usually only applies to the population at large, as opposed to a small group – especially poor people or minorities – who happen to live next to a coal ash debris pile or a polluted waterbody.

The first large-scale federal effort to clean up our surface waters was enacted in 1948. Called the Federal Water Pollution Control Act, its emphasis was on public health. It authorized "the Surgeon General of the Public Health Service, in cooperation with other Federal, state and local entities, to prepare comprehensive programs for eliminating or reducing the pollution of interstate waters and tributaries and improving the sanitary condition of surface and underground waters."[59]

Other measures were included to "assist states, municipalities, and interstate agencies in constructing treatment plants to prevent discharges of inadequately-treated sewage and other wastes into interstate waters or tributaries" as well as efforts to conserve public water supplies, improve fish and aquatic life, promote recreational activities, and manage water usage related to agriculture and industry.[60]

This law was significantly restructured and expanded in 1972 with the passage of the Clean Water Act which establishes the basic structure for regulating discharges of pollutants into the waters of the U.S. and regulating quality standards for surface waters. The Act allowed EPA to implement pollution control standards for wastewater and industrial sources to develop national water quality criteria recommendations for pollutants in surface waters.[61]

The Act has regulated discharges of contaminants since 1972. Much has been accomplished due its passage and it should not be discounted. A study published in 2009 that looked at water quality improvements in the Southern California Bight, a coastal area that extends

from San Diego to Point Conception north of Santa
Barbara, noted the following:

> "While the coastal population grew by 56
> percent and total effluent volume increased 31
> percent from 1971 to 2000, mass emissions of
> nearly all constituents decreased since passage
> of the Clean Water Act, most by greater than 65
> percent. Publicly-owned treatment works were
> the dominant point source of many
> contaminants, but also accounted for the
> greatest reductions in pollutant discharge since
> 1971."[62]

Similar reductions in industrial waste discharges have
been achieved as well. The once flammable Cuyahoga
River is no longer a fire threat and prominent fish
species have started to recover; the Hudson River is
much cleaner and healthier as well. Overall, more than
60 percent of the nation's waters meet the Clean Water
Act's fishable and swimmable goal; in 1972, only about a
third were considered fit for these activities.[63]

These successes are tempered by an increase in
pollution from non-point sources which result from
"land runoff, precipitation, atmospheric deposition,
drainage, seepage or hydrologic modification." Pollution
results when rain or snowmelt moves over and through
the built environment and the ground washing away
natural and human-made pollutants into our waterways
– an impact made worse by intense rain events and
hurricanes.[64]

EPA lists the following pollutants of greatest concern:

- Excess fertilizers, herbicides and insecticides
  from agricultural lands and residential areas; oil,
  grease and toxic chemicals from urban runoff
  and energy production

- Sediment from improperly managed construction sites, crop and forest lands, and eroding streambanks
- Salt from irrigation practices and acid drainage from abandoned mines
- Bacteria and nutrients from livestock, pet wastes and faulty septic systems
- Atmospheric deposition and hydromodification (i.e. channelization and channel modification, dams, and streambank and shoreline erosion)[65]

States report that nonpoint source pollution is now the leading cause of water quality problems and EPA's program to address stormwater – the National Pollutant Discharge Elimination System's (NPDES) newly revised MS 4 permits – is still a work in progress.   It is often difficult to identify this diffuse source of pollution hindering efforts to remediate the problem. Regional and local data collection of sources is also not required under the Clean Water Act, making it difficult to find trends and establish baselines of pollution.[66]

The Center for Effective Government summed up the Clean Water Act as of 2012 on its 40th anniversary in this way:

> "EPA's most recent national water quality inventory reported that 44 percent of assessed miles of rivers and streams, 30 percent of assessed square miles of bays and estuaries, and 64 percent of assessed lake and reservoir acres did not fully support safe fishing and safe swimming. Further improvements to water quality have been hindered by a number of challenges unforeseen in 1972. The impacts of population growth, development, and increased runoff from poorly regulated sources of pollutants were not anticipated when the Clean Water Act was passed. As a result, some of the greatest threats to water quality today are not sufficiently addressed by the existing legal

framework of the Clean Water Act and pollution management practices it contains."[67]

A more recent 2017 EPA report provides further evidence that many of the water impairments remain unabated and that more detailed assessments are needed.[68] While far more needs to be done to ensure clean water for future generations, President Trump's callous desire to gut EPA's funding further impedes these efforts. Meanwhile, our continued dependence on oil and gas has made the Houston Ship Channel one of the most polluted waterways in the country. On March 22, 2014, a barge carrying nearly a million gallons of marine fuel oil collided with another ship causing the contents of one of the barge's 168,000-gallon tanks to leak into Galveston Bay.[69]

No water body can be taken for granted. Estuaries like Chesapeake Bay are the transition zone between land and the sea, where fresh and sea water mix to create one of the most productive natural habitats in the world. These dynamic systems, where temperature, salinity, turbidity, depth and flow all change daily in response to the tides, serve as nurseries to our seas.

The adage that "dilution is the solution to pollution" is no longer acceptable. When we pollute these valuable natural resources with industrial-generated chicken waste and other pollutants, we are losing part of our heritage. When the endless search for oil leads to environmental disasters, we cannot just push these aside as mere accidents. We have made a conscious choice and it is one that will come back to haunt us; nature can be very unforgiving if pushed too far.

Exxon Valdez – Twenty-Five Years Later

Exxon has long claimed that fisheries damaged from 1989 *Exxon Valdez* oil spill recovered quickly. When pink salmon and herring populations crashed after years later, the company said there was no direct link to the spill.   A 2015 study published by NOAA Fisheries experts tells a much different story.

In their laboratory tests, scientists discovered that exposure to even low levels of crude oil caused heart defects in captive juvenile pink salmon and herring despite the fact they appeared normal. According to NOAA toxicologist John Incardona, "That translates directly into reduced swimming ability and reduced survival." As a result, an oil spill can have a dramatic impact on the survival of one-year-old fish leading to future declines in the population. These findings should not come as a surprise.

Nat Scholz, a co-author of the NOAA study, said, "Our findings are changing the picture in terms of assessing the risk and the potential impacts of oil spills. We now know the developing fish heart is exquisitely sensitive to crude oil toxicity, and that subtle changes in heart formation can have delayed but important consequences for first-year survival, which in turn determines the long-term abundance of wild fish populations."[70]

The first study following the Deepwater Horizon Spill in the Gulf of Mexico shows similar effects on several fish species providing more evidence that the toxic agents in crude oil are damaging to the development of fish embryos.[71]

Chapter Fourteen
The Air We Breathe

**"A nation that destroys its soils destroys itself.
Forests are the lungs of our country, purifying
the air and giving fresh strength to our people."**

- Franklin Delano Roosevelt –

The three things we all need are food, water and air. A person can live 30 days without food and three days without water, but only three minutes without air. So why do we continue to foul the one thing every person has the least control over and, at the same time, put our health at risk?

Ever since the beginning of the Industrial Revolution, air pollution has reared its ugly head. At the time, dirty air was considered the cost of doing business. By the 1960s, Congress realized it was time to act. The Clean Air Act of 1970 asserted federal responsibility for cleaning up our air and set national ambient air standards with deadlines. It also codified earlier laws on air pollution; the most successful of these was the Air Quality Act of 1967 that led to all 50 states involved in programs to research and monitor sources of air pollution.[1]

The EPA – which was established the same year – was given responsibility for the promulgation of rules, administration and enforcement of the new law. Numerous state and local governments have enacted similar legislation, either implementing federal programs or filling in locally- important gaps. It was also the first major federal environmental law to include a provision for citizen suits. To establish air quality standards, EPA identified six "criteria pollutants" – particulate matter, ozone, sulfur dioxide, nitrogen dioxide, carbon monoxide and lead.[2]

Most air pollution comes from factories, incinerators, and the production and burning of fossil fuels. The two most prevalent types are ozone (smog) and soot. Ozone occurs when fossil fuel emissions react with sunlight; soot or "particulate matter" consists of tiny particles from dust, smoke, chemicals, dirt, and other gas or solid sources. Even the tiniest particles can penetrate our lungs and bloodstream, posing substantial threats to human health.[3] According to the EPA:

> "An extensive body of scientific evidence shows that long- and short-term exposures to fine particle pollution, also known as fine particulate matter, can cause premature death and harmful effects on the cardiovascular system, including increased hospital admissions and emergency department visits for heart attacks and strokes. Scientific evidence also links particulates to harmful respiratory effects, including asthma attacks.
> Ozone can increase the frequency of asthma attacks, cause shortness of breath, aggravate lung diseases, and cause permanent damage to lungs through long-term exposure. Elevated ozone levels are linked to increases in hospitalizations, emergency room visits and premature death."[4]

Although levels of particle pollution and ground-level ozone pollution are substantially lower than in the past thanks to passage of the law and subsequent amendments, newer scientific studies have shown that some pollutants can harm public health and welfare even at very low levels.[5] For the last 19 years, the American Lung Association has released a *State of the Air* report of the states with the worst air quality. California is a repeat offender. In 2017, the state had the highest smog and particle levels compared to the rest of the U.S – a position they have held for 17 out of the previous 18 years.[6]

In their 2018 report, the State continued its failing ways as "35 million Californians – or 90 percent of the population – reside in counties that received a failing grade for at least one pollutant." None of this is good news for a state that continues to grow, albeit at a much slower rate than before.[7] Its high housing costs also force many workers into longer commutes which only adds to the problem.

California's large population and heavy dependence on the automobile make it difficult to reduce pollution and improve air quality. These two factors contribute to massive traffic congestion in the Los Angeles metro area – population of more than 15 million – what some local DJ's and TV stations have called "Carmageddon." Acording to a 2017 traffic scorecard, Los Angeles topped the list of gridlocked U.S. cities; it also finished number one in the world.

> "Los Angeles took the title for the sixth consecutive year, beating out 1,360 cities in 38 countries around the globe. INRIX – a leader in transportation analytics – calculated the results of its eleventh annual report by combining anonymous, real-time global positioning system probe data from 300 million connected cars and devices with real-time traffic flow data and other criteria, such as construction and road closures."[8]

The below figure shows the most recent data from 2019. While Los Angeles has shown little change since 2017, five U.S. cities are now ranked higher. "Peak hours" is defined as the time spent sitting in traffic congestion during peak time periods.[9]

Figure 7
The 10 Most Congested Cities in the United States

Congestion Rank	Metro Area	State	Peak Hours in Congestion
1	Boston	Massachusetts	149
2	Chicago	Illinois	145
3	Philadelphia	Pennsylvania	142
4	New York City	New York	140
5	Washington	District of Columbia	124
6	Los Angeles	California	103
7	San Francisco	California	97
8	Portland	Oregon	89
9	Baltimore	Maryland	84
10	Atlanta	Georgia	82

Source: Smart Travel website, March 12, 2020

California has long recognized the inherent health risks associated with air pollution. In 1967, Governor Ronald Reagan approved the Mulford-Carrell Air Resources Act to create the California Air Resources Board (CARB), committing to a unified, statewide approach to aggressively address air pollution in the state.

Today, CARB is charged with protecting the public from the harmful effects of air pollution and developing programs and actions to fight climate change. "From requirements for clean cars and fuels to adopting innovative solutions to reduce greenhouse gas emissions, California has pioneered a range of effective approaches that have set the standard for effective air and climate programs for the nation, and the world."[10]

Two air pollutants of greatest concern at the end of the twentieth century were sulfur dioxide (SO_2) and nitrogen oxides (NO_X). Acid rain is created when these two gases are emitted into the atmosphere and then react with water, oxygen and other chemicals forming sulfuric and nitric acids; these then mix with water and other materials before falling to the ground. The major sources of SO_2 and NO_X in the atmosphere are:

- Burning of fossil fuels to generate electricity; two thirds of SO_2 and one fourth of NO_X in the atmosphere come from electric power generators
- Vehicles and heavy equipment
- Manufacturing, oil refineries and other industries

Acid rain has been shown to have adverse impacts on forests, bodies of fresh water and soils, killing insect and aquatic species (some are more affected than others).[11]

In 1852, a Scottish chemist was the first to show the relationship between acid rain and atmospheric pollution in Manchester, England and later coined the phrase "acid rain." By the late 1960s scientists began studying the impacts of acid rain on the environment. The earliest report about acid rain in the U.S. came from the Hubbard Brook Experimental Forest in the White Mountains of New Hampshire – an outdoor laboratory for ecological studies established to research the relationship between forest cover and water quality supply.[12]

Their discovery that rainfall in the White Mountains had turned more acidic which was affecting the ecology in a local stream eventually led Congress in 1980 to pass a law to study the long-term effects of acid rain. Following a visit to Canada, then President Reagan became interested in the damage caused by drifting pollution smokestacks in the Midwest. A report commissioned by Reagan concluded that we needed to cut sulfur emissions. After the report's validity was questioned, Congress failed to pass legislation that would have set a standard for emissions.[13]

Fortunately, further amendments to the Clean Air Act were made in 1990 to address the problem of acid rain by setting a cap and trade program, the first of its kind in the U.S. Emission trading – commonly known as cap and trade – is "a market-based approach to controlling pollution by providing economic incentives for achieving reductions in the emissions of pollutants."

It is usually administered by a governmental body that allocates a limited number of permits to discharge a certain amount of a given pollutant; if polluters want to increase their emissions they must buy or trade with other permit or secondary holders.[14]

This compliance approach to reducing acid rain emissions resulted in two noteworthy outcomes:

> Cost savings – The acid rain cap and trade program passed by Congress in 1990 achieved reductions at two-thirds the cost of achieving the same reductions under a command-and-control system. This program reduced more pollution in the last decade than all other Clean Air Act command-and-control programs combined during the same period.
>
> Innovation – Trading under the acid rain program created financial incentives for electricity generators to look for new and low-cost ways to reduce emissions and to do so early.[15]

Since the 1990s, SO_2 emissions have dropped 40 percent, and according to the Pacific Research Institute, acid rain levels have dropped 65 percent since 1976. As shown below, it only took ten years to make a significant difference in air quality across a large segment of the country.[16]

Figure 8
Acid Deposition Before the Acid Rain Program and Ten Years Later

Source: U.S. Environmental Protection Agency

To build on the success of his father, President George W. Bush proposed in his 2005 State of the Union address to put forward his Clear Skies initiative.

> "My Clear Skies legislation will cut power-plant pollution and improve the health of our citizens. And my budget provides strong funding for leading-edge technology, from hydrogen-fueled cars to clean coal to renewable sources such as ethanol. Four years of debate is enough. I urge Congress to pass legislation that makes America more secure and less dependent on foreign energy."[17]

The Clear Skies legislation was intended to create a mandatory program that would dramatically reduce power plant emissions of sulfur dioxide (SO2), nitrogen oxides (NOx) and mercury by setting a national cap on each pollutant. Had it passed, the law would have provided regulatory certainty for industry and further protected our health and the environment; the legislation never made it out of committee in the Senate. The program only exists now as an archived EPA footnote to history. While mostly solving the acid rain problem was a notable achievement for President George H.W. Bush, not building upon this success with his Clear Skies program was an opportunity missed.[18]

Today, we are more concerned with carbon dioxide and methane emissions, two of the leading greenhouse gases.   Hazardous materials that are airborne also continue to pose a threat to human health, even in small amounts. Almost 200 are regulated by law; some of the most common are mercury, lead, dioxins and benzene. Polycyclic aromatic hydrocarbons, or PAHs, are toxic components of traffic exhaust and wildfire smoke; in large amounts, exposure can lead to cancer or other health issues. The EPA regulates the concentration of PAHs based on their carcinogenicity or genotoxicity (there are 26 PAH compounds that pose the highest risk).[19]

The air pollution problems associated with smog, dust and smoke are only getting worse causing more than 200,000 premature deaths every year in the U.S That is roughly equal to the number of Americans who die annually from diabetes, Alzheimer's or pneumonia added together.[20]   In California, the problem is not ignoring air pollution but having to deal with the overwhelming number of people and their vehicles. The increase in wildfires due to climate change only heightens the risk of smoke inhalation across numerous western states including California.

On the other hand, President Trump preferred to minimize the problem while supporting the fossil fuel industry:

"In August 2018, President Trump unveiled a
plan that would empower states to establish
emission standards for coal-fired power plants
rather than speeding their retirement.   It
represents a major overhaul of the Obama
Administration's Clean Power Plan and his
signature climate policy.
  Trump's plan, which is projected to release at
least 12 times the amount of carbon dioxide into
the atmosphere compared with the Obama rule
over the next decade, comes as scientists have
warned that the world will experience
increasingly dire climate effects absent a major
cut in carbon emissions."[21]

The President's plan affects more than 300 U.S.
power plants providing companies with an incentive to
keep aging coal-fired plants in operation rather than
replacing them with cleaner natural gas or renewable
energy. EPA's own analysis shows the proposal will only
slightly reduce the emission of pollutants – including
carbon dioxide – over the next decade.[22]
  President Trump made his announcement in West
Virginia with the sole goal of propping up the coal
industry. Utility companies and two dozen states – all
but two under Republican leadership – have sued to
block Obama's Clean Power Plan and claim the new rule
will save them hundreds of millions of dollars in
compliance costs and prevent the closure of at least 200
coal plants.[23]
  Florida is one of the states suing to prevent Obama's
plan from taking effect even though they face many of
the greatest risks from climate change. A state should
not be allowed to have it both ways; they cannot on one
hand sue the federal government but then expect
millions in disaster aid when things go badly.
  Air pollution has far-reaching effects on the
environment, everything from public health to climate
change. The impact on poorer communities is often
disproportional. Asthma rates in the Bronx in New York
City are among the highest in the nation, with almost one

in four children affected.[24]   A recent study out of England links air pollution to psychosis in teens.[25]   By adding greenhouse gases to the atmosphere, air pollution is a major contributor to global warming. The progress that has been made so far should not be discounted but it is not nearly enough. Ending our dependence on fossil fuels, especially coal, must be achieved sooner rather than later.

Cutting Emissions Could Prevent Nearly 300,000 U.S. Air Pollution Deaths

Reducing emissions in the energy and transport sectors could prevent almost 300,000 early deaths caused by air pollution in the U.S. by 2030, a new study says. The researchers estimate that saving these lives could benefit the U.S. economy to the tune of $250 billion per year – more than it would cost to put the policies in place.

Once one includes the benefits of emissions cuts for reducing global climate change, these economic gains "roughly quintuple," the researchers say. The findings show that moving to cleaner energy and transport have immediate health benefits for the U.S., in addition to the longer-term benefits for the global climate.[26]

Rejection of Post-Hurricane Harvey Air Pollution Monitoring "Part of a Disturbing Trend of Willful Ignorance"

EPA and the Texas Commission on Environmental Quality knew air pollution was one of the unseen dangers of Hurricane Harvey, but according to news reports they deliberately chose not to use every available tool to discover it. Their rejection of NASA's plan to fly a pollution-spotting plane over Houston after the storm is an abdication of responsibility and part of a disturbing trend of willful ignorance. Their action caused unnecessary risk to the health and safety of Texas families.[27]

Chapter Fifteen
The Lawyer Economy

"The main enemy of the open society, I believe, is no longer the communist but the capitalist threat."

- George Soros -

The Fourteenth Amendment to the U.S. Constitution addresses many aspects of citizenship and the rights of citizens.   Ratified after the Civil War, it primarily addressed the rights of former slaves and over the years has figured prominently in many landmark court cases. How the interpretation of this amendment has affected the environment is less widely known.

As in most countries, U.S. corporations have a right to enter into contracts with other parties and to sue or be sued in court in the same way as individuals. However, since the Constitution was first drafted there has been an on-going legal debate as to what extent other basic rights should extend to corporations.   Thomas Jefferson preferred explicit limitations on the rights of corporations even going so far as to suggest maximum life spans, but his concepts were never put into the Constitution.   Once the Fourteenth Amendment was ratified, it served to expand, not limit, the power given to corporations.[1]

> "A headnote issued by the Court Reporter in the 1886 Supreme Court case *Santa Clara County v. Southern Pacific Railroad Co.* claimed to state the sense of the Court regarding the equal protection clause of the Fourteenth Amendment as it applies to corporations, without the Court having actually made a decision or issued a written opinion on that

point. This was the first time that the Supreme
Court was reported to hold that the Fourteenth
Amendment's equal protection clause granted
constitutional protections to corporations as
well as to natural persons."[2]

As corporate lawyers continued to argue that
corporations were in fact legal persons, the U.S. Supreme
Court embraced this reasoning and even intervened in
state legislative measures that sought to protect the
rights of workers and farmers. To show what degree the
Fourteenth Amendment was corrupted by American
corporations, in the twenty years between 1890 and
1910, there were 288 cases brought before the Court
related to corporations; the number of cases that dealt
with the rights of former slaves was a mere nineteen.[3]

If only the Supreme Court bestowed this kind of
protective status toward the environment. In 1972, the
Court decided that nature did not possess its own rights.

"In the case of *Sierra Club v. Morton*, the Court
rejected a lawsuit by the California-based
environmental group to block a ski resort
development at Mineral King in the Sierra
Nevada Mountains. The Court ruled the Sierra
Club had no legal standing. In his dissent, Justice
William O. Douglas wrote, 'Contemporary
public concern for protecting nature's ecological
equilibrium should lead to the conferral of
standing upon environmental objects to sue for
their own preservation'."[4]

Known for its mining activities, the residents of
Tamaqua, Pennsylvania – population 7,000 – were faced
with a toxic sludge problem and became in 2006 the first
municipality to recognize the legal rights of nature; it is
believed to be the first law of its kind in the world. The
2006 ordinance states the following:

"An ordinance to protect the health, safety, and
general welfare of the citizens and environment
of Tamaqua borough by banning corporations

from engaging in the land application of sewage sludge; by banning persons from using corporations to engage in land application of sewage sludge; by providing for the testing of sewage sludge prior to land application in the borough; by removing constitutional powers from corporations within the borough; by recognizing and enforcing the rights of residents to defend natural communities and ecosystems; and by otherwise adopting the Pennsylvania regulations concerning the land application of sewage sludge."[5]

Regarding rights of nature, the ordinance unequivocally states that: "Borough residents, natural communities, and ecosystems shall be considered 'persons' for the purposes of the enforcement of the civil rights of those residents, natural communities, and ecosystems."[6]

Since then, communities across the nation have since passed similar ordinances. Two years later, Ecuador became the first country to enshrine the rights of nature in its constitution; indigenous activists helped to lead the fight to protect valuable ecosystems and their way of life.[7]

In Chapter Three, we explored the immense power and wealth accumulated by the robber barons. This led Congress to pass several anti-trust laws – the Sherman Act of 1890, the Clayton Act of 1914 and the Federal Trade Commission Act of 1914 – that were designed to prevent collusive practices that result in the restraint of trade, and to promote fair competition by restricting the mergers and acquisitions of corporations especially when a monopoly results.[8]

The most notable break-up of a monopolistic corporation was Standard Oil, a company and corporate trust started in 1870s that served as an industrial empire under the heavy-handed management of John D. Rockefeller. At its height, Standard Oil controlled almost all the oil production, processing and shipping of petroleum products in the U.S. In 1911, the Supreme

Court found that Standard Oil had violated the Sherman Act and broke the monopoly into over 30 separate companies. In its ruling, the Court included the "rule of reason" which states not all big companies are evil but it is up to the courts to decide if economic harm to others has occurred.[9]

Domination of markets is an important issue. As was referenced earlier, companies will go to great lengths to avoid safeguarding the environment; one of those companies was ExxonMobil that arose from the ashes of two previous Standard Oil offshoots – Standard Oil of New Jersey and Standard Oil of New York.[10] But lack of concern for the environment does not end there; companies have also gone to great lengths to prop up their product over the greater good.

In 1932, Standard Oil of California, General Motors, Firestone Tire and Rubber, Phillips Petroleum, and Mack Truck Manufacturing joined forces to form a phony company called National City Lines. The sole purpose of the company was to purchase rail and trolley lines across the U.S., shut them down and then tear up the tracks. In many cases, these services were replaced by bus lines.[11]

Their success pulling off this scam was staggering as approximately 100 streetcar systems in over 25 cities closed. One of those cities was Los Angeles that at the time ran one of the most efficient transit systems in the U.S. Once it was shutdown, people were forced into their cars which led to the network of freeways – and air pollution – we see today.[12]

In what became known as the Great American Streetcar Scandal, this 'con' to promote automobiles over mass transit was perpetuated by the corporations that stood to benefit from increased car, bus and truck sales. In 1949, General Motors and its co-conspirators were convicted in federal court of antitrust violations, but the damage had already been done. The companies were fined $5,000 and the executives a mere one dollar each; two years later, the verdicts were upheld in appeal.[13]

There are many other examples of "corporate malfeasance." The Koch brothers own numerous companies, called Koch Industries, throughout the country that produce a wide array of products. Industries under their umbrella range from ones that refine oil, manufacture paper, process minerals, produce fertilizers, and fashion glass for automobiles and construction applications. They make spandex, resins, chemicals and polymers as well as owning a natural gas and oil pipeline outfit. Because they are a privately held company, their total assets are publicly unknown.[14]

While the Koch brothers are interested in biofuels and own a company that creates electronics for electric cars and surgical robots, they have fought to undermine alternative energy sources and derail public mass transit projects.[15] To undercut the bourgeoning wind industry, the Koch Industries' network of advocacy groups, think tanks and lobbyists fought to terminate the tax credit for wind production. Congress ultimately agreed in 2015 to phase it out by slowly reducing the tax benefit.[16]

Koch Industries also has attempted to slow the exponential growth of solar power. Their lobbyists want state legislatures to curtail net metering, a practice that gives homeowners with solar panels credit for excess energy they generate and transmit back to the grid.[17] Net metering – which can also be applied to wind energy – provides incentives to consumers to invest in alternate energy sources and should be promoted, not lobbied against.

In 2011, President Barrack Obama used his State of the Union address to set a goal for the U.S. to become the first country to have one million plug-in electric vehicles (EV) on the road by 2015. He also set aside federal funds to assist manufacturers develop next-generation electric vehicles and batteries. Despite these efforts, sales of EV in the U.S. did not reach the half million mark until August 2016.[18]

For the U.S. consumer, there is a federal income tax credit that was passed by Congress in 2009 of up to $7,500 for electric vehicle (EV) buyers; the credit applied to the first 200,000 EVs each automaker sells. Even though EVs make up less than two percent of total vehicle sales nationally, Koch Industries is hard at work to kill this subsidy and have now found a friend in President Trump. As a result, the tax credit is currently being phased out. This goes against a long-standing desire of Congress to support emerging industries with tax breaks.[19]

One can argue these tax credits are ineffective in boosting market share or a good buy for the U.S. taxpayer. It has been suggested that since EVs, such as a Tesla vehicle, generally cost more, the tax credit favors the rich. But the decision to support an emerging industry should be left to Congress without any outside influences. Although electric cars are currently dependent on fossil-fuel generated electricity to recharge their batteries, that may change as the country moves to other energy sources. It is the role of Congress and state legislatures to conduct what is commonly referred to as the people's business and to not be influenced by corporate interests.

Since the U.S. Supreme Court has expanded interpretation of the Fourteenth Amendment by defining the word 'citizens' to also mean corporations, Congress could enact a new amendment that revokes these rights and restores the public's right to clean air and water. A group called Reclaim Democracy! is dedicated to establishing appropriate limits on corporate influence and they have drafted the amendment below to preclude corporations from claiming Bill of Rights protections. Their proposal reaffirms our rights as citizens.

> SECTION 1. The U.S. Constitution protects only the rights of living human beings.
>
> SECTION 2. Corporations and other institutions granted the privilege to exist shall be subordinate to any and all laws enacted by citizens and their elected governments.
>
> SECTION 3. Corporations and other for-profit institutions are prohibited from attempting to influence the outcome of elections, legislation or

government policy by aggregate resources or by rewarding or repaying employees or directors to exert such influence.

SECTION 4. Congress shall have power to implement this article by appropriate legislation.[20]

When companies like GE polluted the Hudson River with PCBs, they knew toxic chemicals would cause significant harm to the environment. They made a conscious decision that it was cheaper to dispose of these pollutants in a public waterway than to responsibly clean them up. When they got caught, they hired lawyers to defend their actions in court.

Capitalism runs deep in our society, so the question becomes how do we move forward? The rights of corporations should be limited to economic issues; they also need to embrace a philosophy based on living in harmony with the environment. Of course, it may cost more to do things the right way, although there are many examples where this is not the case; the installation of green infrastructure can often reduce long-term operational costs.

When we start to think of 'waste' as an underutilized resource, whole new markets will be developed. But to make this shift, we need a Congress not nearly as influenced by special-interest lobbyists and shareholders who will hold corporations accountable for their actions. Strong campaign finance laws are an important first step and these reforms need to be enacted before we can seriously address climate change.

In 1993, an Environmental Bill of Rights became provincial law in Ontario, Canada. It gives Ontario residents the right to participate in the decision-making process through an online Environmental Registry. Citizens must be notified of environmentally-significant government proposals and can appeal decisions made by a regulatory agency as well as sue for harm to a public resource.[21]

Americans' environmental rights are much more limited. This can only change through the power of the ballot box. In 2018, drilling bans, carbon fees, gas taxes, and endorsing renewable energy were initiatives considered by a number of states. While some passed and others did not, the momentum is growing to pass climate-friendly measures. Congress needs to support these efforts by enforcing and strengthening existing environmental laws without corporate influence.

If Corporations Can Have Personhood, So Can Lakes

February 26, 2019: It started in a pub. A handful of people hunched over beers in Toledo, Ohio were talking about a water crisis that had plagued the city in 2014. The pollution of Lake Erie had gotten so bad that it had taken a serious toll on their lives. The government, they felt, wasn't doing enough to protect the lake. And so, they wondered: What if the lake could protect itself?

The idea they hatched that night ultimately resulted in a special election, which had the citizens of Toledo voting February 26 on a very unusual question: Should Lake Erie be granted the legal rights normally reserved for a person?

The measure passed easily, which means citizens will be able to sue on behalf of the lake whenever its right to flourish is being contravened – that is, whenever it's in danger of major environmental harm.

If the stakes felt high for the activists who pushed for the Lake Erie Bill of Rights, it's because this was the first rights-based legislation aimed at protecting a whole US ecosystem: the lake, its tributaries, and the many species that live off it.

The law isn't without precedent, though. It's part of the nascent rights of nature movement, which has notched several victories in the past dozen years. Rivers and forests have already won legal rights in countries like Ecuador, Colombia, India, and New Zealand.

Activists in the movement often argue that the environment is the next frontier in humanity's expanding more circle over the centuries, we've extended rights to more and more beings, so why shouldn't nature itself be next?

They reject the conventional Western way of relating to nature – as property that is ours for the taking, as an object rather than a subject – but they recognize they're going to have to work within the existing Western legal system if they want that to change. They're betting that the best strategy for protecting our environment is to stretch America's understanding of what counts as a person.   It's a bold bet, but with climate change decimating the planet at such a ferocious rate, it might be the kind of innovative thinking we need.

"The idea that we can be separate from nature is really a Western reductionist way of looking at the world – we can trace it back to Francis Bacon and the scientific method (which is based on careful observation and applying rigorous skepticism about what is observed)," said Ben Price, the national director for the Community Environmental Legal Defense Fund, a nonprofit public interest law firm that helps people facing threats to their local environment.

To Price, that last best hope rises to the level of an existential need, given the pace of climate change. "We're seeing the results of our narrow-mindedness, of our belief that nature is property and property ownership is the highest right," he said. "The hope is that by beginning somewhere, like the City of Toledo, the conversation enlarges. You never know what's going to be the tipping point."[22]

City of Oakland in California Loses Its Case to Ban Coal Shipments

Associated Press, May 16, 2018: A federal judge in California on Tuesday struck down Oakland's ban on coal shipments at a proposed cargo terminal, siding with a developer who wants to use the site to transport Utah coal to Asia. In his ruling, U.S. District Judge Vince Chhabria in San Francisco said the information the city relied on to conclude that coal operations would pose a substantial health or safety danger to the public was "riddled with inaccuracies" and "faulty analyses, to the point that no reliable conclusion about health or safety dangers could be drawn from it."

City leaders had previously approved construction of a rail and marine terminal in 2013 as part of a larger makeover of an Army base that was shuttered in 1999. The $250 million project in west Oakland is expected to bring thousands of jobs to a historically African-American neighborhood that is among the poorest and most polluted in the region.

Oakland officials said coal was never mentioned as a possibility but lawyers for developers said city officials always knew there would be a mix of goods, including coal. Concerned about pollution caused by coal dust, the city moved in 2016 to ban shipments of coal and petroleum coke, a solid derived from oil refining. The decision came after Utah lawmakers approved a $53 million investment to help ship the state's coal through Oakland to Asia.

Chhabria agreed with attorneys for developers that the city relied on a flawed analysis to justify its ban. As an example, he said the city failed to factor in covers on the coal-carrying rail cars in its emissions estimates for the project. It also had no meaningful assessment of how emissions would affect air quality in Oakland, he said.

The city's opposition to coal operations appeared to stem largely from concerns about global warming, but it was "factually ridiculous to suggest that this one operation resulting in the consumption of coal in other countries will, in the grand scheme of things, pose a substantial global warming-related danger to people in Oakland," the judge said.[23]

Chapter Sixteen
Whose Side is God on Anyway?

"I think that in the discussion of natural problems we ought to begin not with the Scriptures, but with experiments and demonstrations."

- Galileo Galilei -

There is a common misconception that our technological advances have allowed us to become a more enlightened society. We have faltered on many social fronts and when it comes to protecting our environment, those failures are most glaring. In pursuing a policy of sustainability, we can learn more from a sixteenth century scientist and astronomer who was charged with heresy by the Catholic Church than twentieth century Evangelist Reverend Jerry Falwell who said, "I believe that global warming is a myth and, therefore, I have no conscience problems at all and I'm going to buy a Suburban next time."

A sizeable percentage of Christians – most notably Evangelists – place greater faith in the teachings of the Bible while ignoring scientific laws.[1] This includes the belief that the world is only 10,000 years old and that dinosaurs and man roamed the Earth at the same time. Science tells a much different story.

> "Imagine standing on the eastern edge of North America some 400 million years ago. You're in the sands of a shallow sea, volcanoes at your back, Africa looming in the distance. Welcome to Great Smoky Mountains National Park. The impending continental collision will take the ground you're on and raise it to Rocky Mountain heights in a line stretching from Newfoundland to, technically, Morocco. The impact, however, is seen across the globe."[2]

The same geologic pressures created the Rocky Mountains; the region was once an ocean, accumulating layers of sand, mud and volcanic deposits. After hundreds of millions of years, the ever-increasing pressure and temperature "caused massive tectonic collisions" eventually creating some of the nation's most beautiful landscapes.

> "Slice a knife through 2,700 feet of Colorado's crust (or wait two million years for the Gunnison River to do the work for you), and you've got Black Canyon of the Gunnison, a vertical wilderness displaying nearly two billion years of Earth's history."[3]

While people have the inherent right to their personal beliefs, these views have no place in determining public policy. Through advanced carbon dating, we can accurately estimate the age of organic matter and clearly the Earth is older than the Bible's Book of Genesis account – a theory known as creationism.[4]

The world-wide consensus established by numerous scientific disciplines teaches us the formation of the Earth happened around 4.5 billion years ago with the first appearance of life a billion years later. While the origin of man can be debated by the world's religions, the origin of the Earth is not in doubt.

A Gallup poll taken in 2012, showed that 46 percent of Americans believed in creationism followed by 32 percent who believed in theistic evolution – the theory that human beings have evolved from lesser life forms over millions of years under the watchful eye of a higher power. Only 15 percent believed in evolution without God's help.[5]

A more recent Gallup poll taken in 2017 indicates a shift in this trend. The strict creationist view has reached a new low – only 38 percent – while 57 percent believe in some degree of evolution. Since 1982, agreement with the "secular" viewpoint, meaning without divine intervention, has doubled. Perhaps not surprisingly, the level of education one has achieved plays a major role in what people believe. For people without a high school education, creationism is preferred by 48 percent of Americans. For people with a postgraduate education, this number falls to 21 percent.[6]   A more recent poll in 2019 showed similar results.

Digging deeper into how life began there are two men who lived in the first half of the nineteenth century responsible for developing the science of evolution – Charles Darwin and Alfred Wallace. Far more people have heard of Darwin, but Wallace also made important contributions on how the Earth acquired its dazzling biodiversity. While his observations are noteworthy, Darwin is considered the architect of evolution following the release of his book *On the Origin of Species* in 1859.[7]

Its publication stirred up a scientific controversy on how evolution works. It is one of the greatest scientific discoveries of mankind as it describes not just the origin of man, but all living things. Darwin realized that if man could turn wolves into dogs, other life forms could be created naturally. From there he surmised that all species continue to adapt or perish leading to Darwin's theory of natural selection.[8]

A lot more can be said about the science of evolution, but just as important is the concept of "uniformitarianism." This theory states there is one set of natural laws that is consistent from one eon to the next. As we see with the interface between the Colorado River and Grand Canyon, landforms change slowly over time and were not created in one fell swoop by a supernatural power. It is this concept that led Darwin to conceive his theory of evolution.[9]

Believing in the laws of science has nothing to do with the existence of God or a supreme being. President Thomas Jefferson was not a Christian but more likely a Deist. Deism – derived from the Latin word "deus" meaning "God" – is a theological/philosophical position that combines the rejection of revelation and authority as a source of religious knowledge with the conclusion that reason and observation of the natural world are sufficient to determine the existence of a single creator of the universe. As an "Enlightenment Rationalist," Jefferson sought to reconcile his faith and religion through reason and science.[10]

Today we refer to Deism as "theistic evolution." It is a theory that divine direction or God-guided evolution is compatible with our modern scientific understanding about biological evolution and puts all living things on a level playing field.[11] Every modern convenience is the result of some key scientific breakthrough. People have no problem trusting the laws of electromagnetic radio waves that allow our smartphones to work or our ability to create life from a DNA sample, and yet somehow evolution is a form of heresy.

Science has revealed the catastrophic events that led to the demise of the dinosaurs. In 2019, researchers extracted a limestone core from the ocean floor that encapsulated the moment around 66 million years ago when an asteroid slammed into the sea just offshore of Mexico's Yucatán Peninsula. The dark layers in the core exposed the sheer amount of material that piled up hours after the strike; bits of charcoal caused by the raging wildfires that occurred afterward were also found. "The impact triggered a nightmarish sequence of events that sent some 75 percent of plant and animal species spiraling to extinction including all of the non-avian."[12]

As humans, our genetic make-up is strikingly like other animals. We are most closely related to the great apes of the family Hominidae – orangutans, chimpanzees, gorillas and bonobos – as we share up to 98.8 percent of their DNA. Scientists know this is due to "the discovery of the structure of deoxyribonucleic acid, and the technology to sequence the genomes of both humans and animals."[13] Perhaps more impressively, we share 60 percent of our DNA with fruit flies.[14]

Therefore, it should come as no surprise to find that we have a lot in common with our animal friends and often demonstrate similar behaviors. African apes and humans have essentially the same arrangement of internal organs and share the same bones although somewhat different in shape and size; apes can learn to hold pens and draw which is very unusual animal behavior.[15]

> "Humans and chimps, as well as many other great apes, descend from a similar ancestor 5-8 million years ago. During the evolutionary process the two species' genes evolved differently, but many similarities to monkeys and apes are still seen today in humans."[16]

Apes share five personality traits with humans, e.g. openness, reactivity/undependability,dominance, extr aversion and agreeableness.[17] Apes can hug, play and laugh out loud; they mourn their dead and possess the ability to cook. When stressed, they have been known to binge eat. One trait apes do not share with humans is they rarely destroy their own environment. There is one other essential difference – apes are endangered on Earth, humans are not – yet.

Why are people's personal beliefs so important? Our future depends on adapting to the stresses we are exerting on all living things. This includes everything from mass extinctions to climate change. We are altering our natural systems in a way that is unprecedented with no idea how things will turn out. We cannot rest on the belief, "This is all part of God's plan." Instead, we need a science-educated society who can help make the difficult decisions that lie ahead.

Tom Hayden, a former 1960s anti-Vietnam War activist and author of the Port Huron Statement political manifesto for the Students for a Democratic Society, noted we are doomed to "forever roll the environmental stone up a mountain of frustration unless we embrace a vision of the Earth as alive and full of sacred presence." He believed the continuing devastation of the natural world will end when human beings forge a kinship with all living things.[18]

We must reconsider the teaching of creationism in our public schools. It is no more credible as an alternate theory of how life began than saying the Earth is flat – a theory everyone believed until science proved otherwise. When changes in our climate lead to a dramatic rise in sea level, there will be no Noah's ark at the South Street Seaport in Lower Manhattan to rescue the thousands of huddling climate refugees seeking higher ground.

Public funding cannot be used to support religious education in our public schools as the Founding Fathers intended – separation of Church and state. Any public school or school district that teaches creationism should be ineligible to receive federal funding. Parents always have the right to send their child to a private, religious school but not on the back of taxpayers.

The goal is not to trample on religious freedom but to develop a science literate society. We need to expel the belief that domination of the planet is our God-given right and a license for unrestrained plunder. We need a Copernican Revolution to awaken the public to look at the world holistically; and we need a generation who thinks like Galileo, not Jerry Falwell. Perhaps Albert Einstein said it best, "Science without religion is lame, religion without science is blind."

We can learn a lot from the Native Americans who lived here before us. Frank Lloyd Wright once said, "I believe in God, only I spell it Nature." If you believe a supreme being created all living things, then let us protect God's bounty. Let us prepare for the next "Great Flood" when the Greenland ice sheet melts raising sea level by twenty feet.[19]

How the Ancient Dinosaurs Evolved Into Birds

Pterodactyl is the common term for the winged reptiles properly called pterosaurs – giant, leathery flying creatures that lived during the age of the dinosaurs. Their slim bodies and lightweight bones were ideal for flying. They thrived for 160 million years, passing into history after the same asteroid strike that finished off the large dinosaurs.[20]

Today's birds did not descend from pterosaurs, but are more like modern-day dinosaurs having evolved from creatures like the terrifying *Tyrannosaurus rex* (T. rex) and other small, feathered terrestrial dinosaurs.

A bird did not evolve from a *T. rex* overnight, but rather the classic features of birds evolved one by one; first bipedal locomotion, then feathers, then a wishbone, then more complex feathers that look like quill-pen feathers, then wings.   Though people might name feathers or wings as key characteristics distinguishing birds from dinosaurs, but the group's small stature is crucial.   New research suggests that bird ancestors shrank fast, indicating that the diminutive size was an important and advantageous trait, quite possibly an essential component in bird evolution.[21]

Does the sound of a great blue heron conjure up the sounds of a T. rex? With a similar but smaller voice box, the sound is strikingly similar.   Some Native American traditions hold that herons contain the souls of wise men who have returned to earth on mysterious pilgrimages. If true, these wise souls made a good choice: a magnificent bird with a quiet, reflective spirit."[22]

A Piece of the Paleozoic Era

In 2018, an eleven-year-old girl was strolling along the shore of Douglas Lake in Tennessee when she made the discovery of a lifetime – a rare fossil that is over 475 million years old. Her amazing find has already been confirmed by the University of Tennessee.

Her discovery was a trilobite, an extinct bug-like marine animal that lived in the water around the Smoky Mountains during the Paleozoic era. Trilobites were one of the earliest known arthropods – animals that wear their skeletons on the outside, have segmented bodies and don't possess backbones. The trilobite she found is most closely related to the modern horseshoe crab.

Trilobites inhabited the planet for 270 million years before being wiped out in a mass extinction around 252 million years ago. In comparison, modern humans have only existed for roughly 300,000 years.[23]

With a Helping Hand from God

It is a common misconception that communities of faith and environmentalists have little in common. In the U.S. today, 67 percent of Americans say they care about the environment because it is 'God's creation' – and close to half of our members say they attend worship services at least once a month. Most of the world's major religions have long-standing traditions and teachings that inform how humans should interact with the natural world.

Make no mistake – 'creation care' is certainly a growing movement. In the face of unprecedented environmental challenges like global warming, people from all walks of life are coming together to make a difference.

We recently released our "Faith in Action" report, which highlights one exceptional faith-based environmental initiative from each of the 50 states, the District of Columbia, and Puerto Rico. The report illustrates the growing momentum of the "creation care" movement. Lyndsay Moseley, of the Sierra Club's Environmental Partnerships Program, said these initiatives are worth recognizing. "We are inspired by the faith community's leadership in working to protect the planet, and this report is our way of saying 'thank you' to the many people of faith working on creation care initiatives across the country."[24]

According to Galen Carey, the National Association of Evangelicals' vice president of government relations, "Christians should be at the forefront of efforts to reduce air pollution and greenhouse gas emissions because we know that this is our Father's world. We also know that these efforts will particularly benefit our most vulnerable neighbors, those whose health and livelihoods most directly depend on clean air and a stable climate." The World Evangelical Alliance (WEA) has set out to get 20 percent of its members to fully convert to clean energy by 2025 through the use of solar panels on their churches.[25]

Chapter Seventeen
Biodiversity on the Brink

"Sure, pesticides are going to kill a lot of
people, but they may be dying of something else
anyway."

- Othal Brand, member of a Texas Pesticide Review Board,
on Chlordane -

One of the finest environmentalists and writers of her
time, Rachel Carson was a marine scientist who worked
for the U.S. Fish and Wildlife Service. Her love of the
sea resulted in three books about the ocean's
ecosystems, including the Pulitzer Prize-winning, *The
Sea Around Us*. But today she is best remembered as the
woman who challenged the notion that humans could
obtain mastery over nature by chemicals. She believed
"the control of nature is a phrase conceived in arrogance,
born of the Neanderthal age of biology and philosophy
when it was supposed that nature exists for the
convenience of man."

Rachel Carson's 1962 book *Silent* Spring was a
seminal moment in the environmental movement as she
was the earliest scientist to link the demise of multiple
bird species to the deadly pesticide known as DDT. The
book's title comes from a famous line by poet John Keats
– "And no birds sing" and it spoke volumes about the
state of the environment in the 1960s.[2]

DDT (dichloro-diphenyl-trichloroethane) was
developed in the 1940s as the first of the modern
synthetic insecticides. It was initially used with great
success to combat malaria and other insect-borne human
diseases. It also was effective for insect control in
agricultural applications and around homes and
gardens. DDT's efficacy as a pesticide and its broad use

in the U.S. and other countries led to many insect species developing resistance to the chemical; its success was also fleeting once the damage to the environment was unveiled.[3]

In 1957, an article in *The New York Times* caught Carson's attention after Nassau County on Long Island, New York had attempted to ban the use of DDT but failed. Her investigations led to the publication of her most famous book, *Silent Spring*. Released in 1962, Carson showed how DDT moved up through food chains starting with the insects it was designed to exterminate up through the organisms that ate them. In a process known as bioaccumulation, DDT over time found its way into the tissues, organ and fats of the top bird predators such as peregrine falcons, ospreys, bald eagles and pelicans. The effects would prove to be devastating.[4]

Due to its tendency to repel water in aquatic ecosystems, DDT and its metabolites are absorbed by aquatic species including fish. Many birds of prey rely on fish as their main source of food. While pelicans eat a fish-rich diet they are not as picky as ospreys whose diet is almost exclusively fish based. As these birds accumulated DDT and its breakdown products, their eggshells became thinner and they were unable to successfully hatch chicks; the pesticide interfered with the bird's ability to produce calcium leading to broken or infertile eggs.[5]

Beginning in the late 1950s, osprey populations began to plummet along with other birds of prey. Before EPA came into existence, the U.S. Department of Agriculture (USDA) was responsible for regulating pesticides. By the 1960s, some uses of DDT were prohibited due to mounting evidence of the pesticide's declining benefits and environmental and toxicological effects.

Rachel Carson's book only heightened public concern and, in 1972, the EPA banned its use altogether.[6]

Today, DDT is classified as a probable human carcinogen by U.S. and international authorities. It is banned in most of the world except in some African malaria-prone countries.

While concentrations in the environment and in animals began to drop in the U.S., it has a half-life of up to 150 years in aquatic systems. Because of its persistence, only recently have osprey, eagles and other birds started to recover and return to previously-vacated nesting sites.[7]

When one considers the osprey is found on every continent in the world except Antarctica and that the eagle is our national bird, these success stories are noteworthy. Yet DDT's legacy remains today even in songbirds as reported in the magazine *Scientific American*:

> "A recent study (August 2014) reported that birds of prey in South Carolina still carry as much DDT and other legacy pesticides in their bodies as they did before such chemicals were banned in the 1970s, suggesting exposure has not declined substantially over the past 40 years. And in the small town of St. Louis, Michigan, near an old chemical plant, robins are still dropping dead of DDT poisoning, registering some of the highest levels ever recorded in wild birds."[8]

In the Great Lakes, PCBs (see Chapter Thirteen) were found to cause enlarged thyroids in birds. Later studies found that numerous predator bird species were unable to reproduce due to disruptions in their endocrine systems. The problem was linked to chemicals found in the water and the bird's prey; this discovery gave birth to the term "endocrine disruptor."[9]

Birds are not the only creatures affected by chemical pollution. Famous for its marathon migration across North America, the monarch butterfly once numbered in the billions.

The National Wildlife Federation calls the migration "one of the greatest natural phenomena in the insect world," but now due to urban development, climate change and habitat loss from pesticides, their population has crashed by over 90 percent in the past two decades.[10]

Before transforming into a butterfly, monarch caterpillars primarily eat one thing – milkweed plants. The Center for Biological Diversity contends that part of the butterfly's demise is due to the planting of genetically-modified corn and soybean crops. This has led to the widespread use of herbicides containing the chemical glyphosate, most commonly found in Round Up; as a result, milkweed plants are disappearing from the landscape. Scientists fear monarchs could soon become an endangered species and efforts are underway to list it accordingly.[11]

While individual species are important, biodiversity is the key to maintaining healthy ecosystems. The U.S. has over 18,000 native plants species and nearly 3,000 kinds of vertcbrate animals, e.g. mammals, birds, reptiles, amphibians and fish. An accurate accounting of invertebrates such as insects and crustaceans is unknown as they are so plentiful. Flowering plants dominate that list with 16,000 varieties; other plant types include conifers, ferns, mosses and liverworts.[12]

California has the richest diversity of plants and animals in the country; compared to the rest of the world, its flora is a biodiversity hotspot. The state's rich variety of landscapes in addition to its size account for their diversity. It also has numerous endemic species – organisms unique to a specific geographical region that are not naturally found anywhere else.[13]

Texas is second in terms of diversity. Like California, it is a big state with a mix of distinctive ecosystems. At the junction of several great arid ecoregions, Arizona is next on the list; species richness is dominated by desert-adapted plants and animals. The most diverse state east of the Mississippi River is Alabama.[14]

At the bottom of the diversity list is Hawaii, partly because of its small size but also for the large number of extinct or missing species. While the state comprises less than 0.2 percent of our nation's land mass, a quarter of the nation's most endangered species are found here earning it the unenviable title: "Endangered species capital of the world."[15] According to the World Atlas:

"The loss of species in Hawaii is not new news which began as early as the seventh century when Polynesian migrants started arriving on the island accompanied by their dogs, chickens and pigs, invasive species which triggered the end of Hawaiian endemics. A second spate of destruction began in the 1800s when vast tracts of forests were cleared for sandalwood trees and Hawaiian birds were hunted down in thousands for their colorful feathers to adorn the decorated caps worn by the nobility. Large areas of native vegetation were also lost to livestock grazing during this period.

With the arrival of the Europeans in the late eighteenth century, the Hawaiian species suffered a new round of death and destruction when vast tracts of native forests were cleared for sugarcane plantations and grazing lands. The destruction continued into the 1900s and soon, other factors like the influx of large volumes of tourists to the archipelago, growth of human habitation on these islands, global warming and climate change, all led to the wanton destruction of Hawaiian ecosystems."[16]

The Hawaiian monk seal – one of two monk seal species in the world – numbers less than 1,000. The future of the monk seal is in doubt due to high infant mortality, insufficient food, shark attacks and stress from human encroachment. Hawaii's list of extinct birds is greater than 30, ten in just the last 30 years. Due to deforestation, illegal hunting, starvation and predation, the Hawaiian hawk's existence is threatened. The honeycreeper is a large bird that makes its home on the summit of Haleakala Volcano on Maui; there are less than 4,000 birds remaining.[17]

It was President Nixon who urged Congress to pass new legislation to protect at-risk species. Building upon existing law, Congress approved the Endangered Species Act of 1973. Designed to protect critically imperiled species from extinction, it conforms to the provisions of the Convention on International Trade in Endangered Species of Wild Fauna and Flora. The law requires federal agencies to consult with the Fish and Wildlife Service to ensure their actions do not jeopardize critical habitat of any listed species.[18]

The law has been controversial since its passage even though the U.S. Supreme Court found that "the plain intent of Congress in enacting" the ESA "was to halt and reverse the trend toward species extinction, whatever the cost." In 2001 the Bush Administration instituted numerous bureaucratic obstacles to minimize the clear intent of the law.[19]

The best-known case that pitted man against animal under this law involves the northern spotted owl. Believed to have once inhabited forests from San Francisco all the way north to British Columbia, the owl's loss of nesting, roosting and foraging habitat mostly due to timber harvesting and land conversion have led to a decline in the population throughout much of their historic range. More recently, competition with encroaching barred owls who have fewer habitat restrictions have also affected the population.[20]

Northern spotted owls became a lightning rod for protection because of their unique habitat requirements – they only live in a dense canopy closure of mature and old-growth forests that contain snags and are mostly undisturbed. Typically, it takes forests at least 150 to 200 years to attain these characteristics; the birds also require a habitat range of 1,000 acres.[21]

Besides their remarkable beauty, old-growth forests are more complex than any other kind of forest type. They are home to a diversity of vertebrate animals, insects, fungi, mosses and lichens. In addition to the spotted owl, other threatened species, such as the marbled murrelet, are found here as well. These forests provide numerous recreational opportunities while also serving as a hedge against climate change by providing long-term carbon storage.[22]

There are only a few remaining pockets of old-growth forests left. Most of these are protected lands, but this has not stopped politicians supporting the lumber companies and their desire to cut these stands, claiming jobs are at stake. As the controversy pitted individual loggers and small sawmill owners against environmentalists, bumper stickers reading *Kill a Spotted Owl—Save a Logger* and *I Like Spotted Owls – Fried* appeared to support the loggers.[23]

But this was never a battle by environmentalists to save a single species. It was a desire to save a unique ecosystem that is rapidly disappearing. The Endangered Species Act provided an avenue to save what is left of the old-growth forests. Owls are not the reason loggers lost their jobs; most of the western forests were cut a long time ago. There are now an estimated 2,000 pairs of northern spotted owls remaining and they are what conservationists call a legacy species. As for the rest of the U.S., there are currently over 1,540 plant and animal species listed as threatened in the U.S., including about 82 endangered bird species.

How much of our remaining critically-important habitat are we willing to lose? From the 1780s to the 1980s, the lower 48 states have lost more than half of their original wetlands which once totaled over 220 million acres.[25] All of America's wildlife diversity, including birds, is at risk due to habitat destruction, invasive species and climate change with the latter leading us in a direction with unknown consequences. The passage of the Clean Water Act and other environmental statutes have dramatically lessened the rate of wetland loss, but the Trump Administration significantly weakened these laws.

Three species barely hanging on reside only in Florida – the manatee, Florida panther and Key deer. The most recent aerial surveys of manatees in January 2018 indicate there are barely 6,000 of these large animals left.[26] On the other end of the size spectrum, at least compared to its northern brethren, is the tiny Key deer. Its small size is better suited to the heat and humidity of southern Florida. Exclusive to the Keys, it is still found in very small pockets. Powerful storms like

Hurricane Irma in 2017 that hit the Keys are just another threat to its survival.[27]

The wood stork is a large wading bird that stands more than three feet tall with a five-foot wing span. It is the only stork breeding in the U.S. and it feeds by catching small, freshwater fish with its groping bill moving at lightning speed, the fastest of any known vertebrate. Its preference for tropical and subtropical habitats with distinct wet and dry seasons makes it ideally suited for life in the Everglades.[28]

Water is the dominant force in the Everglades which comes from the vast but shallow Lake Okeechobee. This area of southern Florida is characterized by sawgrass marshes – part of a complex ecosystem that includes cypress swamps, tropical hardwood hammocks and the estuarine mangrove forests found along the coast. Shaped by differences in water flows, boundaries between ecosystems can shift over time. But things began to radically change in the late 1800s when man intruded and started developing the area and draining water to support agriculture; as development continued, dikes were constructed to regulate the water supply for economic reasons and to prevent flooding.[29]

As humans tampered with the waterflows to the Everglades and disrupted the ecology, wood stork numbers began to drop. In 1984, they were placed on the Federal Endangered Species list. At the same time, conservation groups were raising concerns about the degradation of the entire Everglades ecosystem. As a result, a comprehensive restoration plan was approved by Congress in 2000. Because the wood stork's habitat requirements are uniquely associated with the conditions found in the Everglades, it is used as an indicator species to measure the effectiveness of on-going ecosystem restoration efforts.[30]

The stork has since been downgraded from endangered to threatened, reflecting a successful conservation and recovery effort spanning three decades. Although its status has improved, the Everglades ecosystem is still endangered. As a low-lying area near the coast, sea level rise and other effects from climate change will be the biggest challenge it has yet to face.

One bird species that did disappear from Florida is the majestic whooping crane. It is the tallest North American bird and one of only two crane species found in North America; it is also highly endangered. After being pushed to the brink of extinction by unregulated hunting and loss of habitat, by 1991 the population was reduced to 21 wild and two captive birds. Since then, conservation efforts have led to a limited recovery. The population now is over 500 birds that summer in Canada and winter in at the Aransas National Wildlife Refuge on the Texas Gulf Coast. Efforts are also underway to reintroduce the whooping crane to Florida.[31]

What we have failed to recognize is that our economic interests are better served when we choose to protect wildlife. According to the non-profit group Beyond Pesticides:

> "The estimated economic costs of losses to biodiversity — for the value of pollinator services, 'beneficial' predators, and birds and aquatic life — are continually changing as more complex and comprehensive studies are published. Earlier studies estimated that the cost of losses to biodiversity might amount to more than $1.1 billion annually. Now, we know that the loss of biodiversity can cost hundreds of billions of dollars annually."[32]

Flocks of birds and schools of fish often group together in large numbers creating a dynamic system in which the parts act as one. It is a behavior that evolutionary biologists refer to as group behavior or "murmuration." Starlings, generally considered an invasive species in the U.S., are most emblematic of this type of behavior. While not fully understood, it is thought there is strength in numbers helping to protect any given individual from predators. When a species population declines, the remaining members are at greater risk from any number of unknown factors. This is just one example of the many ecological principles that determine if a species will thrive or begin to decline.[33]

Now our birds and other wildlife are in the crosshairs of an even larger threat – energy development. In December 2017, President Trump announced plans to scale back two national monuments in Utah to unleash more carbon-emitting energy resources. His plan would reduce the 1.88-million-acre Grand Staircase Escalante National Monument – designated by President Bill Clinton in 1996 – over 45 percent and the 1.35-million-acre Bears Ears National Monument – created by President Barack Obama in 2016 – by 85 percent. Parts of Grand Staircase Escalante could then be developed for its coal resources and Bears Ears for uranium.[34]

In February 2018, both monuments were reduced mostly along the amounts requested by the President. Despite the ongoing legal challenges, the land removed from protective status is open to claims under the General Mining Law of 1872 although to date there has been little interest from energy companies. At the time of his announcement, the President declared, "Some people think that the natural resources should be controlled by a small handful of very distant bureaucrats located in Washington. And guess what: They're wrong."[35]

President Trump cited an antiquated 1872 law for the benefit of two dying industries under the guise it will benefit all Americans, coal and uranium. Just the opposite is true. These treasured lands were set aside by past presidents for the protection and enjoyment of all Americans; developing these lands for coal and uranium for the benefit of large energy companies serves the few, not the many.

Crisscrossing large areas of open land and wilderness with roads leads to habitat fragmentation. There is a direct correlation between the population of a particular species and the size of an area. As we divide a landscape into smaller pieces, a certain percentage of wildlife species will likely disappear. The species-area relationship will be critical as the climate changes presenting conditions that have never been tested before.[36]

Undisturbed areas serve a far more critical role – they help protect biodiversity. Many species are on the move to escape the higher temperatures that are stressing habitats across the globe. If a species is trapped because the land is fragmented and there is no place to go, it will not survive. In the lower 48 states, the largest wilderness areas are in states like Utah which is why Grand Staircase Escalante and Bears Ears were set aside in the first place. They are not just pretty landscapes, but places essential to maintain biologically-rich habitats.

We may have underestimated the effects of climate change on wildlife. All species have specific habitat requirements and some physical characteristics may only occur in limited areas. In the end, the resiliency of any given species will be based on a multitude of factors. The world is rapidly losing its last, undisturbed wilderness areas. One of those areas – the Arctic tundra in Alaska – is also under threat from the Trump Administration that wants to open the area to oil drilling. The U.S. has a larger responsibility to the world in protecting these areas.

Over the last half billion years, there have been five major mass extinctions that altered the diversity of life on our planet. As Elizabeth Kolbert argues in her extraordinary book *The Sixth Extinction: An Unnatural History*, scientists believe we could be facing the next mass extinction – only this one will be caused by humans.[37]

According to Mr. Brand of the Texas Pesticide Review Board, they may be dying of something else anyway but no species should be dismissed with little regard for its survival; this includes the snail darter as described below. If President Trump continues his efforts to weaken the Endangered Species Act, it will be harder for regulators to factor in the effects of climate change on wildlife, thereby threatening the nation's biodiversity.[38]

Congress Decides Some Species Are More Important Than Others

A member of the perch family, the snail darter is a freshwater fish found in the East Tennessee River that drains areas of Tennessee and Alabama. Discovered in 1973 by a University of Tennessee biologist and professor while doing research, two years later it was listed as endangered under the Endangered Species Act. This put the snail darter at the center of a lawsuit to halt the completion of Tellico Dam and Reservoir. While environmentalists argued the dam posed the risk of extinction for the fish by blocking its migratory route, others argued it was being used as a scapegoat to block economic progress.

The case was eventually heard by the U.S. Supreme Court that ruled the Act explicitly forbade the completion of such projects as Tellico "if the Secretary of Interior had determined that such a project would likely result in the elimination of a species." It did not matter that over 100 million dollars had been spent on the project and was substantially finished, the court could not allow the TVA to finish the project. The Court's Chief Justice in the majority opinion wrote, this would force the court "to ignore the ordinary meaning of plain language."

The Court's decision set off a fury in Congress as some members sought to rework the law. Led by then Republican Tennessee Senator Howard Baker, an amendment that exempted the project from the Act was introduced. While it passed in the House, the bill failed in the Senate. This did not deter the Senator as he reintroduced the bill several months later. With bi-partisan support it passed this time around and on September 25, 1979, President Jimmy Carter signed the exemption into law.

In the words of Senator Baker, "We who voted for the Endangered Species Act with the honest intentions of protecting such glories of nature as the wolf, the eagle, and other treasures have found that extremists with wholly different motives are using this noble act for meanly obstructive ends....the snail darter has become an unfortunate example of environmental extremism, and this kind of extremism, if rewarded and allowed to persist, will spell the doom to the environmental protection movement in this country more surely and more quickly than anything else."

Today, the snail darter is a federally protected species; its status is listed as threatened, the result of habitat destruction from the completion of the Tellico Dam. Another factor in its decline is siltation, which degrades spawning habitat and food availability. Other influences include agricultural development, environmental contamination and pollution, and channel modification, all of which affect the water clarity, reproduction success and migration patterns. Like every other species, the snail darter is part of the web of life and should be protected.[39]

Red Knots Are Important Too

Less than two decades ago, more than 100,000 red knots, a shorebird, filled the skies of Delaware Bay during their epic spring migration from South America to breeding grounds in the Canadian Arctic. Today, fewer than 13,000 of the shorebirds remain, a number that continues to decline steadily.

The red knot's remarkable migration is one of the wonders of the animal world, attracting scientists, birdwatchers and wildlife enthusiasts worldwide. As an indicator species for other Arctic long-distance fliers, the red knot has been subject to extensive research on its breeding behavior, wintering ecology, migration patterns and stopover sites.

One of the greatest threats to red knots today is a lack of horseshoe crab eggs to eat at Delaware Bay, a critical stopover and refueling point on the shorebird's migration. When red knots leave Delaware Bay in poor condition due to the lack of these eggs, which are a protein-rich food source, they either die before ever arriving in the Arctic or arrive in too poor a condition to successfully reproduce.

In the 1990s, overfishing for use as bait caused the horseshoe crab fishery to crash, and as this red knot food source diminished, so did the red knot population. Although horseshoe crab harvests are now limited, too many are still being taken from the ocean and egg densities have not yet rebounded. Now, the harvesting of horseshoe crab blood for biomedical purposes may also be playing a role in slowing the recovery of the Delaware Bay horseshoe crab population.

Climate change is another threat facing red knots. Rising temperatures are changing conditions of the shorebirds' tundra breeding grounds, as well as their habitat at the far south and north ends of their range. Sea level rise also threatens to swallow some of the red knot's most important habitat and feeding areas.[40]

Chapter Eighteen

Invaders on the Loose

"Human judges can show mercy. But against the laws of nature, there is no appeal."

- Arthur C. Clarke -

An invasive species is a plant, fungus or animal species – aquatic and terrestrial – that is not native to a specific location but has been introduced to the area. Because these species have no natural predator or other type of control compared to their home environment, they tend to spread to a degree that can cause damage to native plants and animals as well as pose a danger to human health.

Invasive species are among the leading threats to our biodiversity and native wildlife. The potential hazard they pose is based on their geographic range and abundance; when they overwhelm an area, the ecosystem and economic impacts can be devastating. Over 40 percent of threatened or endangered species are at risk due to these unwelcome species from foreign lands.[1]

Dealing with these invaders is nothing new. The gypsy moth was accidently introduced here by an amateur entomologist studying native silkworms after the Civil War. During the larva or caterpillar stage, gypsy moths eat the leaves of trees and can defoliate an entire area. Over twenty insect parasitoids and predators have been introduced over from Asia and Europe to control the moth's population. More recently, a certain fungus species has caused a considerable die-off of gypsy moths.[2] With other invasive species, we have not been so fortunate.

Mute swans – a bird whose heritage as a status symbol for the wealthy dates back centuries – were intentionally introduced to the U.S. by Europeans as decorative waterfowl in zoos, parks and private estates. The first birds to escape captivity occurred early in the twentieth century in New York, while in New England it is believed some birds were intentionally released. By the 1930s, feral populations of swans began to proliferate spreading as far south as New Jersey. In 1962, an escaped Maryland population of only five birds grew to a bevy of 4,000 feral mute swans.[3]

Protected in many states under waterfowl laws, the mute swan population in the Eastern U.S. has grown consistently over the past 40 years. Today there are substantial populations in the Chesapeake Bay, the Great Lakes and areas on Long Island. The birds have thrived in these freshwater habitats because of the similar climatic conditions they enjoy in their native land. Due to their size and outwardly aggressive behavior, they possess the ability to out-compete many native species for food as well as nesting sites. They also face few threats from predators.[4]

While swans may be revered in some parts of Europe, they are considered an invasive species in the U.S. Mute swans are herbivorous foragers and they are voracious eaters. Several recent studies have shown, as their numbers increase, they can severely reduce densities of submerged vegetation to the detriment of other birds; these are the same grasses that shelter other marine species like bay scallops and juvenile lobsters.[5] As their numbers continued to soar, it became evident some type of population control was warranted.

> "In 2003, the U.S. Fish and Wildlife Service proposed to 'minimize environmental damages attributed to mute swans' by reducing their numbers in the Atlantic Flyway to pre-1986 levels, a 67 percent reduction at the time. According to a report published in the Federal Register of 2003, the proposal was supported by all thirteen state wildlife agencies which submitted comments, as well as by 43 bird

conservation, wildlife conservation and wildlife management organizations."[6]

As one might suspect, ten animal rights organizations and most of the comments from individuals were opposed. At the time mute swans were protected under the Migratory Bird Treaty Act due to a court order, but "in 2005 the United States Department of the Interior officially declared them a non-native, unprotected species."[7]

When the Connecticut Audubon Society asked the State to remove mute swans from critical marine habitats, it encountered outrage from bird lovers and animal activists around the state. While neighboring states allow biologists to use certain measures to ensure the eggs are no longer viable, Connecticut is still grappling to come up with an acceptable solution.[8]

In Boston, after the first pair arrived in 1868, a resident pair of mute swans is celebrated every year when released into a lagoon at the Public Garden. The practice was discontinued in the 1960s until the owners of the Park Plaza Hotel arranged for their return. Supported by the Rose Parade charity, this spring tradition is celebrated by the media. No one talks about the fact they are an invasive species.[9] Mute swans may be regal, but they do not belong here and more should be done to encourage states to limit their population; at the very least we need to stop celebrating their spring return.

Under the same misguided notion of aristocracy and ignorance, European starlings were first introduced to the U.S. in 1890. It is believed 100 starlings were released in Central Park in New York City by some unknown person(s) in order to replicate the birds found in the works of Shakespeare. Their yearning to bring these birds to America succeeded beyond anyone's wildest dreams. Due to the bird's ability to exploit a large variety of habitats, nest sites and food sources, the starling population has grown to an estimated 150-200 million birds.[10]

To help protect wildlife, Congress passed the Lacey Act of 1900 – our nation's first conservation law. It prohibited the trade of wildlife, fish and plants that have been illegally taken, possessed, transported or sold in violation of U.S. and Indian law. Since then the law has been expanded to include non-native species that have the potential to become invasive. The Alien Species Prevention and Enforcement Act of 1992 makes it illegal to transport through the mail a plant or animal deemed injurious to Hawaii, a state especially vulnerable to invasive species.[11]

When healthy ecosystems are disrupted by invasive species, it can cost the economy billions of dollars each year. Zebra and quagga mussels provide an illustrative example of how a few introduced species can alter the balance of an entire ecosystem. According to the National Wildlife Federation:

> "Originally from Eastern Europe, these tiny trespassers were picked up in the ballast water of ocean-going ships and brought to the Great Lakes in the 1980s. They spread dramatically, outcompeting native species for food and habitat, and by 1990, zebra mussels and quagga mussels had infested all the Great Lakes. Both have spread to 29 states by hitching rides on boats moving between the Great Lakes and Mississippi River Basins. Artificial channels like the Chicago Area Waterways System facilitate their spread. These man-made channels act like super-highways and are also a pathway for Asian carp, which are currently spreading towards the Great Lakes."[12]

These mussels are filter feeders who have blanketed the bottom of the Great Lakes. Because they eat plankton, water clarity has improved dramatically which is not always a good thing. The clear water has created ideal conditions – i.e. more sunlight – for deadly algal blooms to flourish. With the quaggas mostly found in the deeper, colder waters compared to the zebras, it is estimated there are over 10 trillion of these mussels in the Great Lakes today, taking food away from fish, ruining beaches and blocking water intake pipes. With no known method to eradicate them without harming other wildlife, the cost to the local economy is in the billions of dollars.[13]

Colonization of the Great Lakes by these two species has overwhelmed the normal ecological functions that fish and other wildlife depend on. The disappearing shrimp-like crustacean Diporeia is one of the most important organisms in the Great Lakes food-web, providing a rich source of food to many fish species including smaller fish that are eaten by salmon, trout and walleye. Once supplying 50 percent of the food source for the commercially-important lake whitefish, they now supply only about five percent.[14]

Zebra and quagga mussels do more than outcompete their competition and limit food supply for fish. They attach themselves to native mussels restricting their food intake and movement, eventually killing them. Besides disrupting natural food webs, they also appear to promote the growth of the bacteria responsible for type E botulism. Through bioaccumulation, the toxin is passed through the ecosystem leading to the death of an estimated 52,000 water birds in the period from 2002 to 2006.[15]

The dumping of ballast water or purposely introducing a species are not the only ways an unwelcome visitor arrives on our shores or becomes a nuisance. Other illegal pathways include hitchhikers on imported goods, farm animals that escape and the illegal wildlife trade. Here are some of the notable specimens that have harmed the environment.[16]

- Dutch elm disease is transmitted to trees by elm bark beetles from Asia that carry a fungus. Since 1930, the disease has spread from Ohio through most of the country, killing over half of the elm trees in the northern U.S.

- Cogongrass is an Asian plant that arrived as seeds in packing material. It is now spreading through the Southeast U.S., displacing native plants. It provides no food value for native wildlife, and increases the threat of wildfire as it burns hotter and faster than native grasses.

- Asian carp were imported to the U.S. in the 1970s to filter pond water in fish farms in Arkansas. Flooding allowed them to escape and they are swiftly spreading northward up the Illinois River, soon to invade the Great Lakes. Adult carp have no natural predators here and females lay up to half a million eggs each time they spawn.

- Feral pigs will eat almost anything, including native birds. They compete with native wildlife for food sources such as acorns. They also spread diseases, such as brucellosis, to people and livestock. E. coli from their feces was implicated in the E. coli contamination of baby spinach in 2006.

- Water hyacinth is a beautiful aquatic plant, introduced to the U.S. from South America as an ornamental plant. In the wild, it forms dense mats, reducing sunlight for submerged plants and aquatic organisms, crowding out native aquatic plants, and clogging waterways and intake pipes.

- European green crabs found their way into the San Francisco Bay area in 1989. They outcompete native species for food and habitat and eat huge quantities of native shellfish, threatening commercial fisheries.

- The brown marmorated stink bug is from Asia and they were first discovered in the U.S. in the late 1990s. Their populations are exploding and they are quickly becoming a nuisance to people in their homes and to the agriculture industry.

Florida is home to numerous invasive plants and animals, but the two species that are raising the most havoc with coastal ecosystems are the venomous lionfish and the Burmese python. Found in Indonesia, lionfish were likely released into the wild from home aquariums. Their ornate fins and eighteen spines make them stand out from other reef fish; one writer and diver described them as "red and white Las Vegas showgirls of the sea."[17]

Lionfish are carnivores with huge appetites that feed on small crustaceans and fish, including the young of important commercial fish species such as snapper and grouper; they have the capacity to eat up to 30 times their stomach volume. They also breed about three to four times faster than native fish species posing a serious threat to Florida's saltwater fishing industry – the second largest in the nation – putting over 150,000 jobs at risk. Meanwhile, lionfish continue to populate the waters off Florida despite intense efforts to eliminate them.[18]

Native to Southeast Asia, the other notorious Florida invader is the Burmese python. One of the largest snakes in the world, they were first sighted in the Everglades in the 1980s. In 2000, the python was identified as a breeding population throughout southern Florida. They prey on a wide variety of birds and mammals; the near total absence of mammalian species such as rabbits, foxes, raccoons, opossums and even bobcats corelates directly with the proliferation of pythons. Population estimates range from at least 30,000 to upwards of 300,000.[19]

How they got here is unknown but likely it was the result of imported snakes being released into the wild after they grew too large to keep; it is also speculated they escaped from captivity during Hurricane Andrew in 1992. The importation of Burmese pythons is now banned in the U.S.

Despite efforts to control the population, their numbers appear to be increasing. People that hunt pythons are paid a minimum wage plus a bonus, based on length, for each snake caught. A seventeen-foot female python carrying 73 eggs and weighing over 140 pounds was recently captured in the Everglades. It is thought to be the largest snake ever caught in Florida.[20]

It is estimated that over 50,000 non-native species have been introduced to the U.S, including livestock, crops, pets and other non-invasive species. There is a huge economic cost associated with the damage caused by these unwanted visitors. Estimated at $120 billion per year, the costs include efforts to control and eliminate species causing the greatest destruction.[21]

It is also challenging to ascertain if other invasive species are still entering the U.S. In 1996, Congress passed the National Invasive Species Act in 1996 to regulate ballast water discharges.

The Coast Guard issued ballast water regulations in 2012 and, the next year, EPA set numeric ballast water discharge limits. Only in cases of extreme emergency can ships not comply with the limits.[22] While these regulations may prevent future invasive species from entering our waters, the damage has already been done.

The woolly adelgid is an insect that was introduced on nursery stock from Japan in the 1950s. As a result, eastern hemlocks – a conifer of great value to the lumber industry – are now disappearing along the East coast from Georgia to Maine. The adelgid feeds by sucking on the sap of hemlocks, eventually killing them. In New England, the hemlock is a vital component of the forest ecosystem but now, thanks to warmer temperatures, the adelgid is rapidly moving north decimating huge swaths of trees along its path. In Connecticut alone, about 80 percent of the native eastern hemlocks have been killed.[23]

The only environmentally safe method for treating infecting trees is with a nontoxic insecticidal soap and protective horticultural oil, which is sprayed on the underside of the limbs smothering the insects as they dry. While this treatment can be effective, one can only treat one tree at a time and there are thousands of trees at risk. Most trees also need to be treated on a yearly basis which makes the task that much tougher especially with larger trees. There are toxic systemic insecticides that are applied to the foliage and bark of a tree which can persist in killing the adelgid for up to four years after application, but there are environmental consequences when using a toxic spray in riparian zones, limiting it use.[24]

The bright metallic-green beetle called the emerald ash borer may be barely a half inch long, but it can take down ash trees thousands of times its size. Originally from Asia, the ash borer was first discovered in the Detroit area in 2002; it is alleged to have arrived here on wooden packing materials from China. While the adults just nibble on the leaves causing little harm, it is the larvae that feed on the inner bark of ash trees, disrupting the tree's ability to transport water and nutrients.[25] On its web site, the Arbor Day Foundation notes the following:

> "Ash trees are one of the most valuable and abundant North American woodland trees: estimates of total number of ash trees in the United States alone range between seven and nine billion. The emerald ash borer has destroyed 40 million ash trees in Michigan alone and tens of millions throughout other states and Canada. Small trees can die as soon as one to two years after infestation, while larger infested trees can survive for three to four years."[26]

The beetle is now found in 35 states and five Canadian provinces.[27] The infestation is made worse by heat stress on forests and dying trees only add to global warming as they can no longer absorb and store carbon. Meanwhile new invaders continue to enter the country.

The spotted lanternfly is another Asian native that was discovered several years ago in Berks County, Pennsylvania. It is what they call a "planthopper" similar to the cicada family of insects and aphids. The lanternfly was brought here after a company imported some rocks from China that had egg masses on them. From that single group of rocks, populations of the insect have spread to the other parts of Pennsylvania, as well as Virginia, New Jersey, Delaware and Maryland. And it continues to spread elsewhere.[28]

Unlike the emerald ash borer, spotted lanternflies are far less selective when it comes to what they eat. They are known to suck the sap from more than 70 types of trees ranging from walnut to grape trees. While their feeding usually does not lead to tree mortality, it can cause branch dieback. If a tree shows signs of decline, the lanternfly will move to a healthier specimen; if a damaged tree recovers, the lanternfly will come back for a second helping. Since they pierce the bark to get to the sap, they are creating pathways for harmful diseases to enter. There are some effective measures for getting rid of these pests but when we have an invasive that can fly in masses and is not picky about what it eats, the problem is magnified.[29]

Invasive insects are the biggest problem in terms of preventing their entry into the U.S. and the damage they can cause to our forests.   In their native countries, invasive bugs are kept in check due to the relationship of trees and predators, and predators of predators; trees also might have evolved a chemical defense that protects them.   When those natural defenses are absent – combined with the influences of climate change – our forests come under attack and there is little we can do to stop the destruction.

The wood pallet revolutionized international shipping back in World War II; these same pallets can also provide a free ride to insects entering this country by burrowing into the wood.

Standards were established in 2006 and over 180 countries now abide by the regulations where pallets are either treated with heat or fumigated. While this has helped prevent an unknown number of pests from entering the U.S., unwanted pests are still getting in.[30]

> "Each year some 13 million containers, stacked high with wooden pallets, are shipped to the U.S. 'Inspectors can't possibly ensure all of those are clean,' says forest ecologist Gary Lovett. 'You can imagine, they're looking for a bug inside a board, in a pallet, in the bottom of a shipping container.'
> Lovett argues for ditching wood pallets and replacing them with other materials, like recycled plastic or composite wood materials. One problem – those alternatives cost more. Pallets are an $11.5 billion American business and the industry is against more regulation."[31]

This dilemma highlights the difficulty in developing a sustainable economy. Plastic materials are not always a bad thing, but they are a problem when used in packaging that gets tossed after a single use. Here is an application where plastic and other recycled materials can be turned into reusable pallets, but no one wants to absorb the additional cost. In the meantime, plastic manufacturers complain that if we ban plastic bags jobs will be lost. Perhaps they could make pallets instead. Sadly, most companies and manufacturers are caught between needing to make a profit and protecting the environment in the long term.

When Congress passed the 2018 Farm Bill, there was an effort to strengthen regulating and reporting of invasive pests. Although debated, wood pallets were not banned despite numerous recommendations to do so. In the end, short-term economic interests prevailed as the environmental costs continue to mount.

Throughout history people have imported plants and animals without realizing the consequences. Many plants were brought to the U.S. as ornamentals or for erosion control. But now we know better and we must ask ourselves why we are importing rocks from China? There is no shortage of them in the U.S. and it is wasteful to ship materials half way around the world because of a preference for something different. It is called living within our means, not economically but environmentally. It is the same misguided practice of sending lobsters to Asia.

We can do a lot more to stop the spread of invasive species. Most exotics thrive on disturbances to the natural environment. If we do a better job of restoring the landscape with native plants after a construction project, we lessen the likelihood of invasive plants taking hold. This might cost a little more, but in the long run the benefits are worth it. Homeowners should also request native plants when shopping at their local nursery. And what invasive species is headed here next? First spotted in 2019, the Asian giant hornet is now found in the State of Washington. Known as the "murder hornet," they feed on other insects, especially honey bees, posing a threat to farmers who grow crops.

Here Are Four Other Invasive Species Raising Havoc With Our Landscapes

Japanese honeysuckle is one of many invasive varieties of honeysuckle in the U.S. It was brought to Long Island, NY, in 1806 for ornamental use and erosion control. The plant has become prolific throughout much of the East Coast as it adapts to a wide range of conditions. Japanese honeysuckle is an aggressive vine that smothers, shades and girdles other competing vegetation. Many birds eat the plant's fruit, thereby spreading the honeysuckle's seeds.

Japanese barberry was introduced to the U.S. in the 1800s as an ornamental shrub. Seeds of Japanese barberry were sent from Russia in 1875 as an alternative to European barberry, which suffered from a serious fungus known as black rust stem. The shrub can grow in deep shade and is particularly detrimental to forest lands in the Northeast. The heavily fruiting plant forms dense thickets, crowding out native plants. Like the honeysuckle, its seeds are easily spread by birds.

Japan introduced kudzu to the U.S. at the Philadelphia Centennial Exposition in 1876. It was first promoted as an ornamental plant and later as a forage crop in the Southeast. One million acres of kudzu were planted in the 1930s and 1940s by the Soil Conservation Service to reduce soil erosion on deforested lands. It was not until the 1950s that it was recognized as an invasive species. Once established, kudzu grows at a rate of up to one foot a day and 60 feet annually. This vigorous vine takes over areas by smothering plants and kills trees by girdling them.

The Norway maple came here from England in 1756. The widely adaptable tree quickly became popular and was widely planted as a shade tree. The Norway maple displaces native trees and has the potential to dominate a landscape in both the Northeast and Northwest. It displaces native maples like the sugar maple and its dense canopy shades out wildflowers.[32]

Note: This by no means is a comprehensive list. Other invasive species of concern include English ivy, Japanese knotweed and purple loosestrife. The latter is found across the country and frequently grows in disturbed areas like ditches and highway median strips. While many admire its purple flowers, it can rapidly degrade wetlands diminishing their value for wildlife.

Other invasive plants are well entrenched and create what are called "hybrid" ecosystems. Rather than implementing costly restoration efforts, some places are accepting benign species as "new natives." The idea is to limit their numbers and spread only when they overwhelm native vegetation. While the practice is controversial within the conservation community, it is a recognition that most invasive species are here to stay. [33]

How Climate Change is Affecting America's Pastime

Hillerich & Bradsby Co. has been making Louisville Slugger baseball bats for more than 100 years. Annually, it turns 12,000 to 15,000 white ash trees into bats annually. All the company's white ash comes from forests in northern Pennsylvania and parts of New York.

But the emerald ash borer might change how the industry makes its bats.

The beetles first eat ash tree leaves. Then the females lay eggs in the bark. When these eggs hatch in summertime, larvae chew through the outer bark. The inner, nutrient-carrying tissue of the tree becomes a buffet line. The tree, starved of nutrients and water, eventually dies. Given enough time nearly 100 percent of all white ash – along with green and black ash – will be gone.

The pest was first found in Western Pennsylvania in 2007 after being discovered in Detroit, Michigan five years earlier. Experts say climate change may alter just how far north and south the tree-killing pest will spread. Northern Pennsylvania is right in the emerald ash borer's sweet spot as 47 out of 67 counties have emerald ash borer problems.

What is not in doubt is the white ash trees used in making baseball bats are disappearing. "We haven't seen it affect our ability to get logs yet, but it's knocking on the doorstep," said Brian Boltz, a general manager at Hillerich & Bradsby Co. "It's pretty established both 50 miles north and south of our main harvesting areas. It is only a matter of time." The company can switch to other woods such as maple and yellow birch, but they do not have the same combination of strength and flexibility. This will translate into a lot of broken bats in the future and the use of more resources.[34]

Chapter Ninteen
Nuclear Power: The False Promise

"The saddest aspect of life right now is that science gathers knowledge faster than society gathers wisdom."

- Isaac Asimov -

The push toward using nuclear power in the U.S. to generate electricity began with the Atomic Energy Act of 1954, which encouraged private corporations to build nuclear reactors. Following a significant learning curve and many mishaps, a military plant at Fort Belvoir in Virginia became the first source of atomic power providing electricity to the power grid. The first commercial plant followed the next year in Pennsylvania.[1]

As nuclear power continued to grow throughout the 1960s, the Atomic Energy Commission (now called the Nuclear Regulatory Commission) anticipated that more than 1,000 reactors would be operating in the U.S. by 2000.[2] The electricity produced would be "too cheap to meter" according to some proponents of this new-found energy source.

"Unwilling to risk huge financial liability, private companies viewed even the remote specter of a catastrophe as a major roadblock to their participation in the development of nuclear technology."[3] To ensure the success of the burgeoning industry, the federal government passed the Price-Anderson Act in 1957. The introduction to the Act, starts with the following confession and purpose:

> "An implicit admission that nuclear power provided risks that producers were unwilling to

assume without federal backing. The Price-Anderson Act shields nuclear utilities, vendors and suppliers against liability claims in the event of a catastrophic accident by imposing an upper limit on private sector liability. Without such protection, private companies were unwilling to become involved. No other technology in the history of American industry has enjoyed such continuing blanket protection."[4]

From the very beginning, there has been considerable resistance to the use of nuclear power in the U.S. The first reactor to face public opposition was in 1957 at the Enrico Fermi Nuclear Generating Station. Located about 30 miles from Detroit, Fermi 1 was a prototype fast breeder reactor that suffered a partial meltdown in 1966 and was closed in 1972. This was the worst nuclear accident at a U.S. commercial power plant prior to Three Mile Island. Although there were no injuries or hazardous radiation released, the incident fueled public sentiment that nuclear power was simply too dangerous. More than 50 years after the event, opponents of nuclear power were still wondering if the meltdown at Fermi 1 was "the day we almost lost Detroit."[5]

Fermi 1 had a much different design than other nuclear power plants as it was an experimental "breeder" reactor, meaning it could theoretically create more nuclear fuel than it consumed. This type of reactor is more difficult to operate because of the shorter time frame to regain control in case of a mishap. Today nearly all U.S. commercial nuclear plants have a water-cooled design like the Fermi 2 plant that still operates at the same location as Fermi 1. Plans for a Fermi 3 were later scrapped.[6]

Pacific Gas & Electric hoped to build the first commercially viable nuclear power plant at Bodega Bay, north of San Francisco. The proposal was met with fierce resistance beginning in 1958 forcing the abandonment of plans for the power plant six years later. Historian Thomas Wellock credits the opposition to

Bodega Bay as the birth of the anti-nuclear movement. Plans to build a nuclear power plant in Malibu, California met the same fate as Bodega Bay.[7]

> "There were many anti-nuclear protests in the United States which captured national public attention during the 1970s and 1980s. These included the well-known Clamshell Alliance protests at the Seabrook Station Nuclear Power Plant in New Hampshire and the Abalone Alliance protests at Diablo Canyon Nuclear Power Plant in California, where thousands of protesters were arrested. Anti-nuclear power protests preceded the shutdown of numerous other nuclear power plants."[8]

By the mid-1970s it became clear that nuclear power would not grow nearly as quickly as once believed. "Cost overruns were sometimes a factor of ten above original industry estimates. For the 75 nuclear power reactors built from 1966 to 1977, cost overruns averaged 207 percent."[9]

The dagger that temporarily killed the beast occurred at one of the two nuclear plants at Three Mile Island in March 1979. Located in south central Pennsylvania, a series of mechanical and human errors at the plant triggered the worst commercial nuclear accident in U.S. history. When almost half of the reactor core melted in a large burst of steam trace amounts of radioactive gasses escaped into the surrounding community. It was estimated some two million people were exposed to small amounts of radiation because of the release.[10]

Although there were no known health impacts related to the accident, America's appetite for nuclear power fell to an all-time low and further galvanized the anti-nuclear movement. Stringent new guidelines for operating plants required design changes before any new operating licenses would be granted. This meant higher costs and longer construction times.

As a result, no nuclear plants started after 1974 have been completed in the U.S. The cleanup effort at Three

Mile Island lasted fourteen years at an estimated cost of $1 billion with the damaged reactor entombed in concrete. They also shipped fifteen tons of radioactive fuel and water to a site in Idaho. The second plant here continues to operate but is scheduled to be closed by the end of 2019.[11]

The legacy of Three Mile Island still lingered at the turn of the 21st century when there was a revival of interest in nuclear power. In order to create a "nuclear renaissance" movement, President George W. Bush unveiled the Nuclear Power 2010 Program to reignite the nuclear industry by providing subsidies for a new generation of demonstration plants.[12] But once again a nuclear disaster put an end to the program.

On March 11, 2011, following a 9.0 magnitude earthquake off the coast of Japan, a nearly 50-foot-high tsunami disabled the power supply of the six Fukushima Daiichi reactors. With no ability to cool the reactors, three of the reactor cores melted; this led to massive radioactive releases over several days. The accident was later rated a seven – the highest and most dangerous level – on the International Nuclear and Radiological Event **Scale** (INES). The 1986 Chernobyl disaster is the only other event to be rated so high.[13]

At the time of the earthquake, there were eleven reactors in operation. While all survived the earthquake, the world learned no matter how many safety and back-up systems are in place, one cannot endure a monumental tsunami. Over 100,000 people were evacuated from their homes.[14] Later estimates placed the number of evacuees at 160,000.[15]

Eight years after the disaster, residents are finally being allowed to return to their homes but fears over the possible health effects of radiation exposure remain high. Part of the nearby town of Okuma serves as an "interim" storage site for millions of cubic feet of contaminated soil. The government has vowed to move the soil by the year 2045 but has yet to identify either a place to bring it or any other solution for disposal. Estimated final clean-up costs will approach $200 billion.[16]

Fukushima was the demise of the so-called Nuclear Renaissance. Although Bush's plan generated industry applications for new plants, the scale of the disaster forced a major pullback of proposed plants. In 2017, the parent company of Westinghouse Electric Company filed for bankruptcy because of losses from its reactor construction projects. Currently, only two new nuclear reactors are under construction in the U.S. near Waynesboro, Georgia. At a cost of $25 billion, the project was only able to move forward thanks to loan guarantees from the Obama Administration.[17]

Regardless of how the public feels about nuclear power, it is no longer economically viable without federal loans and subsidies which have existed from the very beginning. This includes how to deal with high-level radioactive waste these plants generate, a responsibility that falls entirely upon the federal government – meaning the U.S. taxpayer.

For the nearly 100 commercial plants currently operating in the U.S., as well as the twenty plus plants in the process of being decommissioned, there is no long-term storage facility for the waste they generate. Approved by Congress in 2002, the proposed $60 billion burial ground called Yucca Mountain in Nevada – a state that has no nuclear plants of its own – has been an unmitigated failure and it is unclear if the project will ever be completed. In 2011 the Obama Administration cut its funding despite the fact the government already has spent $15 billion studying the location. In the meantime, most U.S. nuclear plants have resorted to the indefinite on-site storage of waste in steel and concrete casks – hardly a permanent solution.[18]

Another subject the nuclear industry does not like to talk about is the over 15,000 abandoned uranium mines in the U.S. Most of these were established under the General Mining Law of 1872 that does not require reclamation or remediation – another example of an antiquated law that protects corporations and not the public interest.[19] Wyoming is home to the largest uranium mines in the U.S. It also possesses the largest capacity for uranium enrichment; a process necessary to produce the required fuel rods.[20] This is the same state trying to stop efforts to develop renewable energy.

Others have suggested nuclear power should be a key component in the battle against climate change. Although proponents falsely claim that nuclear power is carbon-free and does not contribute to global warming, this is only part of the story as told by the Seacoast Anti-Pollution League (SAPL) in New Hampshire that led the fight against the Seabrook Nuclear Power Station.

> "While a nuclear plant emits negligible CO_2 in operation, the mining, milling, fabrication and especially enrichment of uranium fuel rods are very carbon-intensive. In fact, there are whole utility-size coal power plants that are devoted to powering existing U.S. uranium enrichment facilities. The huge amount of materials, mainly energy-intensive concrete, required to construct the containment structures for nuclear plants is also very carbon-intensive. Conservative analyses have found that nuclear power is seven times more carbon-intensive than its closest renewable competitor – wind power generation."[21]

Because of their need for an endless supply of coolant water, nuclear power plants also pose a vulnerability that is not shared by most other energy generating facilities. While the Fukushima disaster was the result of a natural occurrence beyond anyone's control, climate change presents a whole new set of challenges. Many nuclear plants are located at or near sea level putting them at increased risk from sea level rise and the ravages of more intense storms. On the other hand, many plants are in areas experiencing severe drought. Lack of an adequate water supply could force partial shutdowns; the same is true of extreme heat waves.[22]

To address water shortages at some older plants, recirculation systems are being explored instead of the traditional once-through cooling systems. These may or may not solve the problem but will certainly add to the operating costs. In 2017, the U.S. Energy Information Administration reported that renewable energy sources remain in a statistical dead heat with nuclear power in relation to their respective shares of the nation's electrical generation, with each providing roughly twenty percent of the total.[23] As the problems facing the nuclear industry continue to escalate, the cost of renewable energy is headed downward.

Most climate experts recognize climate change is the paramount issue facing the world, but nuclear energy is not the path to eliminating fossil fuels from our future despite the backing of several prominent climate scientists including the renowned Dr. James Hansen. In a 2014 letter, over 300 U.S. and international concerned groups responded to his support for nuclear power.

> "Indeed, Dr. Hansen and his colleagues tout so-called 'advanced' nuclear technology, which is nothing more than regurgitated attempts by the industry to bring tried-and-failed alternative designs such as expensive and dangerous breeder reactors to commercialization. We have clean, affordable, safe, reliable and proven solutions available to us. These safe and clean sources can be brought to scale creating an electric grid that relies much more heavily on increased energy efficiency, variable wind and solar photovoltaic (PV), distributed power, demand response and storage technologies.
>
> This energy path can reduce greenhouse gas emissions much more quickly, cost-effectively and safely than any nuclear option. The markets are responding and there is clear evidence that they are catalyzing an unprecedented technological revolution in the power sector."[24]

Nuclear power has never been the panacea claimed by its proponents. It only survives on the backs of ratepayers or with government handouts and subsidies. No other industry dares ask to get paid up front for building facilities – what they politely refer to as "construction work in progress" – and no other industry enjoys the indemnity protections afforded to them through the Price Anderson Act. No other source of energy produces the waste product radioactive isotope U238 with a half-life of 4.5 billion years only to discover there is no known viable place to safely dispose of it.[25]

Nuclear energy is a centralized, uncompromising power source managed by large corporations that causes incalculable harm to the environment. Building more nuclear plants will not lead us to a better and safer world. We need to figure out how to lower our carbon emissions. Nuclear energy is not the answer and it is time embrace legitimate renewable energy sources.

The Yucca Mountain Nuclear Waste Dump, a Political Hot Potato, is Back

CNBC, March 16, 2017: Under a 1982 law, the federal government was supposed to begin moving nuclear waste to a permanent location by 1998. There is currently more than 78,000 tons of waste stored at U.S. nuclear power plants where leaks are common.

The industry has pressured Washington to find a solution. Energy companies have mounted legal challenges that have cost the government more than $5 billion in settlements according to the lobbying group the Nuclear Energy Institute. That cost could balloon to $29 billion by 2022. States that currently store nuclear waste have also pushed for a resolution.

Congress hoped to restart licensing activity at the Yucca Mountain repository and fund an interim storage program. That would allow development at the remote site located about 100 miles from Las Vegas to start up again following the suspension of the facilities license by President Barack Obama in 2010.[26] The funding was never approved by the Senate thanks to the advocacy efforts of Senator Dean Heller (R-NV) who later lost his re-election bid in 2018.[27]

An Island Unto Itself

The Guardian, July 14, 2014: The issue of Turkey Point nuclear plant located 24 miles south of Miami. Its operators point out its reactor vessel is built twenty feet above sea level and they insist it can survive sea surges and hurricanes. But critics argue that ancillary equipment – including emergency diesel generators that are crucial to keeping cooling waters circulating in the event of power failure – are not so well protected. In the event of sea rise and a major storm surge, critics claim a power supply disruption could cause a repeat of the Fukushima accident of 2011. In addition, inundation maps show that with a three-foot sea-level rise, Turkey Point will be cut off from the mainland and will become accessible only by boat or aircraft. And the higher the seas go, the deeper it will be submerged.[28]

Chapter Twenty

The Hummer is the Antichrist of the Environmental Movement

"It's time we reconsidered the wisdom of driving a four-thousand-pound vehicle to take a two-hundred-pound person to buy a quarter-pound hamburger."

- Ted Turner. -

According to the Cynic's Dictionary, an automobile is a "progenitor of suburbs, shopping malls, motels, traffic jams, 'Baby on Board' signs, drive-in funeral parlors and endless rivers of asphalt."

No single vehicle better represents total disdain for the environment than the Hummer. Based on the military Humvee, the Hummer was first marketed in 1992 as a brand of trucks and SUVs by AM General – makers of the Humvee. In 1998, General Motors purchased the brand name and marketed three brands, · the original version and two smaller versions, the H2 and H3. Following the economic downturn of 2008, sales began to fall off proving an old axiom that recessions can benefit the environment. The last Hummer H3 rolled off a GM assembly line on May 24, 2010.[1]

The original Hummers were significantly bigger than other SUVs. Even compared to other heavy passenger vehicles, they also suffered from poor fuel economy due to their weight. Because of their class size, the EPA never published their fuel economy although there are claims the mileage is better than later models. It is estimated that the H2 averaged 14 mpg on the highway and 10 mpg in the city; there was also a diesel option that improved these numbers.[2]

A full reckoning of the environmental costs from automobiles is uncalculatable but when first introduced,

they were viewed as the solution to a growing problem
– too many horses:

> "Historian Clay McShane has estimated that
> during the latter part of the nineteenth century
> the horses in New York City dropped 800,000 to
> 1.3 million pounds of manure every day, much
> of it on the streets. With the addition of all the
> urine, and the corpses of animals that dropped
> dead from disease or exhaustion and were often
> left where they fell, crowded city streets were
> dirty, foul-smelling and fly-ridden, especially in
> hot weather. It is easy to see why many
> urbanites hailed the coming of 'horseless
> carriages'."[3]

It did take not take long before folks began
complaining about the automobile's effect on their
quality of life. In the urban areas, people complained
about exhaust pollution, congestion, traffic accidents
and the demise of downtown; in the countryside, people
complained about the noise and dust. But as cars
replaced the horse and trolley, it was the ability to move
away from the city and the subsequent rise of the
suburbs that had the greatest impact.

> "Almost like a plough breaking the plains, the
> automobile transformed cities and reshaped the
> nation's landscape making it virtually
> unrecognizable from the unpaved version of the
> previous century."[4]

Once the first automobile rolled off the assembly line,
it was destined to be the dominant form of
transportation in the U.S. As expressways and limited-
access highways were added to the mix, cities were
further committed to a one-dimensional transportation
system. In 1970, there were 111,000,000 motor vehicles
– cars, trucks and buses – driving on the nation's
3,730,000 miles of road.[5] By the year 2010 – 40 years
after the first Earth Day celebration – there were over

240,000,000 vehicles on the road; by 2013, that number rose to 256,000,000 and nearly 272,500,000 by 2017. In the span of just seven years, we added an additional 32,5000,000 vehicles to our already crowded roads.[6,7]

All told, there are approximately 4,120,000 miles of roadways across the 50 states; about two-thirds – or 2,750,000 miles – are paved. Between 1970 and 2017, the number of vehicles increased by 161,500,000 while only 360,000 miles of new roadway were constructed.[8] In less than 50 years, we went from 29.75 vehicles per mile of roadway to over 66 vehicles per mile – more than double. When we consider the fact that a third of our roads are dirt with minimal use, it is no wonder people complain about increased traffic jams; we only need to ask the citizens of Los Angeles about the perils of commuting.

Of course, many factors need to be considered when examining road availability and the root causes of congestion. There are road widening projects that expand vehicle capacity (called lane miles) and how far we drive each day affects traffic volume; but when–we consider that our Interstate System is only 47,575 miles long and carries about one-quarter of all traffic, it comes to 1,492 vehicles per mile of highway.

The fact remains while the number of vehicles continues to rise, it is no longer practical or cost effective to build new roads. In addition, the number of miles driven by Americans increased for a sixth consecutive year in 2016, topping 3.2 trillion miles.[9]

> "In April 2010, the EPA and the Department of Transportation's National Highway Traffic Safety Administration (NHTSA) formulated a national program that would finalize new standards for model year 2012 through 2016 passenger cars, light-duty trucks, and medium duty passenger vehicles. With these new standards, vehicles were required to meet an average emissions level of 250 grams of carbon dioxide per mile by model year 2016. This was the first time the EPA had taken measures to

regulate vehicular greenhouse gas emissions under the Clean Air Act."[10]

At the same time, under the original Energy Policy and Conservation Act of 1975 passed in response to the 1973 oil crisis, the Obama Administration introduced Corporate Average Fuel Economy (CAFE) standards. A major selling point of the law was consumers would save money on gas especially if the price at the pump went up.[11] In August 2012, President Obama expanded on these standards for vehicles in model years 2017 through 2025, issuing final rules that set strict emission per mile standards by model year 2025.[12]

The program also includes targeted incentives to encourage early adoption and introduction into the marketplace of advanced technologies to improve vehicle performance, including:

- Incentives for pure electric and plug-in hybrid electric vehicles, and fuel cells vehicles;
- Incentives for natural gas vehicles;
- Credits for technologies with potential to achieve real-world greenhouse gas reductions and fuel economy improvements that are not captured by the standard test procedures.[13]

In June 2015, the Obama administration released the President's "21st Century Clean Transportation Plan" with the goal of reducing carbon pollution by converting the nation's century old infrastructure into one based on clean energy. The goal was to reduce emissions to battle climate change by utilizing more sustainable forms of transportation such as public transit.[14]

> "President Obama recently unveiled an ambitious new plan to pump $32 billion more annually into sustainable 21st century transportation infrastructure. With a dual focus on jumpstarting economic investment and reducing carbon pollution, the plan aims to drive

innovations in public transit, intercity rail and electric vehicle technology, and other clean fuel alternatives. In short, the kind of sustainable investments that are gaining momentum at the local, regional, and international level."[15]

In December 2015, Congress passed the Fixing America's Surface Transportation Act (FAST). The bill's focus was on improving the Interstate System by reducing traffic and lowering emissions but largely overlooked the nation's climate concerns. To further his own agenda,-President Obama proposed a phased-in tax of up to ten dollars per barrel of oil up that would fund infrastructure improvements and drive down the incentive to consume oil. In the end, House Republicans, along with powerful oil companies, announced their disapproval and it never got out of committee.[16]

As more and more Americans embrace bigger and heavier vehicles such as crossovers, SUVs and pick-up trucks, technological advances since the Hummer have also increased fuel-efficiency removing the incentive to purchase a smaller car. Researchers at the University of Michigan calculated the increase in miles per gallon (mpg) thanks to CAFE's implementation. Starting in 2008, there was an average increase from 25.5 to 31.2 mpg by 2016.[17]

In 2017, President Trump requested EPA to conduct a review of fuel economy standards while indicating he might challenge the waivers held by California and other states that allow them to impose tougher emission-cutting requirements.[18] In January 2020, the President announced a compromise. Instead of eliminating fuel standards all together, the federal government would increase the standard 1.5 percent per year from 2021 to 2026 – well below the five percent annual increase proposed by the Obama Administration. Environmentalists and some Senators were hardly thrilled by his proposal. Because of the large number of vehicles in California and their efforts to promote fuel-efficiency, the state has significant influence on automakers even if President Trump attempts to lower fuel standards.[19]

While all this innovation is positive, it has done little to convince Americans to switch to electric vehicles (EVs). By November 2016, there were 540,000 electric cars on the road in the U.S.; this represents a microscopic .22 percent of all vehicles. In that same year, of the approximately 17.5 million vehicles produced, EVs accounted for only 134,000 of these or .77 percent.[20]

Even though Tesla and fourteen other major car manufacturers produce EVs, they have failed to capture the imagination of most Americans. In 2018, there were fifteen models offered in the U.S. that sold less than 1,000 units; two of these models – B250e and S550e – were produced by Mercedes and sold only 135 and 96 units respectively.[21] And Americans continued to shun all types of EVs in 2019 even though 45 new models were introduced, as sales decreased by 6.8 percent from the previous year.[22]

Ironically, some of the very first cars made were electric as well as steam driven. Utilizing a rechargeable battery, the electric car was perceived as a promising alternative to the loud and smelly gas-powered engine. In 1900, more than a quarter of the 4,200 American cars produced that year were electric but their popularity was short-lived.[23]

Featuring big, bulky batteries with limited shelf life, their range was limited to twenty miles. Even the illustrious Thomas Edison could not produce a viable battery with the power and range of gas engines. Once oil was discovered near Beaumont, Texas and Henry Ford began mass producing his gas-powered cars, the dream of an electric vehicle came to an end. It would take another 85 years before they would make a comeback.[24]

Today consumers face many choices today when purchasing a vehicle. The options range from traditional fuels like gasoline and diesel to hybrids and EVs. The diesel engine is significantly cleaner than in the past and while diesel fuel generally provides more miles per gallon than gasoline, it also has a slightly higher carbon content and yields, after refinement, only eleven gallons per barrel of oil compared to twenty for gasoline.[25]

Both types of fuel pollute the environment – diesel engines emit suspended particulate matter and nitrogen oxides while gasoline motors release hydrocarbons, carbon monoxide and carbon dioxide. In the U.S., there also has been slower than estimated reductions in emissions from heavy-duty diesel trucks, hampering progress when it comes to cleaner air; compared to a well-engineered, luxury diesel-powered car, these large trucks are a much bigger problem.[26]

The other issue concerns the reliability of the emissions data being provided by vehicle manufacturers; in 2015, Volkswagen was caught installing sophisticated software – "defeat devices" – designed to cheat strict emissions tests in eleven million cars worldwide.[27]

Despite the environmental problems with larger vehicles, Americans still prefer them. During the first three months of auto sales in 2019, a total of 3.9 million vehicles were sold. Passenger car sales continue to trend downward, their sales usurped by popular crossovers and SUVs. The top three selling vehicles were all pick-up trucks – Ford F-Series, Dodge Ram and Chevrolet Silverado; there are no EVs in the top 25. As gas prices remain low, consumer preferences are not likely to change anytime soon.[28]

In other parts of the world, travelling by rail, including high-speed trains, is far more prevalent. In the U.S., outside of the Northeast, passenger rail traffic is not widely used. While trains contribute their own air pollutants including carbon dioxide, in most cases they are more efficient than automobiles in moving passengers from one location to another.[29]

To evaluate passenger train efficiency there are two key factors that come into play – percent of occupancy and type of fuel used. If a half-empty train is powered by electricity that comes from burning coal, automobiles with several passengers and a full plane are much better. For domestic travel in the U.S., it has been shown that buses are the most efficient option.[30]

When it comes to railroads, we generally tend to think about moving freight. Intermodal – meaning several modes of transportation – freight trains carry goods and materials in a container over long distances before being met by a truck. Like ship containers, they are sealed and can be easily transferred to something else like a truck; these containers improve security, help reduce damage and loss, and allow the freight to be shipped faster.

An intermodal train can carry as much freight as several hundred big rig trucks and it is far more fuel efficient. Partly because these long-haul trains make infrequent stops, a ton of freight can be moved nearly 500 miles on just a gallon of diesel fuel. By removing the need to ship these goods cross country by truck, we can also reduce highway gridlock as well as the costs associated with maintaining existing highways and building new ones.[31]

Given this fact, one would expect freight shipments to be on the increase in the U.S., but that is not the case. A 2017 State of Logistics report shows that the faster modes of transport such as airplanes have grown year after year. These faster modes are also forecast to continue to grow for the next five years. Slower modes – such as freight trains – are forecast to show negative growth.[32]

Despite all the scientific evidence showing that we need to dramatically reduce our carbon emissions, we are turning away from a highly efficient intermodal system to other methods whose only advantage is speed. Next day shipping guarantees often involve the use of airplanes. There are situations where getting something quickly is necessary, such as a replacement part that runs machinery. But this is the Achilles heel in our economy. Our entire system is based on selling more goods and services; we accomplish this by making lots of stuff and shipping it to every corner of the planet as quickly as possible. This is not how we build a sustainable economy.

Americans are not about to abandon their automobiles or stop buying the latest gadgets. What we can change is our vehicles and the movement of goods. This is where the Green New Deal (see Chapter Twenty-Eight) comes in. We need to rethink the structure of our transportation system. This will be more fully discussed in the last section, but hydrogen fuel cells represent a promising new technology.

Hydrogen Fuel Cells

Soon, it is possible we will be using fuel cells to generate electrical power for all sorts of objects we use every day. Much like the batteries that are found under the hoods of automobiles or in flashlights, a fuel cell converts chemical energy to electrical energy. Most fuel cells in use today use hydrogen and oxygen as the chemicals.

Stationary fuel cells are the largest, most powerful fuel cells. They are designed to provide a clean, reliable source of on-site power to hospitals, airports, military bases, schools, and homes.

Fuel cells could also power our cars, with hydrogen replacing the petroleum fuel. This could be a game changer when it comes to transportation as hydrogen-fueled vehicles produce much smaller quantities of greenhouse gases and none of the air pollutants that create smog; when pure hydrogen is used as a fuel, the only byproducts are heat and water.

While many vehicle manufacturers are actively developing fuel cell technologies, the biggest hindrance is access and cost. Although hydrogen is the most abundant element in the universe, it is difficult to store and distribute. Canisters of pure hydrogen are readily available from hydrogen producers, but as of now, one cannot just fill up with hydrogen at a local gas station.[33]

California's Hydrogen Highway – The Road to the Future

As zero-emission vehicles (ZEVs), hydrogen-powered fuel cell electric vehicles play a significant role in reducing California's greenhouse gas and smog emissions. The California Air Resources Board's most recent Advanced Clean Cars program builds upon the ZEV regulation in place since 1990, and encourages rapid increases in deployment of ZEV technologies, such as hydrogen fuel cell and battery-electric vehicles.

Deployment of sufficient fueling infrastructure for the coming ZEV fleet is a necessary first step. The California Hydrogen Highway Network was initiated in April 2004 by Executive Order under Governor Arnold Schwarzenegger. The mission was to assure that hydrogen fueling stations were in place to meet the demand of hydrogen fuel cell electric vehicles entering California roads. A shared vision between state government, academia and private industry guided efforts that led to the initial policies and funding that set hydrogen on a path to rapid progression.

With an initial target of 100 operating hydrogen fuel stations, as of 2018 there are 36 open stations and funding for an additional 28; the fully operational stations are servicing nearly 5,000 hydrogen-powered vehicles. Gov. Jerry Brown's commitment to address climate change follows in the footsteps of Gov. Schwarzenegger's bold vision for the future.[34]

Compare California's vision to that of Wyoming. To boost the coal industry and other fossil fuel producers, the state Legislature in 2017 drafted a bill – known as the "Electricity Production Standard" – to impose a penalty of ten dollars per megawatt hour for generating electricity from solar and wind energy. The bill would allow oil, natural gas, coal, nuclear and hydro power to be used by Wyoming utility companies for electricity generation at no penalty.

Talk about going backwards. Fortunately, the bill did not pass and it was sent back to committee for further study. In addition to violating the basic tenets of a free-market system, the bill would effectively kill the state's growing wind industry.[35]

Chapter Twenty-One
What in the World is Mcdonaldization?

"We're developing a new citizenry. One that will be very selective about cereals and automobiles but won't be able to think."

- Rod Serling -

McDonaldization is a term concocted by sociologist George Ritzer in his 1993 book, *The McDonaldization of Society*. He describes it as the process where society embraces consumerism and takes on the characteristics of a fast-food restaurant – standardized with a focus on efficiency and predictability.[1]

McDonald's is the prototype for today's fast-food culture. One can go anywhere in the country and the same things appear on the menu and the layout will be familiar. Never mind most of their food is "manufactured" and generally unhealthy. Their chicken McNuggets contain over 30 ingredients and while chicken is listed first, it provides only twenty percent of the protein compared to boneless white chicken. The real nutrient secret lies with all the other ingredients – some real, some not – that are used to make a product that children seem to love.[2]

The nuggets are prepared in a vegetable oil stew of canola oil, corn oil, hydrogenated soybean oil, citric acid and finally tertiary butylhydroquinone. Say what? Better known as TBHQ and a form of butane, "this powerful petroleum-based preservative which is also found in varnishes, lacquers, pesticide products, cosmetics and perfumes may be used to help the chicken and other ingredients maintain their distinct shapes." Banned in the United Kingdom (U.K.), this toxic chemical has been shown to cause DNA damage in animals.[3]

Through devious labeling, McDonald's does not tell us their seasoning contains monosodium glutamate – better known as MSG – which is added in the form of autolyzed yeast extract.

Dimethylpolysiloxane is also added as an antifoaming agent. Like TBHQ, this silicon-based polymer is used as a lubricant and conditioning agent with numerous commercial applications including silly putty and breast implants. Another appealing ingredient is Sodium Aluminum Phosphate – an acid used with baking powders during the chemical leavening of baked goods.

Once we unmask the secrets of the devious tricks behind each nutritional label, we have a better understanding what we are eating. While the label for McNuggets says they are "made with 100-percent USDA Grade-A chicken," this is not the same as "made from." As a result, we have no way of knowing the percentage of chicken in each nugget, just that chicken meat was used during the manufacturing process.[5]

The accompanying tangy barbecue sauce has its own long list of ingredients starting with high-fructose corn syrup plus sodium benzoate added as a preservative. Although it was the first food preservative to be approved by the FDA, many experts question the health risk associated with this chemical due to its ability to convert to benzene – a known carcinogen. While more research is needed to link it to cancer, it is one more chemical being added to our food.[6]

So far, we have only looked behind the curtain on how McDonald's makes their nuggets. Their hamburgers are tied to the same corn growers and their unhealthy feedlots discussed earlier. A 32-ounce soda or double-thick shake contains over three ounces of high-fructose corn syrup, which contains no essential nutrients and in excessive amounts has been linked to obesity and diabetes. It takes a third of a pound of corn to produce this much syrup for a single drink.[7]

Should we be concerned if the ingredients in our food are made with synthetic products from an oil refinery or chemical plant? In part the answer lies with how we feel about consuming "cheap calories" that will eventually lead to obesity, Type II diabetes and heart disease.[8]

In the end, McDonald's is joined at the hip to the agricultural and chemical industrial complex that dominates today's food industry. But McDonald's reach in shaping the values of consumers does not end with their food selections. Much of their sales and marketing campaigns are aimed at children through their toy giveaways and other promotional items. More on this later.

To better understand consumerism in the U.S., we need look no further than the toy industry. While America's children represent barely three percent of the global youth population, we consume 40 percent of the world's toys. In the process, we are creating the next generation of consumers which dramatically impacts our values and role in trashing the environment. Three-quarters of garages surveyed in one study were so full of toys, sports equipment, garden tools and other paraphernalia homeowners could not park their cars inside. Many of these items are made of plastic and will eventually be discarded.[9]

Self-storage facilities first appeared in Texas during the late 1960s at the height of the counterculture movement. The industry grew slowly through the 1990s when demand started to outpace supply. From 2000 to 2005, over 3,000 new facilities were built every year in the U.S. and Americans had found a new place to store all our stuff.[10]

> "At year-end 2017, a total of between 44,000 and 52,000 self-storage facilities have been developed   in the U.S. on industrial and commercial land parcels. There are more than 2.3 billion square feet of available self-storage space in the U.S., or a land area equivalent to three times Manhattan Island; industry revenues topped $38 billion in 2018."[11]

To make the stuff being put in these storage units, one needs a lot of natural resources. Between 1900 and 1989, the U.S. population tripled while our use of raw materials grew by a factor of seventeen; by 2009, we were using one-third of the world's paper and a quarter of the world's oil. "A decade ago, a child born in the U.S. would create thirteen times as much ecological damage over the course of his or her lifetime than a child born in Brazil and consume 53 times more goods and services than a person raised in China."[12]

If the rest of the world lived like the U.S., it would take the resources of more than four planets. With only five percent of the world's population, we use twenty percent of the world's energy; one American consumes as much energy as 128 Bangladeshis and 370 Ethiopians. And if those figures are not staggering enough, we generate 40 percent of the world's garbage. The average American will create 52 tons of solid waste by age 75.[13]

One can make a case that the amount of garbage we generate is related to the size of our houses. If we have a lot of rooms to fill, it follows we need to buy a lot of stuff. In 1966, the average size of new homes under construction was 1,570 square feet. By 1975, that figure showed a modest gain to 1,660 square feet; 40 years later, this number grew to 2,740. Only in the last two years has square footage dropped slightly.[14]

Beginning in the 1980s, upper middle-class families began seeking larger homes in the suburbs which led to the term "McMansion" – generally described as an oversized home containing at least 3,000 to 5,000 square feet of living space. Such houses are designed to fill the gap between the smaller "starter homes" and the custom-built mansions found in exclusive neighborhoods.[15]

> "The allusion to the McDonald's restaurant chain is important to understand when it comes to a McMansion. The name suggests that, much like the hamburger chain's franchises, a McMansion could spring up anywhere at any time. Builders rarely consider factors such as

local architectural traditions when contracted to build a house like this. A 5,000-square foot McMansion with numerous gables and boxy additions could appear next to a traditional ranch-style home, creating a noticeable change in the neighborhood.

Improvements in home building designs and techniques encouraged the popularity of McMansions among young professionals with growing families. For relatively the same price as a traditional two-bedroom house, potential homeowners could have a spacious two-story McMansion built on a lot far from city life. Hundreds of planned communities with idyllic names such as 'Pleasant Grove Estates' or 'Hickory Hills Place' sprang up all over the United States, each offering lots and other amenities for buyers."[16]

The McMansion is aptly named as on any given Saturday its occupants can be seen piling into the family SUV for a visit to their local fast-food restaurant. On the surface, there is nothing wrong with this scene as it represents life in suburban America today. As the largest quick service restaurant chain worldwide in terms of both revenue and brand value, the problem lies with how McDonald's obtain and process their food. According to their own website:

> "Farming practices vary, but most of the cattle we use for our **beef** are raised in the United States on grass for the first part of **their** lives. Later, the cattle are provided a balanced diet of grains, grasses and minerals."[17]

McDonald's also claims they have a sustainable supply chain based on the three E's – ethics, environment and economics. As discussed in Chapter Twelve, the beef they purchase from the big meat producers such as Cargill is hardly ethical or good for the environment. And just like their nutrition labels, to say their beef comes from cattle raised on grass for the "first their part of their lives" is widely misleading; in fact, they are bred to eat corn and then shipped to feedlots.[18]

Companies that McDonald's has worked with in the past include Cargill, Smithfield Foods, Kraft, PepsiCo, Coca Cola, Tyson and Griffith Laboratories – a leader in the food science industry. None of these names scream sustainability but instead represent some of America's largest corporations. They also share one other common trait with McDonald's, they are driven by expansion and increased profits.[19]

Many argue this erosion of values – putting what we want now ahead of what is best for society in the long term – is the root cause of a culture that cherishes possessions over an equitable economic system. It is likely the path of unbridled consumerism will come back to haunt us. And we should not go blaming Walmart or similar retailers. It is the U.S. consumer who demands large quantities of low-priced goods. What cannot be ignored is Walmart's destructive impact on our main streets. Their road to success has created ghost towns by pulling business away from small retailers.

Some put the blame on the doorstep of the Baby Boomers, claiming this generation took us from the "golden age" of environmentalism to a world filled with McDonald's golden arches. It may not have been done with malicious intent, but it happened unimpeded on their watch; they went from activists to bystanders content to collect their Social Security Checks. As the largest population bubble, this is part of the population dilemma – more consumers than producers.

In his book *How Baby Boomers Broke America*, author Steven Brill argues the key measures of the nation's public engagement and confidence – voter turnout, knowledge of public-policy issues, faith that the next generation will fare better than the current one, and respect for basic institutions, especially the government – are far below what they were 50 years ago when President John F. Kennedy's New Frontier was about seizing the future. "It is difficult to argue that the cynicism is misplaced...it is clear the country has gone into a tailspin over the last half-century."[20]

We can blame the Baby Boomers all we want but everyone is complicit. No single generation defines a culture. When we measure success by the amount of production – what we call the gross domestic product – we inevitably ignore other important values such as shared economic prosperity and social well-being. This includes providing a healthy environment that sustains all forms of life.

Economist John Kenneth Galbraith, a leading proponent of twentieth century American liberalism, believed America's demand for goods and services is not organic but created by the consumer. That once a person's basic needs for food, clothes and shelter are satisfied, advertisers then create the demand for the consumption of goods which leads to a reduction in public spending and investment.[21]

> "Whether the problem be that of a burgeoning population and of space in which to live with peace and grace, or whether it be the depletion of the materials which nature has stocked in the earth's crust and which have been drawn upon more heavily in this century than in all previous time together, or whether it be that of occupying minds no longer committed to the stockpiling of consumer goods, the basic demand on America will be on its resources of intelligence and education."[22]

The Republican-led Tax Cuts and Jobs Act passed in 2018 – whether intentional or not – does exactly the opposite by rewarding corporate America with huge tax cuts while diminishing federal revenue needed for investment in things like education and transportation infrastructure.

The tax cuts primarily benefit the wealthy and have added substantially to the national debt. Eventually, any revenue shortfalls must be paid for with tax increases or spending cuts.

Other developed countries are looking to move in a new and untested direction. In May 2019, France, Belgium, Denmark, Luxemburg, Netherlands, Portugal, Spain and Sweden – all members of the European Union (EU) – issued a joint statement calling for net-zero gas emissions by 2050 at the latest. To accomplish this, they have challenged the EU to spend a quarter of its budget to fight climate change. Although the other twenty EU countries have not initially endorsed the proposal, the group of eight hopes their plan can "go hand in hand with prosperity and set an example for other countries to follow."[23]

Cutting emissions is just one part of the equation. Here is how *The Atlantic* defined a sustainable community back in 2011, what they called "Sustainaville."

> "Sustainable communities share a common purpose: places where people thrive to enjoy good health and create a high quality of life. A sustainable community reflects the interdependence of economic, environmental, and social issues by acknowledging that regions, cities, towns and rural lands must continue into the future without diminishing the land, water, air, natural and cultural resources that support them. Housing, transportation and resource conservation are managed in ways that retain the economic, ecological and scenic values of the environment. And they are communities where the consumption of fossil fuels, emissions of greenhouse gases, water resources and pollution are minimized."[24]

While many American cities and towns have adopted some or even many of these principles, the U.S. is light years away from true sustainability which means more windmills and fewer fast-food restaurants. Until there is a radical rethinking of our values, change will be problematic in absence of some cataclysmic climate event. If the melting of the Greenland ice sheet began to rapidly accelerate leading to a dramatic rise in sea level, public pressure could lead to a call to action. No one knows what will ignite such a response. It could be another Hurricane Sandy or an unrelenting heatwave that leads to more massive fires across the West. Regardless, a discussion on what a post-consumption society might look like needs to begin before it is too late to respond. Only by creating new public institutions focused on the common good can we move toward a more sustainable society.[25]

Would You Like a Gas Guzzler with Those Fries?

The New York. Times, August 10, 2006: When General Motors introduced the three-ton, 11-miles-to-the-gallon Hummer H2 four years ago, it redefined American extravagance. But now, with gas prices hovering at three dollars a gallon and threatening to go higher, sales of Hummers are declining as Americans become increasingly conscious of gas mileage.

McDonald's, however, appears not to have gotten the message. This week, the restaurant chain started putting toy Hummers in children's Happy Meal boxes, calling it the "Hummer of a Summer" promotion. Television and radio ads, which started running this week, feature a family riding in a Hummer on their way to a McDonald's.

With enough visits to McDonald's, children will be able to collect eight different Hummers in a variety of colors, including two versions of the H1, the original and most monstrous member of the Hummer family. The promotion runs until the end of August and is aimed at young boys. Girls can choose to get Polly Pocket fashion dolls in their Happy Meals instead.

In a written statement, McDonald's chief marketing officer, said the promotion was intended to bring "the fun and excitement of Hummer vehicles to McDonald's youngest guests." The company did not make anyone available for an interview.[26]

California Company Sells "Luxury" Ice Cubes for $325 Per Bag

According to Gläce Luxury Ice, their product is superior to regular ice because it is purified of minerals, additives and other pollutants. Gläce Ice claims that the design of their cubes – which come in cube or sphere shapes – provide minimum dilution, maximum cooling, and should be enjoyed with "premium spirits." If you're drinking top-shelf liquor, you'd better be enjoying it with top-shelf ice.

That is the idea behind a California company that sells "luxury" ice cubes for $325 per bag. Gläce Luxury Ice says that its ice is of higher quality than regular ice, which is made with local tap water and may contain impurities and carcinogens, resulting in poor tasting and potentially unhealthy ice, according to the company's website. Gläce Ice, on the other hand, is purified and protected in a resealable package, which ensures its purity, according to the company.

"Our elegant design provides minimum dilution and maximum cooling, greatly enhancing enjoyment at the point of consumption," the website reads. "Gläce Luxury Ice provides consumers with a top-shelf choice for ice that matches their premium spirit selection."[27]

Note: The San Francisco based company ships overnight 50-cube bags around the globe via FedEx with its attendant wastefulness and pollution. Of course, the product must be kept frozen the entire time. Do these consumers know that mineral free purified water is available on the shelves at their local market? One can then freeze the water and make his/her own ice cubes at a fraction of the cost. It is called an ice tray.

Chapter Twenty-Two

America the Wasteland – What A Mess We Have Made

"Progress may have been all right once, but it went on too long."
- Ogden Nash -

The average American produces about 4.4 pounds of trash daily; this compares to the global average of 2.6 pounds. With a population of 324 million in 2016, every day the nation generates more than 700,000 tons of solid waste – enough to fill some 60,000 garbage trucks.[1]

From 1960 to 1990, the tonnage of garbage grew dramatically. In 1960, the U.S. population was around 180 million; the amount of solid waste generated that year was 88 million tons. By 1990, these numbers had grown to 248 million people and 208 million tons. In a span of just 30 years, we went from .048 million tons per million people to 0.83 tons. By 2016, the population stood at 324 million producing 262 million tons for an average of .80 tons. While we are no longer increasing the tonnage per million people, the population continues to climb meaning the total amount of solid waste increases annually.[2]

The flattening of tonnage per million people is not due to less packaging but increased recycling rates. Up to one-third of our waste is recycled while the rest is incinerated or buried in landfills. Many experts believe we could easily double the amount of material being recycled but it would require an overhaul of how we manufacture and package goods as well as redesigning the entire handling and shipping of recyclables. More on this later.

According to the EPA, many of the country's landfills have been closed either because they had reached full capacity or they were contaminating local groundwater supplies. In 1990, there were over 6,630 active landfills in the U.S.; just five years later that number dropped to just shy of 3,330. By 2015, there were less than 2,000 landfills (some of the more recent reduction can be explained by consolidation). The large number of closures following 1990 correlates with the dramatic rise in the amount of solid waste during the previous 30 years.[3]

If we cannot bury it, the next best alternative is to burn it. The first incinerator in the U.S. was built in 1885 on Governors Island in New York and it was not until the late 1950s when the first hazardous waste incinerator was built. Today, there are some 80 plants with 220 operational units for incinerating garbage – down substantially from 25 years ago.[4]

While the burning process does produce energy, it also can lead to the release of toxins into the air and create ash that requires disposal in hazardous-waste landfills.

> "When this trash is incinerated it releases 28 times more dioxin than coal and six times more mercury and lead; it also releases more than double the amount of carbon dioxide emissions. These toxic pollutants do not disappear; the more you capture them at the smokestack, the more toxic the fly ash that must be mixed with the bottom ash and transported for proper disposal."[5]

With proper treatment, the metals in the ash can be separated and bound with other pollutants to be used later as pavement fill.[6] And the energy created sounds like a good idea until one accounts for the entire cycle of how products are made and then shipped to be burned. According to the Global Alliance for Incinerator Alternatives that draws on an earlier, peer-reviewed life cycle assessment of waste management options:

> "Three to five times more energy can be 'saved through alternative strategies such as waste prevention, reuse, recycling, and composting

than can be generated by burning.' An incinerator can burn a ton of paper and generate about 2,280 KWH of energy. However, recycling that same ton of paper saves almost 9,780 KWH by saving the upstream 'embodied energy' needed to manufacture and supply new, virgin paper, including the fuel and energy costs associated with harvesting timber, powering paper mills, and transporting to market.

Burning garbage to generate power is neither clean nor renewable. Yet, aging, costly, and polluting solid waste incinerators have been bolstered by a dirty secret – 23 states legally classify incineration as 'renewable' in their energy goals and commitments."[7]

When one looks at the economics of incineration, "waste to energy" becomes a very expensive slogan that does nothing to reduce the amount of solid waste being generated. In fact, even though companies get paid for the energy they produce, incineration has been shown to be more expensive than nuclear – both to build and operate. These plants also release carbon dioxide which intensifies the impact of carbon emissions.[8]

Then there is the problem of hazardous waste. Historically, it was disposed of in regular landfills until we learned the inevitable seepage was leading to groundwater contamination. Today, hazardous waste is handled with much more care. There are now lined landfills that are properly solidified to prevent leakage; there are also different treatments available to stabilize the active ingredients of any hazardous material. Most flammable materials, such as lead acid batteries and electronic circuit boards, can be recycled into industrial fuel.[9]

A material is defined as hazardous based on several factors including ignitability, corrosivity, reactivity and toxicity. Enacted in 1976, the Resource Conservation and Recovery Act (RCRA)regulates the treatment, storage and disposal of hazardous with EPA responsible for its enforcement.[10] It also oversees the clean-up at over 1,300 of the most toxic and contaminated sites. Known as Superfund sites, New Jersey – the densest state by population – has the most sites at 113 with California and Pennsylvania not far behind; North Dakota is the only state with none.[11]

The list includes some of the worst toxic sites imaginable such as the Love Canal neighborhood in Niagara Falls, New York. Advertised to be a dream community, by 1910 this man-made canal quickly turned into a municipal and industrial chemical dumpsite owned by Hooker Chemical Company. After covering the site in dirt, Hooker sold the site to Niagara Falls in 1953 for one dollar. About 100 homes and a school were then built here. What happened next will go down near the top of the list in the annals of environmental disasters.[12]

> "Twenty-five years after the Hooker Chemical Company stopped using the Love Canal here as an industrial dump, 82 different compounds, 11 of them suspected carcinogens, have been percolating upward through the soil, their drum containers rotting and leaching their contents into the backyards and basements of 100 homes and a public school built on the banks of the canal. A sign posted by one of its residents read 'Give Me Liberty, I've Already Got Death'."[13]

Today, EPA's "cradle-to-grave" hazardous waste management system is designed to keep America safe from these dangerous materials and to prevent future Love Canals. In general, compliance rates appear to be sufficient – or at least better than before – to protect the environment although there are still many holes in the system such as dealing with coal ash. The growing amount of waste being generated also makes it increasingly critical that EPA and every other government entity remain diligent in keeping this system functioning properly. There are few new facilities being built to deal with hazardous waste and budget cuts to EPA and other government programs only serve to put our health and safety at further risk.[14]

Some routine products we depend on can still cause big headaches after we are done with them. Discarded vehicle tires have become a significant environmental enigma. According to the award-winning website, The Spruce, used tires are problematic for lots of reasons:

> "The sheer volume of tires discarded each year – over 290 million – makes safe disposal difficult. Discarded tires are an ideal breeding ground for mosquitoes and other disease-carrying animals because their hollow, rounded shape holds water for a long time. When disposed in a tire stockpile, used tires are often burned outdoors, which creates an ugly black smoke that contains toxic compounds.
>
> Tires are also a problem in landfills: their hollow, rounded shape takes up valuable space in landfills. Additionally, tires often do not stay buried. They have the unfortunate habit of trapping gases like methane and carbon dioxide (both potent greenhouse gases) and then 'bubbling up' through landfills, ripping through landfill liners in the process."[15]

What has improved dramatically is the number of trashed tires that are now being recycled. Of the 290 million discarded every year in the U.S., over 80 percent are recycled or reused in some fashion. Some 130 million of these tires are used to make a tire-derived fuel or TDF; the rest are sold as retreads that are molded into new tires or shredded to be used in multiple types of construction projects including playgrounds.[16]

Of course, TDF is not without its own controversary. Tires contain a long list of toxic chemicals that are emitted when burned, everything from benzene, metals and lead to PCH's, butadiene and styrene; the latter two are synthetic rubber components and highly dangerous to humans when inhaled. Additionally, toxic dioxins are released due to the high content of chlorine found in tires – an unfortunate side effect of incineration.[17] And who uses TDF?   The biggest buyer is the cement industry, followed by the general public, paper mills, electric utilities, dedicated tire-to-energy facilities and industrial/institutional boilers.[18] Far more research is needed to ensure the burning of this fuel is environmentally sound.

To cover the dangers from all the chemical compounds being used today would take volumes.

According to the American Chemical Society which maintains a database of known substances,humans have found or made over 50 million different chemicals. While it took 33 years for the first 10 million registered chemicals, the last 10 million that made it into the database took less than a year. "A novel substance is either isolated or synthesized in the world every 2.6 seconds and the rate new chemicals are being produced is astounding."[19]

Every year U.S. factories and manufacturing plants release over six billion pounds of toxic chemicals into the environment.[20]   Unfortunately, the average consumer has little control over this flood of chemicals other than purchasing products that are less of a threat to a person's health. Sometimes though we have little choice; our living room couches being one of them.

> "Back in the 1970s, California introduced strict flammability standards for upholstered furniture sold there. To meet these standards, manufacturers added flame-retardant chemicals to foam used in furniture sold everywhere. Because California is such a big market, furniture sold across the country is often manufactured to their standards. In fact, a 2012 study analyzed couches bought in the U.S. between 1985 and 2010 and found that 85 percent of them contained flame-retardant chemicals."[21]

Studies have since linked flame-retardant chemicals to numerous health problems. In 2014, California eliminated the need for flame-retardant chemicals based on revised flammability standards and requires that furniture be marked accordingly. Many chain stores now carry retardant-free couches, but the burden is on the consumer to read the label. And when couches with the retardant are thrown away, the chemicals in them tend to persist in the environment.[22]

If this is not bad enough, a new source of hazardous waste has appeared – the growing number of natural disasters as a result of climate change. The increase in more intense storms means an increasingly larger flow of everything from furniture – such as flame-retardant couches – to abandoned cars and much of this material may contain hazardous substances. We have all seen the piles of trash in front of people's homes that have been destroyed by these storms. The volume of waste resulting from Hurricane Harvey in Texas is staggering.

> "Hurricane Harvey damaged and destroyed countless structures, including 111,884 homes and counting. This destruction resulted in huge amounts of debris, but the Texas Commission on Environmental Quality (TCEQ) said it is still too early to tell just how much. Comparing this hurricane's reach to that of Hurricane Katrina, however, they estimate that Harvey could leave 200 - 300 million cubic yards of waste behind – two to three times as much as the debris left by Katrina. That's enough waste to fill Houston's NRG Stadium 60 to 90 times over, and it's two to three times the volume of compacted trash landfilled by the entire state in all of 2015,"[23]

As our population continues to expand, we need to slash the amount of solid waste we generate and the best solution is not to produce it in the first place. The mailing of catalogs reached its peak in 2007 when over 17 million were mailed in the U.S. – 59 for every man, woman and child. By 2016, this number had dropped to 11 million. However, according to analysts and retailers, catalogs remain their most effective driver of online and in-store sales for many brands even in this digital age.[24]

Consumers may still desire catalogs, but what happens when they keep sending them long after your interest in that company has waned or your name is sold to someone else who sends you their catalog? Check any waste bin at your local post office and it will be filled with them. Of course, catalogs are only one part of the junk mail vortex of waste. The real problem lies with how the U.S. Postal Service functions today.

The Postal Service is older than the nation. Our first Postmaster General Benjamin Franklin used mail wagons that delivered mail between Philadelphia and New York City. As the country grew, the Postal Service made it possible to connect the early settlers of the West with family back home in the East. The Pony Express, the mail carriers who connected the two regions of the country, operated for only eighteen months but captured a place in American folklore.

Today, the Postal Service is a shell of its former self and loses billions of dollars every year. Instead of fixing the problem, Congress appropriates additional funding to cover its losses. Indisposed to adapt to a rapidly-changing technological world with increasingly limited resources, the Postal Service is emblematic of a government agency not changing with the times. The deluge of junk mail is a twentieth-century shotgun approach to advertising – blanket the market with the hope someone will notice – and the taxpayer continues to subsidize this wasteful behavior. While the Postal Service will claim they rely on third-class mail, in fiscal year 2019 it provided less than 25 percent of revenue but it was more than 50 percent of the total volume.[25]

It is time to reinvent the Postal Service before Congress decreases its financial support by markedly raising the price on third-class mail. The supermarkets, drug store chains, big-box stores and a myriad of other businesses that send out these flyers will likely complain along with every local Chamber of Commerce. Many non-profits and environmental groups also use third-class mail with no regard to the waste generated.

By eliminating most of the junk mail, fewer workers and smaller buildings will be possible. It will also greatly diminish the waste stream, saving energy and scarce resources. More in line with online shopping, it should concentrate on its more profitable and growing small-package business while reducing its overall footprint. The Postal Service of the future should be housed in an energy-efficient building with delivery trucks that run on renewable biofuels or are EVs.

The first step towards sustainability is to stop doing things the same old way. Every year we toss 350 million bushels of litter out of our vehicle windows and throw away 30 billion Styrofoam – also known as known as polystyrene – cups.[26]   But before we talk about better packaging and banning Styrofoam (in 2019, Maine become the first state to ban all types of Styrofoam containers), we need first to see why recycling efforts are falling flat on their face, a trend sending anxious ripples through the industry.

Americans have never been very good when it comes to recycling. The amount we recycle appears to have peaked at around 34.5 percent of what is disposed as of a few years ago.[27] Compare this rate to Germany which boasts a 65 percent rate and Taiwan's 55 percent; even more extraordinary, Norway recycles 97 percent of its plastic drink bottles. The reasons behind these success rates are simple – there are consequences to not recycling and the costs are borne by the manufacturer and/or consumer and in some recycling systems, retailers participate in the collection process.[28]

Americans also seem to believe recycling will end their guilt over being wasteful. It is called "wishful" recycling where people imagine that their trash might have some value and should be

re-purposed including used diapers. Recycling rules can be complicated and vastly different depending where one lives, but diapers have never been recyclable.[29]

Recycling has never been a panacea to solving our waste problem, but now a far more serious quandary has emerged with no immediate solution. According to a March 2019 article in *The Atlantic*, major changes are coming to how the world recycles its waste:

"For decades, we were sending the bulk of our recycling to China — tons and tons of it, sent over on ships to be made into goods such as shoes and bags and new plastic products. But starting in 2018, the country restricted imports of certain recyclables, including mixed paper — magazines, office paper, junk mail — and most plastics. Waste-management companies across the country are telling towns, cities and counties that there is no longer a market for their recycling.   These municipalities have two choices: pay much higher rates to get rid of recycling, or throw it all away."[30]

Just when we are creating more waste than ever, recycling is coming to a halt. And this does not just affect the U.S. as other developed countries were sending their recyclables to China as well. Has the world reached its capacity for solid waste? A few nations like Thailand and Vietnam have absorbed some of the load but their waste management systems are not nearly as developed as China's. Vietnam is temporarily no longer accepting plastic scraps; Cambodia, Malaysia and Philippines are no longer accepting any plastic waste.[31] As a result, California's largest operator of recycling redemption centers – RePlanet – shut its doors in August 2019; the company's decision was driven by increased business costs and falling prices for recyclables.

Across the U.S., communities are now learning the hard way that for too long we have consumed inexpensive products that do not last and must be thrown way. While there is available landfill capacity, this often involves shipping the waste long distances at a huge cost adding to the release of carbon emissions into the atmosphere.

Philadelphia is well known for its recycling program. Following the China ban, the city decided to landfill half of their recyclables and incinerate the rest. This decision came as a surprise to many and the city has now elected to landfill anything that cannot be recycled.[32] This disruption to their waste stream does not come cheap.

In 2012, the city earned $67 per ton for their recyclables; just three years later they had to pay companies to take the same materials. It now will cost the city and its taxpayers $78 per ton to landfill its recyclables, a difference of $145. This comes at a time when the city's financial resources are being stretched to the limit.[33]

If there is no place to send our recyclables for repurposing, they will only add to the solid waste stream. If communities charge too much for picking up trash, this will encourage more illegal dumping. We need to dramatically reduce the amount of waste and switch to more sustainable packaging. It takes over 400 years for water bottles to decompose in a landfill; glass takes one million years to decompose and some sources suggest it never breaks down.[34]

We also annually throw away eighteen billion disposable diapers. It takes over 82,000 tons of plastic and 250,000 trees to make all these diapers. Although it is illegal in most states to dispose of dirty diapers in a landfill, there are few other alternatives if that is where one's trash goes; once there, it can take between 250 to 300 years for plastic diapers to decompose. Since cloth diapers are no longer popular, the next best solution is to use biodegradable diapers.[35]

In 2011, the U.K. opened a facility for recycling dirty diapers and other absorbent hygiene products meaning it can be done. In the U.S. there are no such facilities. In California, the city of San Clarita has created a trial diaper recycling program but is concerned about the costs. More people means more diapers and even if birth rates drop in the future, the use of incontinence products will rise as Baby Boomers live longer than previous generations.[36]

Disposable diapers are about convenience which brings us to the preference for on-the-go coffee. No longer do Americans have time to brew a pot of coffee at home, so they have turned to the plastic single-serve K-Cup. Talk about waste, the K-cup was invented by the Keurig Green Mountain Coffee based in Vermont to be followed by lots of imitators. The K-Cup is designed to be thrown away and although it is small, we are throwing away billions of them – enough to wrap around the world ten times.[37]

> "Worst of all, as Keurig tries to live up to its 'brew a better world' motto, their short-term environmental solution is to incinerate K-Cups. Through their Grounds to Grow On program they encourage their customers to mail their empty K-Cups back to Keurig where the plastic pods are burned in energy incinerators. Incinerating trash is known to waste energy and to put harmful, cancer causing toxins into our air, water, and soil."[38]

We know the best solution would be to make K-Cups reusable or compostable, but that may not be possible due to how the coffee is brewed so quickly at a hot temperature. And this has been the problem all along – we bring things to market without any idea how to dispose of them.

Consumers are often confused by the rules for separating their recyclables. The manufacturers blame consumers, but there is no uniformity of packaging. The emphasis is always on marketing the product, not what to do with it when it's used up. We tried to make recycling easier by going to a single-stream system, but this resulted in contaminating the more valuable recyclables.

A lot has changed since 1933 when a British chemical company first discovered polyethylene, the resin used to make plastic bags. It took until 1982 when two of America's largest grocers – Kroger and Safeway – began the switch from paper bags to plastic. Then in 1990, the small island Village of Nantucket located off the coast of Massachusetts was the first U.S. community to ban retail plastic bags; the first country to ban them was Bangladesh in 2002. By 2010, major bag producer Hilex Poly with support from the fossil fuel industry began its campaign to block a statewide ban in California.[39]

Petroleum is used to manufacture numerous suitable plastic items such as plexiglass or acrylic glass, but when plastic is consumed for single-use convenience packaging, it is problematic. Lower oil prices only serve to bolster the production of plastic bags. Many cities and states are addressing the problem head on by charging customers for plastic bags or by an outright ban.

San Francisco was the first major city in the U.S. to ban plastic bags starting in 2007 allowing only reusable bags followed by a ban on plastic bottles in 2015. This is part of the city's 2020 zero-waste plan; next on the list is a ban on plastic straws. The State of California followed San Francisco's lead by banning plastic bags; the law took effect in 2016.[40]

As many other cities and states consider passing a similar ban, the plastic industry is not going down without a fight. In what is nothing short of corporate bullying, the Strategic Litigation Against Public Participation – or SLAPP – was created by the industry to intimidate activists who were raising alarm bells about the use and disposal of plastic bags. SLAPP accomplishes this by filing lawsuits that are intended to censor and silence their critics by claiming conspiracy and defamation. This includes suing every city and county in California that has passed legislation against bags hoping to burden them with outrageous legal costs.[41]

These types of tactics run counter to the most sacred principles of a democracy. This is capitalism run amuck and why we need stricter environmental laws. The District of Columbia and 28 states have adopted anti-SLAPP statutes that protect a person's freedom of speech and the right to protest activities they deem to be dangerous.[42]

Idle resources are a drag on the economy and many recyclables like aluminum still have value. Paper is one of those materials if we stop contaminating our waste stream and go back to separating our trash. Recycled paper saves trees and energy while reducing the amount of solid waste and release of greenhouse gases. To make the switch, we must implement economic incentives so businesses, governments and people will prefer recycled paper. If cheap virgin wood fiber is available, the paper industry will continue to do business as usual.[43]

Another potential reuse for paper is to produce an alternative to peat moss which is not a renewable natural resource. An American company called PittMoss has developed a revolutionary new process that turns recycled paper into an environmentally-friendly garden peat moss substitute that requires less watering. It only takes a little ingenuity to find a use for yesterday's newspaper and many other things.[44]

If only more cities adopt a zero-waste mentality like San Francisco, it would go a long way to solving the solid waste problem.   At the same time, the federal government has left communities to fend for themselves while providing little leadership on a national level to inspire communities to do better. China on the other hand is now in the process of phasing out plastic bags and single-use plastic packaging.

The Basel Convention on the Control of Transboundary Movements of Hazardous Wastes and Their Disposal is an international treaty that was established in 1989.   Its purpose is to govern the classification   and   cross-border   movement   of "hazardous" and other wastes. The intent is to minimize the amount and toxicity of wastes generated and to ensure their environmentally sound management as closely as possible to the source of generation.[45]

There are 187 countries as well as the European Union that are parties to the Convention including Iran, Yemen and the State of Palestine. There are two nations that signed the Convention but never ratified it – Haiti and the U.S. As a non-party, we cannot reap the benefits of a shared approach to dealing with hazardous materials and to join we must provide statutory authority to implement its requirements. Now the Convention is tackling the issue of plastic waste. Like withdrawing from the Paris Climate Agreement, the U.S. is once again out of step with the rest of the world.[46]

Americans are greedy consumers and irresponsible about throwing trash out their car or truck window. Aside from the unsightly mess, plastic products that lie by the roadside can leach phthalates. These are esters of phthalic acid that give plastic its flexibility and softness that can soak into the groundwater and act as an endocrine disruptor – a hormonally active agent that affects humans and wildlife.[47]

Our love of electronic devices has also created another new waste steam – e-waste. Over three million tons of e-waste are discarded annually in the U.S., mostly computers, monitors and televisions. About 25-30 percent of this waste is recycled and the bulk of metals found in landfills comes from electronic devises. Roughly 80 percent of e-waste generated in the U.S. is exported to Asia, a trade flow that is a source of considerable controversy. The EPA has been active in working with other nations to exchange best management practices in dealing with e-waste.[48]

We are fashioning a society that ignores the laws of nature. Instead of composting our leftover food waste, it is either trucked to a landfill or incinerated. When organic waste sits in a landfill, it decomposes and emits methane – a greenhouse gas at least twenty times more potent than carbon dioxide; as a result, landfills are the third-largest source of methane emissions in the country.[49]

A more sustainable practice would be to take the millions of tons of nutrient-rich yard waste and food scraps and instead of creating methane, we would compost all our organic waste and produce valuable fertilizer. We choose to do the opposite and pump fossil fuel out of the ground – adding to the vicious cycle of carbon emissions – and manufacture commercial fertilizer instead. Whereas nature-made fertilizer releases nitrogen much more slowly, man-made fertilizer leads to polluted runoff that is contributing to the dead zones in the Gulf of Mexico and other critical waterways.[50]

Composting is a lot easier in a rural setting than in urban areas, but large cities across the U.S. are already doing it. The Seattle City Council, following the lead of other west-coast progressive cities and well-known for its comprehensive recycling program, passed an ordinance in 2015 prohibiting food from the city's residential and commercial garbage. All businesses and residences must comply and if their garbage bin contains more than ten percent food or compostable paper a bright red tag is tied on it; increasingly larger fines are involved as well.

The compost generated is used at local parks and gardens.[51]

Some might find this "Scarlet Letter" approach appalling, but the city believes public shaming is the most effective way to enforce the law as it creates a stronger culture of stewardship. Using a fee-based system for garbage, recycling and composting means equitably paying for the waste an individual or business generates.

Buckminster Fuller, an American architect and futurist, believed we are ignorant of the potential for turning pollution into a useful resource. To create a healthier environment, we need to modify our wasteful, destructive behavior while promoting personal responsibility and collective stewardship. When buying products online, consumers should make sure to indicate they do not want printed catalogs sent to their home. Sometimes it is the little things that can make a big difference.

Why Catalogs May Work But Are Bad for the Environment

Product Stewardship Institute, June 1, 2015: Restoration Hardware's record-breaking, 3,000-page annual catalog in 2014 boosted sales for the year. But it also sparked a flurry of negative comments on social media about the paper waste from folks who had no interest in purchasing from the company.

So, let's talk about the downsides of all these unwanted catalogs. Aside from Restoration Hardware's catalog doorstop arriving on our porches, it's rare that we consider the impacts of the paper industry. But in fact, its impact is huge. The Department of Energy stated that the paper industry is the fourth largest industrial user of energy, behind chemical production, petroleum and metal refining. Meanwhile, ForestEthics estimates that mail advertisements generate over 56 million tons of greenhouse gases every year.

It's important to recognize the companies that are printing catalogs more responsibly, such as Patagonia, who uses Forest Stewardship Council (FSC) certified paper to print their catalog. Even Restoration Hardware purchased carbon offsets for their massive sourcebook. These options are better, but unfortunately, they're not sufficient. Neither is recycling, as it simply cannot neutralize the paper, energy and carbon costs required to produce new catalogs. And limited recycling infrastructure in some areas means that about 40 percent of all unwanted catalogs end up in landfills without having ever been opened.[52]

Plastic Bags Appear in the Guinness World Records as the World's "Most Ubiquitous Consumer Item"

Parties to the Basel Convention (as referenced above) have adopted amendments that will dramatically expand the Convention's international controls and trade bans applicable to plastic wastes shipped across borders for recycling. The amendments will be legally binding on the 187 parties to the agreement and will have a lasting impact on the global circular economy for plastics. As a non-party to the Convention, the United States will be uniquely and adversely impacted by the new restrictions.

Driven by concerns over the crisis in marine plastic litter, the fourteenth conference of the parties adopted a historic package on plastic wastes, including: An amendment to Annex II of the Convention that will, in effect, bring most plastic wastes under the control of the Convention, unless certain narrow exceptions apply. It will mandate an update to existing technical guidelines for the environmentally sound management of plastic wastes.[53]

Chapter Twenty-Three
Sixty Thousand Orangutans

"In pushing other species to extinction, humanity is busy sawing off the limb on which it is perched."

- Paul Ehrlich –

It is predicted the world's population will grow to 8.7 billion by 2035 from the current 7.7 billion in 2019 and these newcomers, in addition to the basic necessities, are going to want electricity.[1] With the expansion of the middle class in developing countries, the Organization for Economic Cooperation and Development (OECD) estimates the demand for electricity in 2035 will, compared to 2011, increase by 80 percent. Much of this new electricity will come from fossil fuels.   This projection comes at a time when many climate scientists are warning the world that we must switch to cleaner energy by 2030 to avoid a climate catastrophe.[2]

Supporting a sustainable population is always controversial as no one knows how many people is too many. Some social scientists argue over-population is not the issue but rather poverty is the real problem. If more people could provide for themselves, the world would be a better place and we could reduce activities that are harmful to the environment such as slash and burn agriculture. This may have been true at one time, but no longer. Reinventing the world's delivery of energy is a monumental task. The more people we must deal with, the harder it will be to make the switch.

The Catholic Church has a long-standing tradition of being against birth control. There are an estimated **1.2 billion** Catholics in the world according to the Vatican; more than 40 percent of the them live in Latin America – a region where people are fleeing to America.[3] The challenge for the Church is how to balance their traditional beliefs with their concern for world poverty.

We cannot escape the reality there are too many people living on a planet with finite and dwindling resources. As the world's population climbs to eight billion, what is the impact on other animal species? There are some 60,000 orangutans left in the wild (estimates for the largest tree-climbing mammal range from 45,000 to 75,000).[4] Wildlife are feeling the population squeeze and will be forced to deal with the same displacement forces from climate change as people, only their options for finding a new home will be much more limited.

A country's population growth is determined by the number of births minus deaths and immigration/emigration. At the end of 2018, the U.S. population exceeded 328 million and we are currently adding a person every sixteen seconds.[5] It is very likely we will reach 400 million sometime around 2050. This translates to an increase of 70 million in just the next 32 years. For comparison, the entire U.S. population did not reach 70 million until 1895 when there were 44 states in the Union.[6]

Others have projected a much larger population increase. According to a Pew Research Center study, the American population will explode, going from 328 million in 2018 to 428 million by 2050 – a 100 million increase in just over 30 years. They estimate over 80 percent of this growth will result from immigration, which is difficult to predict.[7] Until very recently, we welcomed immigrants with open arms; public policy currently is to restrict immigration. Science is also allowing people in the U.S., on average, to live longer which impacts death rates; U.S. fertility rates are also in the decline.

What these projections cannot account for is the mass migrations of climate change refugees as happened following the devastation of Puerto Rico from Hurricane Maria in 2017. It is estimated some 200,000 Puerto Ricans relocated to Florida in the months following the storm. Some of these refugees may eventually return to their homes, but those who stay may be displaced again as parts of Florida become unlivable.[8]

Future migrations following catastrophic events could be much larger. Bangladesh is the eighth most populated country in the world with over 160 million people, most of whom live in a river floodplain surrounded by mountains. As the sea level continues to rise, it is likely millions of people will be displaced. Where will they go? Major climate disruptions could lead to mass migrations across the globe. Just as America sees its own citizens fleeing places like Phoenix and Las Vegas due to heat and drought, we could start to experience refugee fatigue.

But, of course, we are already seeing a mass migration of climate refugees to the U.S. The recent flood of immigrants from Central America is partly the result of unprecedented drought and winds in the western highlands of Guatemala. In his June 5, 2016 column "Food Doesn't Grow Here Anymore," *The New York Times* columnist Nicholas Kristof poignantly documents why Guatemalan families are sending their children on the treacherous journey north. It is better than starving to death. When aggravated drought alters the climate so people are unable to grow food, their land is worthless.[9] To prevent these kinds of migrations, U.S. foreign aid should be used to feed those in need.

We have no choice but to lower our carbon emissions. The data is clear. In 2017, our release of CO_2 emissions (which includes fossil fuel consumption) was per capita 15.7 tons; the world per capita value was 4.9 tons. This means we are producing CO_2 emissions at a rate more than three times the world average; but one needs to look behind the numbers to fully grasp why the world must embrace renewable energy sources and curb population growth.[10]

Accounting for all greenhouse gases and why we are headed to a point of no return includes many factors. When we cut down a large swath of the Amazon rain forest, we are losing the ability to absorb excess carbon dioxide. It is what the United Nations Climate Change Secretariat refers to as the "greenhouse gas inventory sector that covers emissions and removals of greenhouse gases resulting from direct human-induced land use such as settlements and commercial uses, land-use change, and forestry activities." Emissions from international shipping are also not included in national figures.[11]

Population comes into play when we look at total emissions. Since 2006, China has been emitting more total carbon emissions than the U.S. but their population far exceeds our own. The below figure compares total emissions to per capita output.[12]

Figure 9

Total CO₂ Emissions by Country In 2017 Versus Per Capita Emissions

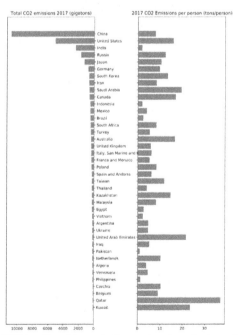

Source: Wikipedia, List of Countries by Carbon Dioxide Emissions; created May 24, 2019

The countries with the highest per capita rates but small populations are Qatar and Kuwait, two of the world's leading oil producers. Saudi Arabia and United Arab Emirates, also large producers of oil, are next in terms in per capita emissions. India, the world's second most populated country, ranks third in total emissions because of the sheer number of people.

A reliable indicator of the environmental impact of resource exploitation is average energy consumption. Americans are energy hogs. With only five percent of the world's population, we consume seventeen percent of the world's energy according to the latest data (2017) provided by the U.S. Energy Information Office.[13]

It is not just energy Americans are profligate in using. We utilize more than our fair share of a multitude of natural resources. We use 23 percent of the coal, 27 percent of the aluminum and 19percent of the copper consumed by the world. In fact, we generally dwarf other developed nations when it comes to sustainable practices.[14]   Our "ecological footprint" is a measurement of the amount of natural resources required to produce what a person consumes. If everyone on the planet had the same standard of living as the average American, it would require four Earths to supply the requisite resources. While these types of calculations have their critics, the basic premise cannot be ignored. We are living beyond our means.[15]

Ignoring the fact that we depend on the rest of the world to provide most of the goods we now consume, if we were to become more self-reliant how do we determine what is a sustainable population level? Is it 400 or 500 million or have we reached our limit? The biocapacity of any society is governed by access to employment, housing, transportation, public services, energy, food, fresh water, etc. Many of the elements required to maintain a high standard of living face limitations which are being exacerbated by climate change.

Scientists who study the interactions between man and the environment believe our economic system is not in balance with the laws of nature. In his 1971 ground-breaking book *The Entropy Law and the Economic Process*, Nicholas Georgescu-Roegen argues that the world's mineral resources are irreversibly degraded when used for economic activity and therefore limited.[16]

It does not have to be this way. Humans have the capacity to control their own destiny, which is why the proposed Green New Deal is focused on an economy that exploits renewable resources and the equitable sharing of wealth. What we lack is the political will to think differently. Mike Lee, a Republican Senator from Utah, has suggested the solution to climate change is more babies which will lead to greater innovation.[17] The last thing we need is more people.

Washington Becomes First State to Legalize Human Body Composting

EcoWatch, May 22, 2019: Washington became the first U.S. state to legalize human composting, offering residents a more environmentally friendly way to dispose of their remains. The bill, signed by Governor Jay Inslee, would allow people who die in Washington after May 2020 to forgo burial or cremation and have their bodies turned into soil through a process called "recomposition."

The deceased are placed in a steel container filled with alfalfa, wood chips and straw. Natural organic reduction heats the corpse to a temperature that destroys any pathogens; everything including bones and teeth turn into compost. After 30 days, the body decomposes into two wheelbarrows of soil that can be used to plant flowers or trees. The soil has been tested to meet all federal and state standards for pollutants like metals.

Washington already has "green" cemeteries where people can be buried without embalming, coffins or headstones. Each after-death action comes with its own set of environmental impacts, from embalming chemicals that leach into groundwater to transportation emissions. Many cremation facilities lack modern filtration systems and spew carbon dioxide and mercury into the atmosphere. Cemeteries themselves carry an environmental cost as many depend on fertilizers and large amounts of water to maintain that clipped, mowed look. "In this country, we have a massively dysfunctional relationship with death...and a lot of our state laws stand in the way of people returning to simple, natural, uncomplicated, inexpensive ways of doing things."[18]

This is the Environmental Catastrophe You've Probably Never Heard Of

World Economic Forum, April 24, 2019: Most cities are, quite literally, built on sand. As global urbanization continues apace, the demand for concrete (and the sand that goes into it) increases.

By 2100, it's estimated that up to 23 percent of the world's population – a projected 2.3 billion people – will be living in the 101 largest cities. But to house those people, industrial sand mining or aggregate extraction – where sand and gravel are removed from river beds, lakes, the oceans and beaches for use in construction – is happening at a rate faster than the materials can be renewed, which is having a huge impact on the environment. A billion tons of aggregate (sand and gravel) are extracted from the Earth each year, according to a report from the World Wildlife Fund, making it the most mined material in the world.

While around a third of the planet's land surface area is made up of desert, it's the wrong kind of sand for the construction industry, because the particles are rounded by the wind and don't bind together in cement and concrete as well as the more angular particles found in river beds and lakes. Ironically, Dubai is importing sand from Australia to keep up with its building needs.

Sand mining of river deltas, such as the Yangtze and Mekong, is increasing the risk of climate-related disasters, because there's not enough sediment to protect against flooding.[19]

In 2018, there was a total of over 120 million tons of sand and gravel consumed in the U.S. for industrial purposes. Most of the produced material was used as hydraulic fracking sand and well-packing or for making cement.[20]

Chapter Twenty-Four
Nero's Fiddling While Rome Burns

"Global warming is the greatest hoax ever perpetrated on the American people."

- Senator James Inhofe (R-OK) -

According to a report released by the United Nations Intergovernmental Panel on Climate Change in October 2018, the world has twelve years left (ten years as of 2020) "to make massive and unprecedented changes to global energy infrastructure to limit global warming to moderate levels." Pulling no punches, the panel stressed we must act now or face severe consequences.[1]

Not all scientists agree with the UN's assessment, but if we do nothing by 2030 things could get a whole lot worse. While there has been some incremental progress, most of the world is still dragging its feet when it comes to significantly reducing carbon emissions. This foot dragging is confirmed by the latest data from the Mauna Loa Observatory in Hawaii. On May 13, 2019, the concentration of CO_2 in the atmosphere surpassed 415 parts per million – far higher than at any point in the last 800,000 years since before the evolution of homo sapiens.[2]

Instead of leading the technological revolution around green energy, the Trump White House is more interested in propping up the dying coal industry and opening the Arctic to oil exploration. However, ignoring the impending climate crisis is not unique to our President; Exxon has been at it since 1981 – a full seven years prior to climate scientist James Hansen testifying before Congress that global warming was caused by the buildup of greenhouse gases in the atmosphere.

An email from one of their chemical engineers provides verification the company was cognizant the burning of fossil fuels would alter the climate and that regulations to limit carbon emissions would harm their bottom line.[3] In 2015, Exxon's attempts to deny how much they knew about the link between fossils fuels and climate change were made public:

> "Exxon first got interested in the potential for carbon-cutting regulations that could hurt its bottom line in 1981 when it was seeking to develop the Natuna gas field off Indonesia according to Lenny Bernstein, a 30-year industry veteran and Exxon's former in-house climate expert. 'This is an immense reserve of natural gas, but it is 70 percent carbon dioxide,' he wrote in the email. By the time he learned of the project in 1989, it was clear that developing the Natuna site would set off a huge amount of climate change pollution.
> However, Exxon's public position was marked by continued refusal to acknowledge the dangers of climate change, even in response to appeals from the Rockefellers, its founding family. Over the years, Exxon spent more than $30 million on thinktanks and researchers that promoted climate denial, according to Greenpeace. As for Bernstein, he later served as lead author on two of the United Nations' IPCC climate science reports."[4]

Today, Exxon acknowledges the risks associated with climate change and no longer funds climate denial groups. Its change of heart though did not dissuade New York State Attorney General Barbara Underwood from filing in 2018 a securities-fraud lawsuit against Exxon Mobil Corporation "alleging that the company misled investors regarding the risk that climate change regulations posed to its business." While some may applaud making the company pay for its past ills, it does little to regulate the burning of fossil fuels.

The U.S. energy system is incredibly complex and it will take years if not decades to untangle it.

In addition to a reliance on coal to generate electricity, the shale boom has markedly reduced U.S. dependence on imported energy and kept oil-related products, including gasoline, from large price increases. In 2019, the U.S. Energy Information Administration (EIA) forecast demand for energy will continue to rise as follows:

> "The numbers in oil's favor are overwhelming. The global oil-based passenger vehicle fleet is around 1.5 billion, with 95 million new ones being bought this year alone. In total, there are less than 5 million electric cars in operation, a growing niche market but nowhere near lowering oil demand in any significant way. In fact, just achieving a 20 percent market share of total global car sales by 2040 would be a huge achievement for those running on electricity – but not nearly enough to significantly reduce oil needs since more oil-requiring planes and heavy-trucks will compensate."[5]

The U.S. must first move away from our oil dependence when it comes to transportation, but we are no closer now than we were twenty years ago. As the Trump Administration attempts to put a freeze on the Obama-era fuel economy standards, the country is moving away from reducing the need for gasoline. By subverting the previous efforts under President Obama to create a so-called "national program" to develop a greenhouse gas emissions standard for cars and trucks, the EPA instead has chosen to challenge California's decision to enforce the Obama-era rules; thirteen other states also currently follow California's standards. Even the major automakers are concerned about building cars under dissimilar standards.[6]

Without a major disruption to the world's oil supply or a drastic change in federal policy, Americans are likely to continue purchasing gasoline-powered vehicles despite the increasing warning signs that severe climate disruption is on the horizon. While the Covid-19 pandemic caused an unprecedented drop in U.S. traffic, gasoline prices also plummeted leading to an eventual surge in truck and SUV sales. It will be incumbent on the next Administration to realize the sense of urgency and come up with a transportation plan based on cleaner energy.

As mentioned earlier, hybrids and EVs are no panacea but if everyone suddenly switched to hybrids, it would be a step in the right direction as it would reduce gasoline consumption. The challenge with EVs in the U.S. is that one must charge the battery and burn fossil fuels to generate the electricity. In 2018, about 4,178 billion kilowatt-hours (kWh) – or 4.18 trillion kWh – of electricity were generated at utility-scale electricity generation facilities.

The U.S. is the world's second biggest consumer of electrical energy behind China. Here is a breakdown of electricity generated by the energy source. Fossil fuels and nuclear energy provide 83 percent of the nation's electricity with renewable energy lagging far behind. Wind and hydropower are the only renewables that total more than two percent.[7]

Figure 10

U.S. electricity generation by source, amount, and share of total in 2018

Energy source	Billion kWh	Share of total
Total - all sources	4,178	
Fossil fuels (total)	2,651	63.5%
Natural gas	1,468	35.1%
Coal	1,146	27.4%
Petroleum (total)	25	0.6%

Petroleum liquids	16	0.4%
Petroleum coke	9	0.2%
Other gases	12	0.3%
Nuclear	807	19.3%
Renewables (total)	713	17.1%
Hydropower	292	7.0%
Wind	275	6.6%
Biomass (total)	63	1.5%
Wood	41	1.0%
Landfill gas	11	0.3%
Municipal solid waste (biogenic)	7	0.2%
Other biomass waste	3	0.1%
Solar (total)	67	1.6%
Photovoltaic	63	1.5%
Solar thermal	4	0.1%
Geothermal	17	0.4%
Pumped storage hydropower[3]	-6	-0.1%
Other sources	13	0.3%

Source: U.S. Energy Information Administration, 2018

As air pollution has become a major issue in China, the Chinese government has shut down coal-burning plants around Beijing. It is also closing hundreds of coal mines and restricting the construction of new coal power plants. China's commitment to renewable energy technology has made the country a major maker and exporter of solar panels, supplying some two-thirds of the world's annual supply; they also produce half of the world's wind turbines.[9]   As President Trump and Republicans leaders continue to criticize the proposed Green New Deal, claiming it will cost millions of jobs, the Chinese are training their workers for a clean energy future. According to CNN Business News:

> "Even in China where coal is – or was – king, the government still recognizes that the economic opportunities of the future are going to be in clean energy. More than 2.5 million people work in the solar power sector alone in China, compared with 260,000 people in the U.S.
> China is betting big on renewable energy. It pledged in January to invest 2.5 trillion yuan ($367 billion) in renewable power generation – solar, wind and hydro – as well as nuclear energy by 2020. The investment will create about 10 million jobs in the sector; China currently boasts 3.5 million jobs in clean energy, by far the most in the world."[8]

China is not the only country that is far ahead of the U.S. when it comes to renewable energy. Because of its unique geology, Iceland now derives all of its energy for electricity and home heating from geothermal and hydroelectric power plants. Scotland produced enough electricity from wind turbines in the first half of 2019 to power the country twice over. Denmark has produced similar results. Ideally situated for capturing the power of the wind, almost half of its electrical power comes from wind generation. In 2019, Denmark also launched the *E-Ferry Ellen*, the world's largest all-electric ferry.[10,11]

With populations under six million people, it is a challenge to compare Denmark and Scotland with our own needs; Iceland's population is less than half a million. Therefore, a better example is Germany with a population of over 83 million. In 2011, Germany made a commitment to close their nuclear plants by 2022. In the meantime, they have become the world's largest producer of solar power accounting for close to ten percent of their electrical power; the U.S. generates less than two percent of its power from solar (see Figure 10).[12]

New Zealand has passed a bill that sets a goal of zero emissions while the United Kingdom is taking a more direct approach by banning coal altogether. With the promise of "zero-carbon operation" of the electricity system by 2025, the U.K. is already demonstrating it is possible.

> "For the first time since the world's first coal-fired plant opened in London in 1882, the U.K. has gone a week without burning the highly-polluting fossil fuel, *The Independent* reported on May 8, 2019. All coal generators were offline from 1:24 p.m. May 1 through 1:24 p.m. May 8. The record follows closely on a five-day coal-free stretch over the Easter weekend. As more and more renewables come on to the energy system, coal-free runs like this are expected to be a regular occurrence.[13]

Closer to home, Costa Rica is at the forefront of renewable energy production in Central America. Thanks to its rich natural resources, the country has invested heavily in renewableenergy. During 2017, Costa Rica achieved a 300-day in a row mark when its electric system operated exclusively with renewable sources meeting 99.62 percent of their electricity needs.

Over 78 percent of their electricity is generated from huge hydroelectric plants; the rest comes mostly from wind and geothermal. Since 1949, the Costa Rican Institute of Electricity has promoted a model based on equal access for all citizens, sustainability and national security.[14]

As our country continues to subsidize the fossil fuel and nuclear industries, there will be no large-scale shift to green power. This has not stopped Georgetown, Texas from switching to renewable power to meet all its electrical needs. The City first signed a 144-megawatt wind power agreement in 2014; this was followed by a 150-megawatt solar power contract. In addition to providing competitive electric rates and a hedge against price volatility for energy produced by fossil fuels, Georgetown earned the distinction as one of the largest municipally-owned utilities in the U.S. to supply its customers with 100 percent solar and wind energy.[15]

In 2016, Georgetown signed a new power agreement with SunEdison to purchase 150-megawatts of solar power starting in 2016. SunEdison will provide electricity to Georgetown through 2041 at a lower overall cost than its previous wholesale power agreement. It is worth noting, this electricity is delivered over miles of large transmission lines and not generated locally.[16]

Georgetown is not only a shining example for other communities to follow, but their switch to green energy comes with a bonus – the power being generated requires no water other than what is used to produce solar equipment. As many parts of the country are experiencing record droughts, renewable energy is one way to conserve water for more critical uses. Unfortunately, while other industrial nations such as the U.K. and Germany are making major strides toward reducing their carbon footprint, Georgetown is not representative of the rest of the country.

So why is the U.S. out-of-step with the other major industrial nations? Instead of embracing the Paris Agreement that was adopted in 2016, we continue to finance the use of fossil fuels. A report published by the Rainforest Action Network in March 2019 found "33 global banks have poured $1.9 trillion into climate-changing projects worldwide" in the past three years; the list contains many of America's largest financial institutions including the top four lenders – JP Morgan, Wells Fargo, Citi Bank and Bank of America. Also listed at the bottom of the report's so-called "Dirty Dozen" banks are Morgan Stanley and Goldman Sachs.[17] The Rainforest Network in their 2019 report, *Banking on Climate Change*, notes the following:

> "The Paris Agreement calls for finance flows to be 'consistent with a pathway toward low greenhouse gas emissions.' This 2019 fossil fuel finance report card shows that the big global private banks are clearly failing miserably at this goal – even though many of these banks claim to support the Paris Agreement. Jamie Dimon, the CEO of JPMorgan Chase, is perhaps the most hypocritical in this regard, as he has declared his support for the Paris Agreement and his opposition to President Trump's attempt to withdraw from the accord, while at the same time presiding over a bank that is financing climate change projects more than any other in the world."[18]

This does not mean financial institutions are immune to changing their behavior. J.P. Morgan is now among the leading international banks that marketed the world's first general purpose bond linked to meeting the United Nations' Sustainable Development Goals (SDG). In December 2019, Goldman Sachs updated its Environmental Policy Framework. The investment firm will no longer finance certain harmful types of energy projects such as new oil and gas development in the Arctic.[19] But until we are willing to change our economic system to coexist with the environment, the fossil fuel industry will continue to dictate the supply of our energy.

Besides the increased frequency, weather and climate disasters are becoming far costlier. According to NOAA's 2017 report, the seven years with the most billion-dollar disasters have all come in the last decade. Of the total inflation-adjusted costs since 1980, over 25 percent have come since 2015, including the record $312.7 billion in 2017.[20] According to NOAA:

"During 2018, the U.S. experienced a very active
year of weather and climate disasters. In total,
the U.S. was impacted by 14 separate billion-
dollar disaster events: two tropical cyclones,
eight severe storms, two winter storms, drought,
and wildfires. The past three years (2016-2018)
have been historic, with the annual average
number of billion-dollar disasters being more
than double the long-term average. The number
and cost of disasters are increasing over time
due to a combination of increased exposure,
vulnerability, and the fact the climate change is
increasing the frequency of some types of
extremes that lead to billion-dollar disasters."[21]

New Orleans was previously devastated by
Hurricane Katrina. Despite upgrades to its levies and
flood gates, the City remains vulnerable to increased
flooding. Billions of dollars were spent in the process;
now more money is being spent to build levies around
surrounding communities. That job is far from done. In
July 2019, Hurricane Barry dumped 10 to 15 inches of
rainfall across most of Louisiana and Mississippi leading
to widespread local flooding and damage.[22] As more
super storms are in the long-term forecast, New Orleans'
future remains uncertain.

Potential economic loss from climate changes can
take many forms. Rising sea levels are already being
blamed for declining real estate values in coastal
counties from Maine to Mississippi. According to a 2019
report by the First Street Foundation, "owners of coastal
properties are getting hit by a rising tide of bad news as
higher sea levels slashed home values in seventeen states
by $15.8 billion over a dozen years." Florida suffered the
greatest loss in relative home values, with New Jersey
and New York not far behind. Among urban areas,
Ocean City in New Jersey was the biggest loser – a
consequence of Hurricane Sandy. These losses will
continue to mount in the future unabated.[23]

Dealing with the huge financial costs associated with climate change is not limited to the U.S. Indonesia – the fourth most populous nation in the world, behind China, India and the U.S. – provides the perfect case study of too many people having to search for higher ground. In 2019, BBC News reported the following:

> "Indonesia is considering moving its capital from Jakarta. While overpopulation is also a determining factor, Jakarta has a much more unique problem as well: It's sinking. That's right—parts of the capital city have dropped about ten inches every year as a giant seawall, once intended to protect the city, began sinking itself.
>
> The proposal to move is not new; past leaders have long pushed for a different capital city. Only recently though has the discussion gained momentum as Jakarta reels from many storms and is unable to cope with flooding issues. President Joko Widodo has a tough battle ahead as not everyone agrees that moving the capital city is the right solution. Plus, many ask if the next capital city might struggle with overpopulation and environmental issues as well."[24]

We know a lot about the physical and potential economic impacts of climate change, but it is the biological effects that should concern us the most. The Earth and its many life forms have evolved over millions of years and we are altering the future at an unprecedented pace. As the polar ice caps melt, the world's tropical zones are expanding at a rate of about 30 miles per decade; in the northern hemisphere, the Tropic of Cancer has moved northward from Mexico to include all the states along our southern border. This means hotter and drier weather for many of these states – a forewarning for places like Phoenix and Las Vegas.[25]

These rapid shifts i climate zones will reshape the planet and not always in a good way. While warmer temperatures can increase growing seasons in the U.S., it also gives a boost to weeds and pests. And a longer growing season does us no good without an adequate water supply. It is the intersection of these climate forces that makes it difficult to predict winners and losers in the battle to grow crops and sustain life; not only are plants and animals, including humans, on the move, but so are diseases.

As the distribution of species shifts, the balance of nature can be disrupted leading to massive die-offs. If native insects are not present when the birds need to eat them, they will not survive. "Insects are the glue in nature and there is no doubt that both the numbers and diversity of insects are declining; at some stage the whole fabric unravels and then we will really see the consequences."[26]

Many scientists believe we are sleep walking into a mass extinction that will have major implications for our most valuable ecosystems. The world's coral reefs are the rain forests of the oceans and they could be mostly nonexistent in just 30 years. In Florida, new research has shown that warmer ocean temperatures are not the only factor resulting in the decline; pollution also is a factor by adding reactive nitrogen that speeds up the process. As reported by *The Washington Post* in 2016:

> "If carbon dioxide concentrations continue increasing at the current rate, the impact of global warming and ocean acidification could combine to slow coral growth by almost 50 percent, according to the EPA. Scientists say 90 percent of the world's corals will probably be dead by 2050. In the U.S., the biggest impact will be to Florida's coral reefs system which is the third-largest barrier reef ecosystem in the world that's currently dissolving like a 'sugar cube in water.' First reported off the coast of Miami-Dade County in 2014, the Florida Reef Tract has also been experiencing an outbreak of a coral disease termed Stony Coral Tissue Loss Disease SCTLD)."[27]

Coral reefs are enormously important to our own survival. As a place where fish and other sea life thrive, coral reefs serve as a barrier against waves and ocean currents, but more importantly help regulate the amount of carbon dioxide in the water. "Coral's limestone shell is formed by the ocean's processing of carbon dioxide; without coral the amount of carbon dioxide in the ocean rises, which in turn, affects all living things on Earth."[28]

At the same time, the world's oceans are losing oxygen. In 2018, a sweeping analysis in the journal *Science*, put it starkly:

> "Over the past 50 years, the volume of the ocean with no oxygen at all has quadrupled, while oxygen-deprived swaths of the open seas have expanded by the size of the European Union. The culprits are familiar: global warming and pollution. Warmer seawater both holds less oxygen and turbocharges the worldwide consumption of oxygen by microorganisms as agricultural runoff and sewage drive suffocating algae blooms."[29]

These are the challenges the world must face in the coming decades. Meanwhile, the planet continues to get hotter. Antarctica locks up to 90 percent of the world's fresh water as ice; a study completed in 2018 confirms its ice sheets are melting at a rate three times higher than just a mere ten years ago. If all the ice on Antarctica were to melt, it would raise sea levels by 200 feet. This would be enough salt water to flood the lower ten floors of Trump Tower in Manhattan.[30]

Individual statistics are important and often disputed as to their accuracy, but it is the overall weight of the evidence that cannot be ignored. This chapter started with a warning from the United Nations Intergovernmental Panel on Climate Change and a reference to setting a new CO_2 record. "We don't know a planet like this," was the reaction of meteorologist Eric Holthaus. As seen below, the rapid rise in CO_2 levels started with the onset of the Industrial Revolution with no end in sight.[31]

Figure 11
Scientists: Global Carbon Dioxide Hits Record Level

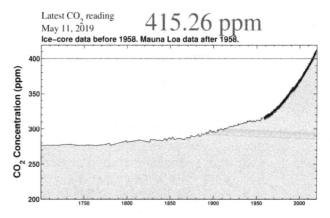

Source: Save Our Roots, An Indigenous Environmental Network Campaign to Defend, Protect, and Renew the inherent Rights of Mother Earth based on Natural Law and Our Original Instructions

With overwhelming evidence that climate change is real, past deniers are taking a new tack – the U.S. cannot afford to tackle climate change and that other countries like China and India are just as much at fault. Playing the blame game will do nothing to save our coastal cities from being flooded by rising seas.

In one generation, the climate experienced across the U.S. is projected to change in dramatic ways; in Alaska, it is already happening. In 2019, all-time summer heat records were shattered across the state. Starting on the Fourth of July, temperatures across Alaska were 20 to 30 degrees higher than average with numerous locations reaching 90 degrees and above. And the heat wave was not short-lived. In Anchorage, the highs reached 80°F for six consecutive days – doubling the previous record.[32]

A heat wave of this magnitude occurs when a large dome of high pressure for a long period of time keeps clouds away. This allows for warmer temperatures than normal for the region to persevere. Normally, warmer summer conditions in Alaska occur during El Niño conditions, but that was not the case in 2019. Climatologists are at a loss as to why this is happening now.[33]

> "Humankind, in two centuries, has transformed the climate. It has reversed a 50-million-year cooling trend. Scientists conclude that the profligate combustion of fossil fuels could within three decades take planet Earth back to conditions that existed in the Pliocene three million years ago, an era almost ice-free and at least 1.8°C and possibly 3.6°C warmer than today. So cogent have been the warnings from the distant past that researchers argue that the epoch in which modern humans flourished – geologists call it the Holocene – effectively came to an end midway through the twentieth century."[34]

We have now entered a new epoch known as the Anthropocene, defined as the current geological age where human activity is the dominant influence on climate and the environment. Just when bold federal action is needed, the EPA – following years of industry requests – is drafting new pollution rules that will reduce the cost of compliance. In May 2019, EPA Administrator Andrew Wheeler released a memo "urging the agency's top officials to revise the way EPA weighs the costs of regulating pollutants against the benefits of limiting their release for public health and the environment."[35]

Critics of the proposed changes note there is no known safe level of fine particle pollution exposure and changes to the existing rules will endanger public health. In 2017, the Trump Administration proposed repealing Obama's Clean Power Plan that targeted greenhouse gas emissions from power plants – which, if enacted, would have reduced fine particles and cut CO_2 emissions. In EPA parlance, this is called a "co-benefit." It will no longer be considered when performing a cost/benefit analysis if Administrator Wheeler has his way. This latest effort to undermine environmental protections is bound to be challenged in court.[36]

The Trump Administration has embarked on a campaign to grow the economy at any cost and to minimize any negative impacts on public health. Emails obtained by the *Los Angeles Times* in the aftermath of Hurricane Harvey, document how NASA researchers were prepared to measure pollution levels in the Houston area – one of the most industrialized hubs in the nation – using a plane equipped with the world's most sophisticated air samplers. Prior to takeoff, the plane was grounded by EPA and Texas officials. This was after residents complained about dizziness and nausea following the storm. NASA scientists were "stunned by the decision" and the full environmental impacts of Harvey will now never be known.[37]

President Trump is not the only one refusing to embrace the development of renewable energy; Congress is complicit as well. The 2020 Defense Appropriations Bill passed out of committee contains language that could hamper the development of wind energy. As currently written, the bill requires the Department of Defense to report "on the potential impacts to national security of offshore wind, and potential mitigation options." According to the American Wind Energy Association, this authority already exists and is redundant.[38]

Similar language also appears in the Interior Appropriations Bill that addresses the need to "accommodate all affected interests including national defense, security, environmental, maritime safety, fisheries, and particularly locally affected community concerns." Again, the Wind Energy Association says these issues are already part of the regulatory process.[39]

This leaves one to question whether renewables are held to a higher standard than the coal and oil industries? We already know the environmental damages being caused by the latter. The longest oil spill in U.S. history is fifteen years old and still ongoing. According to the president of the company that operates the oil platform, the spill that has been leaking oil into the Gulf of Mexico for a decade was caused by "an act of God."[40]   As reported by CBS News:

> "In 2004, Hurricane Ivan destroyed the MC20 oil platform operated by Taylor Energy. The company has spent over $400 million working alongside the U.S. Coast Guard to contain and clean up the spill which Taylor estimates has been leaking at a rate of about ten gallons a day for years. But Florida State oceanographer and oil spill expert Ian MacDonald, who has studied the site for the government using underwater technology, thinks the leak is closer to 96 barrels a day.
>
>   MacDonald convinced the Coast Guard that more oil is leaking than previously thought. The Coast Guard is now working with a private contractor to cap the well and will demand Taylor Energy pay the bill. But the fight over the spill has moved from the Gulf to a courtroom because Taylor has pursued legal action to block the containment."[41]

Yet we continue to invest in the fossil fuel industry. A 23-mile pipeline, stretching from New Jersey to the Rockaways – which was devastated by Hurricane Sandy – in New York, is proposed as part of its Northeast Supply Enhancement project.   It will upgrade the existing 10,000-mile-long Transco pipeline which provides natural gas to New York City and Long Island. The pipeline is to be built by Williams Transco, an Oklahoma-based energy company with a notoriously poor safety record according to 350 Brooklyn, a group that supports renewable energy sources and is opposed to the project. If built, it will carry fracked gas from the Marcellus Shale region in the Appalachian Basin.[42]

In May 2019, the New York State Department of Environmental Conservation (DEC) denied permits to Williams for their proposed pipeline, noting that the company had failed to provide "reasonable assurance" it would mitigate the potential impacts from the disruption of sediments. "The Department received over 14,000 public comments on behalf of over 45,000 individuals and organizations opposed to the project; as expected, Williams reapplied two days later."[43] In May 2020, the Department announced its subsequent denial of the required Clean Water Act Section 401 Water Quality Certification for the pipeline stating "the project would not meet New York State's rigorous water quality standards."[44]

The company argued construction of the pipeline will create thousands of jobs and aligns with the city's goal to reduce carbon dioxide since natural gas is "cleaner" than oil and coal.   What the company does not tell us concerns the environmental costs associated with fracking. Saving carbon emissions in one place does no good if you are releasing them somewhere else.   All energy comes with a price. Digging a pipeline under New York City Harbor is one option; laying a power line on the ocean floor to connect windmills to the power grid is also an option.

As reported by *The New York Times*:

> "Seeking to meet growing electric demand in the Hamptons with renewable energy, the Long Island Power Authority approved the nation's largest offshore wind farm on January 25, 2017, set for the waters between the eastern tip of Long Island and Martha's Vineyard. With as many as 15 turbines capable of powering 50,000 average homes, it is the first of several planned by the developer, Deepwater Wind. It will be in a 256-square-mile parcel, with room for as many as 200 turbines, that the company is leasing from the federal government."[45]

Cape Wind off the coast of Massachusetts in Nantucket Sound was once hailed as America's first offshore wind farm. Opposed by everyone from the Kennedy family to the Koch brothers, its developers relinquished their offshore leases in 2017 after losing their power contracts two years earlier. Even though the wind farm would be nearly five miles offshore, wealthy families living there opposed the project on the grounds it was a visual eyesore and would depress house values. If completed, the project would have supplied three-quarters of the electrical needs of Cape Cod and the islands of Nantucket and Martha's Vineyard.[46]

President Trump has been a vocal critic of wind power ever since his battle with Scottish officials over a plan to build what he called a "really ugly wind farm" within sight of his golf resort in Aberdeen. More recently, he has claimed that the noise from wind turbines can cause cancer; the American Cancer Society has stated there is no credible evidence to support his claim. Of course, there is ample evidence linking the particulate pollution from coal plants to lung cancer and heart disease.[47]

The President has also criticized windmills as a "killing field" for birds. The evidence suggests otherwise. "Estimated bird deaths from wind turbines are small when compared with other human-caused sources of avian mortality such as from domestic cats; the greatest threat to birds today is climate change."[48] The safety record for wind energy is improving along with the technology and, when built offshore, underwater power transmission lines do not leak.

As wind power ramps up, so does the engineering. Windmills now have bigger rotors and blades which increase the capacity to generate electricity. These larger units are best suited for the open ocean as opposed to land. In Europe, windmills are gradually moving offshore. As wind power evolves over time, its capability to produce electricity may soon surpass natural gas and coal.[49]

Meanwhile, solar power is more affordable and widespread in the U.S. than ever before. Since 2010, the cost of photovoltaic solar panels has dropped more than 60 percent making solar electricity economically-competitive with conventional energy sources in several states, including California, Hawaii, Texas and Minnesota. As a result, the number of solar jobs is on the rise.[50]

> "As the cleanest domestic energy source available, solar supports broader national priorities, including national security, economic growth, climate change mitigation, and job creation. Solar's abundance and potential throughout the U.S. is staggering –
>
> Photovoltaic panels on just 0.6 percent of the nation's total land area could supply enough electricity to power the entire U.S.
>
> Photovoltaic can also be installed on rooftops with essentially no land use impacts. Concentrating solar power is the other method for capturing energy from the sun, and seven southwestern states have the technical potential and land area to site enough capacity to supply more than four times the current U.S. annual electricity demand."[51]

This evaluation of the huge potential of solar energy comes from the U.S. Department of Energy's Office of Energy Efficiency and Renewable Energy. To further capture and utilize the sun's energy, there are significant market barriers and grid integration improvements that need to be addressed as well as permitting challenges and the need for adequate financing. One area that needs more research and innovation is battery storage. But the road ahead is a bright one for solar energy. As technological advances increase efficiency and drive down costs, utilities will begin to rely on solar for baseload (the minimal level of demand on the grid) power.[52]

America is at a crossroads when it comes to energy production. President Trump and his allies want to double-down on fossil fuel whereas others like

Congresswoman Alexandria Ocasio-Cortez (D-NY) have proposed a "Green New Deal" which would transform the economy while addressing climate change. She has been called everything from a socialist to a terrorist and that her vision for the country is not what Americans desire. But it is the proponents of fossil fuels whose vision is clouded by the past; the nation's security and economic growth depends on adapting to a world that will look very different 30 years from now.

Too Big to Ignore: Subsidies to Fossil Fuel Master Limited Partnerships

Earth Track, April 19, 2019: A new report released today by Oil Change International and Earth Track exposes a largely unaccounted for subsidy to the fossil fuel industry, valued at roughly $4 billion per year and growing.

New analysis quantifies the value of tax avoidance by the fossil fuel industry through a corporate structure called "master limited partnerships (MLPs)." Though eliminated for most U.S. industries more than a quarter century ago, special rules protected eligibility for fossil fuels, and have allowed a growing range of oil and gas activities to escape corporate income taxes entirely.

Existing estimates of the taxpayer costs associated with fossil fuel MLPs are deceptively low, reducing the pressure to end this tax break. MLPs, such as those created by Enbridge, Sunoco and TransCanada, not only enable firms to avoid their corporate income taxes on profits, but also to delay most tax payments on distributions to partners by many years. As *Forbes* has said, MLPs are an "income and a tax shelter rolled into one investment."

The MLP structure, according to the new report, cost the U.S. treasury as much as $13 billion in lost tax revenue between 2009 and 2012, a figure six times larger than previous estimates. Fossil fuel interests continue to convert to MLPs at an alarming rate through asset spin-offs, mergers and by seeking expanded eligibility granted not only by Congress, but also through rather secretive Internal Revenue Service rulings. "Not only does the U.S. oil boom imperil our communities and climate, but the increasing use of master limited partnerships allows the industry to pay even less of its share of the taxes needed to support those same communities," said David Turnbull, campaigns director of Oil Change International. "The fossil fuel industry is busy destroying our air, water, land and climate, all the while finding new ways to avoid taxes."[53]

The Tax Cuts and Jobs Act of 2017 did little to change the subsidies received by the fossil fuel industry. In addition to cutting corporate tax rates, it lowered the tax burden on MLPs thanks to a special amendment proposed by Senator Cornyn of Texas (R-TX). An analysis by the Taxation and Economic Policy Institute in Washington, D.C. found that, due to the new tax law, many profitable companies are paying no federal incomes taxes – and often getting refunds – and the biggest winners were firms involved with fossil fuels.

Of the 60 Fortune 500 corporations that paid zero federal income on $79 billion in U.S. pretax income, 22 are linked to fossil fuels; i.e. oil, gas and pipelines, and gas and electric utilities.

The list includes many of the largest and most powerful corporations in America such as Chevron, Kinder Morgan, Duke Energy and Haliburton.[54]

Wildfires Force 10,000 to Flee as Alberta Repeals Carbon Tax

EcoWatch, May 31, 2019: More than 10,000 people have been forced to evacuate as wildfires spread in northern Alberta, Canada's CBC News reported Thursday. Smoke from the fires has choked skies across the province, raising the Air Quality Health Index in its capital city of Edmonton.

The fires prompted Alberta Premier Jason Kenney to cancel a celebration of the repeal of the province's carbon tax. Kenney had promised to repeal the carbon tax and roll back other climate change policies in the April 16 general election. A bill to repeal the tax was the first his government introduced after gaining power. Canada's Environment Minister Catherine McKenna criticized the repeal and said she was working on a national tax.[55]

Canada has shown it is no more committed to dealing with climate change than the U.S. A leader in the development of tar sands, Canada is just as complicit as our own country in heating up the planet.[55]

Chapter Twenty-Five
Juliana, et. al. v. United States

"It is not enough to change our light bulbs. We will have to change our leaders."

- Thomas Friedman –

Since our earliest roots, America has never forged a consistent environmental ethic. The great conservationists of the twentieth century – Teddy Roosevelt, John Muir and Gifford Pinchot – were successful in protecting and preserving the nation's most spectacular natural wonders against their wanton destruction; the early environmentalists like Rachel Carson and Barry Commoner warned us about the risks of chemical pollution and untethered capitalism. And over a hundred years ago, a newspaper blurb first cautioned the world about the link between burning coal and a warmer Earth. On August 14, 1912, a New Zealand newspaper wrote:

> "The furnaces of the world are now burning about 2,000,000,000 tons of coal a year. When this is burned, uniting with oxygen, it adds about 7,000,000,000 tons of carbon dioxide to the atmosphere yearly. This tends to make the air a more effective blanket for the Earth and to raise its temperature. The effect may be considerable in a few centuries."[1]

Mankind cannot say we did not know better. We made our choice at the start of the Industrial Revolution and future generations will pay the price. But "business as usual" may no longer hold sway if a group of U.S. teenagers are successful in demanding the federal government act on their behalf in the fight for a sustainable plant.

Represented by the non-profit organization Our Children's Trust, *Kelsey Rose Juliana, et al. v. United States* is a lawsuit filed in 2015 on behalf of 21 teenage plaintiffs against the U.S. and several executive branch positions including President Donald Trump and former President Barack Obama. The Trust is a nonprofit organization based in Oregon that has filed several lawsuits on behalf of youth and their right to a stable climate system.

The plaintiffs include teenager Xiuhtezcatl Martinez, the members of his organization Earth Guardians, and climatologist James Hansen, acting as a "guardian for future generations." Some fossil fuel and industry groups intervened as defendants but were later dropped at their request following Trump's election.[2]

The lawsuit asserts "that the government violated the youths' rights by encouraging and allowing activities that significantly harmed their right to life and liberty, and sought the government to adopt methods for reducing greenhouse gas emissions." Under common law (taken from English law as adopted and modified here by the federal government), the "public trust doctrine" establishes the legal right of the public to use certain lands and waters. The legal interest of the public is not absolute and may be enforced concurrently with private ownership; it is determined by a balancing of interests such as the public's right to access the shoreline in the zone that separates low from high tide.[3]

Juliana, et al. v. United States seeks to expand the definition of the public trust doctrine. The lawsuit is at the leading edge within an area of environmental law known as "atmospheric trust litigation." According to the suit, the federal government has the responsibility to manage the nation's natural resources in the best interest of the public. Similar lawsuits in the past have been dismissed by the courts. But in 2016, Judge Ann Aiken of the U.S. District Court of Oregon, upheld the concept that access to a clean environment was a fundamental right, allowing the case to move forward. The case then proceeded through the federal courts.[4]

> "On July 30, 2018, the Supreme Court issued a brief order, denying the government's request for a stay as premature. The Court expressed skepticism about the lawsuit, as well as noting that 'the breadth of the plaintiffs' claims was striking.' It requested that the District Court issue a prompt ruling on the government's motions challenging the overall justiciability of those claims."[5]

On June 4, 2019, a three-judge panel from the Ninth Circuit Court of Appeals – all of whom were appointed to the bench by former President Obama – held a hearing on the government's motion.[6] The Circuit Court granted an interlocutory appeal thereby putting the earlier ruling by Judge Aiken on hold.

When first filed, few people believed the case would ever see the light of day. The government has argued it is without merit based on current law; the plaintiffs believe that every American has a fundamental right to a clean and healthy environment. The case may well hinge on the Supreme Court's interpretation of the Fifth Amendment of the U.S. Constitution, as follows:

> "The Due Process Clause provides two main protections: procedural due process, which requires government officials to follow fair procedures before depriving a person of life, liberty, or property; and substantive due process, which protects certain fundamental rights from government interference."[7]

It will be up to the court to decide if the federal government's subsidies to the fossil fuel industry and failure to act in minimizing the impacts from climate change constitutes a violation of rights guaranteed under due process. It is now evident that the federal government, including our presidents, has known about the risks of climate change as far back as the 1960s.

During the discovery process, the plaintiffs have constructed a timeline when past U.S. administrations "knew about the connection between fossil fuels and climate change." It begins with the presidency of Lyndon Johnson who issued a report in 1965 that talks about climate change as a "catastrophic threat."[8]

> "The legal proceedings involving 36,000 pages in all have required the government to make some startling admissions in court filings. It now acknowledges that human activity – in particular, elevated concentrations of greenhouse gases – is likely to have been the dominant cause of observed warming since the mid-1900s and that global carbon dioxide concentrations reached levels unprecedented for at least 2.6 million years. It also acknowledges that climate change is associated with increases in hurricane intensity, the frequency of intense storms, heavy precipitation, the loss of sea ice and rising sea levels, and that the effects on agriculture could lead to food scarcities."[9]

Whatever the outcome of the case brought by Kelsey Rose Juliana and her supporters, the federal government can do much more to mitigate the release of greenhouse gas emissions. In 2006, during the Bush Administration, the Supreme Court ruled in *Massachusetts v. EPA* that the federal government has the authority to regulate auto emissions that contribute to climate change per the Clean Air Act.[10] Despite growing concern in the country over climate change, President Trump continues to placate the auto industry and has lowered emission standards.

Kelsey Rose is not the only one suing those responsible for helping disrupt the climate. In November 2018, the Pacific Coast Federation of Fishermen's Associations filed a lawsuit calling out oil companies for spoiling the fishing industry in California and Oregon. Their claim asserts "the energy providers failed to warn their clients about the effects fossil fuels have on the climate." At issue is the impact on the Dungeness crab fishery due to warmer sea temperatures.[11]

The State of New York is also suing ExxonMobil, but not for their role as a contributor to climate change. Their lawsuit alleges that the company was "engaged in a longstanding fraudulent scheme to deceive investors, analysts and underwriters concerning the company's management of the risks posed to its business by climate change regulation." The suit was filed in 2018. The exposure of emails dating back to the 1980s show Exxon knew about the potential impacts of climate change.[12] As reported by *The New York Times* in 2018:

> "Exxon essentially kept two sets of books when accounting for the effects of climate change, prosecutors said. The company told the world that it was prepared for the more stringent regulations that would inevitably be required to combat global warming. But Exxon's internal estimates discounted the potential future costs of climate policies, even though the threat of government action exposed the company to greater risk from climate change regulation than investors were led to believe."[13]

On December 10, 2019, ExxonMobil prevailed in its closely-watched legal battle "beating back claims that it misled investors for years in how it calculated the financial risks of climate change." However, New York Supreme Court Judge Barry Ostrager ruled the company had not violated any state securities laws and the lawsuit was without merit.[14]

> "Nothing in this opinion is intended to absolve ExxonMobil from responsibility for contributing to climate change," Ostrager wrote in his ruling. "ExxonMobil does not dispute

either that its operations produce greenhouse gases or that greenhouse gases contribute to climate change.   But ExxonMobil is in the business of producing energy, and this is a securities fraud case, not a climate change case."[15]

The State of Rhode Island has gone one step further by putting out the "welcome sign" for those seeking damages due to climate crisis. In July 2018, the State filed suit against 21 fossil fuel companies seeking to hold them accountable "for knowingly contributing to a climate emergency that is causing catastrophic consequences to Rhode Island, our economy, our communities, our residents, our ecosystems."[16]

"The Ocean State accused fossil fuel producers of 'externalizing the responsibility' for the consequences of the human-caused crisis — such as sea level rise, drought, extreme precipitation, and heatwaves, and the damage those events cause — by expecting taxpayers to foot the bill."[17]

The fossil fuel companies requested the case be moved to federal court claiming municipalities and states have no jurisdiction when it comes to climate liability lawsuits. On July 22, 2019, their motion was denied by Judge William Smith of the U.S. District Court for the District of Rhode Island who wrote in his opinion:

"Because there is no federal jurisdiction under the various statutes and doctrines adverted to by defendants, the court grants the state's motion to remand. Climate change is expensive, and the state wants help paying for it and the defendants, collectively, have extracted, advertised and sold a substantial percentage of the fossil fuels burned globally since the 1960s. This activity has released an immense amount of greenhouse gas into the Earth's atmosphere, changing its climate and leading to all kinds of displacement, death – extinctions, even – and destruction.

What is more, defendants understood the consequences of their activity decades ago, when transitioning from fossil fuels to renewable sources of energy would have saved a world of trouble. But instead of sounding the alarm, defendants went out of their way to becloud the emerging scientific consensus and further delay changes that would in any way interfere with their multi-billion-dollar profits."[18]

A similar outcome occurred earlier in Baltimore, Maryland. On June 11, 2019, a federal judge ruled that Baltimore's climate liability suit that was filed in 2018 against 26 fossil fuel companies can be heard in state court. In her decision, District Judge Ellen Hollander stated that "the fossil fuel defendants relied on a proverbial 'laundry list' of grounds for dismissal and that Baltimore's public nuisance claims can only be decided in a state court since nowhere in their suit are any federal statues or regulations even mentioned."[19]

These cases are a stark reminder of what happened to the tobacco companies. For years, they denied that cigarettes were addictive and caused lung cancer despite decades of research that proved otherwise. The Tobacco Master Settlement Agreement was then approved by the four largest U.S. tobacco companies and the attorneys general of 46 states. The defendants agreed to pay a minimum of $206 billion over the first 25 years of the agreement and to cease several harmful activities such as targeting youth with their advertising.[20]

Lawsuits aside, we know what is at stake. Extreme weather will occur more frequently and larger wildfires will burn relentlessly; crop yields will plummet and thousands of species will be at risk of extinction. "That is if the planet heats up another two degrees; at a temperature rise of three or four degrees, we enter a 'hothouse Earth' stage that could render many parts of the planet uninhabitable."[21]

Meanwhile, "the Trump Administration has refused to publicize dozens of government-funded studies that carry warnings about the effects of climate change, defying a longstanding practice of touting such findings by USDA's acclaimed in-house scientists." Some of the recent findings document how rice loses vitamins when grown in a carbon-rich climate and the adverse impacts on grasses critical for raising cattle. All the studies were peer-reviewed by scientists and approved by the USDA's non-partisan Agricultural Research Service Agency.[22]

In 2008, the Svalbard Global Seed Vault opened. Known as the world's "doomsday vault" of seeds, it was constructed in Norway above the Arctic Circle next to the northernmost town in the world with more than 1,000 residents. But as the polar region where it is located warms faster than any other area on the planet and the Siberian permafrost melts, the vault's future is at risk.[23]

What is happening to Svalbard is why Kelsey Rose and her generation are suing the U.S. government for a more secure future. On Earth Day in 2019, students around the country protested to demand tough action on climate change. And slowly Americans are beginning to wake up to the new reality.

According to the latest NPR/Ipsos poll, 78 percent of Americans now support schools teaching about climate change, including 84 percent of parents with children under age eighteen. Parents also believe climate change should be introduced to students at a young age. Only ten percent of Americans think schools should not teach anything about climate change.[24] While one can argue it is essential that schools teach our children about climate change – something that will impact every aspect of their life – it is easy to respond in the affirmative to a poll question. It does nothing to reduce our carbon emissions. Far greater action is required.

Satellite Photos Show Massive Swaths of The Arctic Engulfed in Flames By 'Unprecedented' Wildfires

Business Insider, July 24, 2019: Satellite images posted online show wildfires burning through large portions of the Arctic, including Russia, Alaska, and Greenland. Satellite imagery showed huge pillars of smoke visible from space.

According to the World Meteorological Organization, unusually hot and dry conditions in the northern hemisphere have created the ideal conditions for wildfires and warned in a recent report that conditions in the Arctic are "unprecedented." While wildfires in the Arctic are common in the summer, climate change, with rising temperatures and shifts in precipitation patterns, is amplifying the risk of wildfires and prolonging the season.

Since the beginning of June, the Copernicus Atmosphere Monitoring Service (CAMS) observed more than 100 intense and long-lasting fires in the Arctic Circle. It said the total carbon dioxide sent into the atmosphere was more than the entire annual emissions of the nation of Sweden.[25]

Earth Overshoot Day

Huffington Post, July 29, 2019: Today we crossed an alarming threshold. This date marked Earth Overshoot Day, the point each year at which humanity starts to consume the world's natural resources faster than they can be replenished. According to the Global Footprint Network, an international nonprofit that calculates our annual ecological budget, it took us only 209 days to burn through a year's worth of resources including everything from food and timber to land and carbon. We are using up nature 1.75 times faster than it can be replenished. To do this sustainably, we would need the resources of 1.75 Earths. Once we bust through this budget, we start devouring resources at an unsustainable rate.

The burden of this ecological debt is getting heavier. We started overconsuming resources back in the 1970s, and since then it has gotten progressively worse. Since

1985, Earth Overshoot Day has continued to creep forward and this year, it falls on the earliest date yet as shown below.[26]

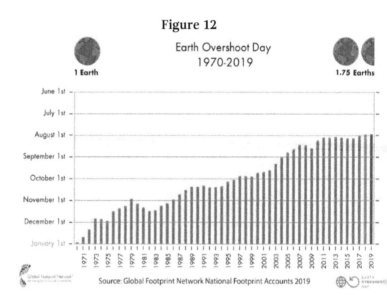

Figure 12

1 Earth

Earth Overshoot Day
1970-2019

1.75 Earths

Source: Global Footprint Network National Footprint Accounts 2019

Part Two:
What a Sustainable Future looks like

"Remember, democracy never lasts long. It soon wastes, exhausts, and murders itself. There never was a democracy yet that did not commit suicide."
- John Adams -

"If it can't be reduced, reused, repaired, rebuilt, refurbished, refinished, resold, recycled or composted, then it should be restricted, designed or removed from production."
- Pete Seeger, Folk Singer and Social Activist -

Chapter Twenty-Six
Going Carbon Neutral

"People will come to love their oppression, to adore the technologies that undo their capacities to think."

- Aldous Huxley -

Life-style choices are made every day. People will commute twice as far to take a better job somewhere else. An avid birder will drive hundreds of miles to view a rare bird to complete his/her checklist. The NFL plays some games in London, making it a road trip for both teams. Can the Earth afford to fly football players and their entourage across the ocean so the English can watch an American football game live? Probably not, but this is the world we live in.

Although millennials are thought to be the most environmentally-educated generation, that does not always translate toward creating a greener planet. A recent study showed that 76 percent of millennials indicated a preference for brands that are ecologically conscious and they would like companies to be more environmentally responsible.[1] But the products they most crave are destroying the environment at an increasingly faster rate.

With a two-year average life cycle, smartphones have become disposable devices that are hardly carbon-neutral. Mining the rare materials inside a smartphone represents 85 to 95 percent of the device's total CO_2 emissions for two years; buying one new phone takes as much energy as operating and recharging it for an entire decade. Keeping a smartphone for just three years can help reduce a person's carbon footprint, meaning it is better to buy a new battery than a new phone. Apple has also disclosed that new versions of their phone often create more carbon than older models; this is especially true for larger phones.[2]

Rapid, technological advances have made living responsibly far more difficult than in the past.

In the end, it is not just millennials – we are all complicit.

> "A new study published in the *Journal of Cleaner Products* in 2018 analyzed the carbon impact of the whole Information and Communication Industry (ICT) from around 2010-2020, including PCs, laptops, monitors, smartphones, and servers. Even as the world shifts away from giant tower PCs toward tiny, energy-sipping phones, the overall impact of technology is only getting worse. Whereas ICT represented one percent of the carbon footprint in 2007, it's already about tripled, and is growing rapidly."[3]

The iCloud also uses lots of electrical power. The companies with the best advanced technology are using power sources developed in the 1800s; burning coal to operate the world's most sophisticated economy is indefensible. While many of today's servers are more energy efficient than in the past, we have created a vicious cycle as the rapid rise in mobile apps necessitates more servers requiring new sources of energy. And the cycle continues – the more information in the iCloud means more powerful phones to run more complex apps

But this increased demand for power is insignificant compared to what it takes to mine the new cryptocurrency. Bitcoin is nothing more than a series of mathematical puzzles that must be solved via a computer network. To figure how much power is required to run the network depends on the number of what are called "sums" that are calculated every second.

> "These individual sums are called hashes, and there are vast numbers of them – so many, in

fact, that you must think of them in terms of millions of hashes (known as megahashes) or billions of hashes (gigahashes). As of 2018, the computers on the bitcoin network were doing 342,934,450 gigahashes per second.

At this rate, the bitcoin network runs at 342,934,450 watts – roughly 343 megawatts. Calculations based on data from the International Energy Association reveal that the average U.S. household consumes about 1.2 kilowatts of power, meaning that 343 megawatts would be enough to power 285,833 U.S. homes."[4]

While it is difficult to assess the real impact of the electrical demands due to the emergence of cryptocurrency, it is just another example of charging ahead with a new technology with little understanding of its environmental impact. A survey published back in 2016 found that over sixteen million Americans – or eight percent of the general population – owned some form of cryptocurrency and five percent owned Bitcoin.[5]

The number of Americans owning Bitcoin pales compared to the number of e-commerce consumers which has led to other unintended consequences. In 2018, there were nearly 259 million digital shoppers in the U.S. – a clear majority of adults. As e-commerce has exploded over the past ten years, it was first imagined that consolidating products and delivering them to homes via a single truck would require fewer road miles as opposed to shoppers driving their cars. For a variety reasons, this never materialized.

Access to online shopping has not stopped us from shopping locally. The Internet also allows greater access to products from all over the globe. The further a product is shipped, such as flying lobsters from Maine to Asia, the less any energy savings. "In 2017, United Parcel Service disclosed that the e-commerce boom had decreased the number of packages it dropped off per mile, leading to more trucks on the road and higher greenhouse gas emissions."[6]

Greater efficiency and fuel economy are further diminished by the push for next day delivery. As CNN Business reported in 2019:

> "Inefficient routes are not only more carbon-intensive – they're also more expensive for the shipper. If fast delivery is free, it's only because the retailer is subsidizing that delivery to fight for customers at a time of fierce competition and rapid growth. That means consumers aren't feeling the true cost – either environmental or financial – of getting their e-commerce goods super quickly."[7]

Jared Diamond in his book *Collapse: How Societies Choose to Fail or Succeed*, validates the premise that "all of our environmental problems are unanticipated harmful consequences of our existing technology." This is reflected in many of the electronic devices we now purchase.

The chemical used in making flat-screen televisions is a potent greenhouse gas – 17,000 times more potent than carbon dioxide. Called nitrogen trifluoride – or NF3 – it has been labeled "the missing greenhouse gas" by atmospheric chemist Michael Prather. NF3 isn't covered by the Kyoto Protocol because it was being produced in such small amounts when the treaty was signed in 1997, an example of technology once again outpacing our ability to regulate it.[8] Fortunately, some companies are finding alternatives to NF3 that are carbon neutral and cheaper to produce.[9]

As technology rushes ahead and the Trump Administration attempts to prop up the coal industry, many states are moving in a different direction. In 2018, California became the first state in the nation to mandate carbon-free electricity generation by 2045 with the goal of achieving total carbon neutrality. There is currently one operating nuclear plant – Diablo Canyon – that provides 8.7 percent of the state's electricity; the plant is scheduled to be decommissioned in 2025 and with no other reactors scheduled to go online, California will then be nuclear free.[10]

Beginning in 2020, California will also require that newly constructed homes must install solar panels. Opponents argue this measure will be costly for homeowners in a place where home prices are already much higher compared to other states. But that is the short view. California's Energy Council estimates the addition of solar panels will increase the average monthly mortgage by $40 but this is offset by saving an average of $80 on energy costs – a net savings of $40 while reducing the need for electricity generated using fossil fuels. California understands the risks associated with climate disruption and is acting accordingly.[11]

Other states are also developing plans to become more carbon neutral. In 2019, Washington State passed a bill to require utilities to stop using coal-generated power by 2026 which will compel all retail sales of electricity to be greenhouse gas-neutral by 2030. On August 16, 2019, Wisconsin Governor Tony Evers (D) signed an executive order calling for the state's energy usage to be 100 percent carbon free by 2050, making it the first Midwest state to enact such an ambitious goal.[12]

New York has passed a Clean Power Law that strives to reduce greenhouse gas emissions 40 percent below 1990 levels and to generate half of its electricity needs from renewable energy sources. Hawaii has approved a Power Supply Improvement Plan with a goal of powering the Islands' multiple grids with 100 percent green energy by 2040 (the original goal was 2045).[13]

At the same time, ballot initiatives to address climate change did not fare well in 2018. In the State of Washington, voters failed to approve the nation's first fee on carbon emissions and, in Colorado, a measure that would have banned oil and gas drilling on 85 percent of the state's land, did not pass. Arizona also defeated a measure that would have upped the state's renewable energy target to 50 percent (the current goal is fifteen percent) and Alaska voters rejected a proposal for new regulations on projects that threaten salmon habitat.

The fossil fuel industry spent more than $73 million to ensure the Washington and Colorado initiatives did not pass.[14]

While these results are disappointing, it will not deter the growth in renewable energy. Much of the Midwest is ideally suited to generate wind power and Iowa's nearly 4,700 wind turbines produced 34 percent of the state's electricity in 2018, the second-highest amount in the U.S. That percentage is likely to grow to 40 percent in the next few years.[15]

The U.S. also leads the world in geothermal power generation. The first modern geothermal heating plant was built as far back as 1894 in Boise, Idaho. An unlimited power source, geothermal energy comes from the heat of the Earth and can be harnessed directly for heating and cooling applications. It also can be turned into electricity. Best of all, it is a baseload energy source meaning it is always available 24/7. The Geysers Geothermal Complex north of San Francisco in California is the world's largest geothermal facility with eighteen power plants.[16]

The use of natural gas as a bridge fuel to renewable energy cannot last forever. Studies show that the amount of methane being released is higher than previous estimates – likely the result of natural gas production and transportation. By reducing fracking, we can reduce greenhouse gas emissions and protect our diminishing water resources. "Using natural gas instead of oil is like a drug addict replacing heroin with methadone – a step in the right direction, but one that fails to provide the meaningful and long-term recovery we need."[17]

This does not mean shutting down all the gas-fired power plants, at least in the short-term. Aging oil and gas plants can successfully be converted to natural gas if done right. The Salem Harbor Generating Station in Massachusetts was built as a coal-fired power plant in 1950s and later expanded to a coal/oil-fired facility. Faced with mounting pressure to make New England coal-free, the plant was sold in 2012 and now has a much brighter future.

> "Footprint Power has developed a state-of-the-art generating facility that reduces gas usage in New England, reduces costs of wholesale energy, dramatically reduces system-wide emissions including greenhouse gases, and paves the way for greater reliance on renewable resources in the future. The new Salem Harbor Station which went online in 2018 is a 674-megawatt (MW) natural gas-fired, quick-start, combined-cycle electric generating facility on a 23-acre portion of the original 65-acre Salem Harbor site."[18]

To eliminate the burning of coal not just in New England but across the country, Michael Bloomberg is putting his wealth to good use. The former Mayor of New York City has a plan to close the nation's remaining 241 coal plants. Bloomberg and his foundation joined forces with the Sierra Club in 2011 to launch Beyond Coal with the goal of closing at least a third of the country's coal plants; his new initiative is called Beyond Carbon.[19]

Bloomberg has pledged $500 million toward the effort beginning in 2019. According to a spokesman for the philanthropist, "Most of the money will be spent over a three-year period and will go toward lobbying efforts by environmental groups in state and city governments and public utility commissions; some funding will also go toward electing local officials who are focused on clean energy." The Washington and Colorado climate initiatives in part lost because the fossil fuel industry has money to burn when it comes to protecting their turf; now the other side has the financial resources at their disposal to grow the climate movement.[20]

As a key partner of the Beyond Carbon initiative, the Sierra Club issued the following statement:

> "The task before us is clear: we must phase out coal by 2030, stop the fracked gas rush, and

move toward 100 percent clean energy with no delay. With the support of Bloomberg Philanthropies and partners like the environmental justice allies that are a part of this announcement, we'll help achieve this goal and support communities and workers in the transition to clean energy. With Beyond Carbon, we have the opportunity to build a clean energy economy filled with family-sustaining union jobs."[21]

On the heels of Bloomberg's pledge, the largest commercial insurance company in the U.S. announced it will no longer insure coal. In yet another sign of the unsustainability of coal, Chubb became the first commercial insurance company in the U.S. to make this policy change. "The company will stop insuring new coal-fired power plants and phase out coverage of coal mining companies by 2022; Chubb will also restrict coverage to power companies that produce more than 30 percent of their energy from coal and cease new investments in coal companies."[22]

Chubb – the market leader when it comes to insuring the U.S. power sector – has sent a clear message to the entire nation that the coal industry is bad for business and bad for the climate. This move came after significant pressure from leading climate and consumer-rights organizations, including the Sierra Club, that make up the Insure Our Future campaign.[23]

Many groups and associations are also joining the carbon neutral bandwagon and the dump coal movement. In 2017, the nation's largest outdoor-recreation companies elected to pull their two annual trade shows from Salt Lake City, Utah. Fed up with the state's effort to persuade President Trump to de-designate much of Bears Ear National Monument, the Outdoor Industry Association ended their twenty-year relationship with the state.

The feud was ignited when Patagonia – an industry powerhouse and advocate for protecting the environment – announced they would pull out of the show. Patagonia's Founder, Yvonne Chouinard, said, "The outdoor industry creates three times the amount of jobs than the fossil fuels industry" referencing the $12 billion in consumer spending and 122,000 jobs that outdoor recreation creates for the State of Utah each year.[24]

Thanks to Governor Gary Herbert's and the state legislature's successful campaign– with the support of their congressional delegation – to get President Trump to undo the federal protection of Bears Ear National Monument, Utah will no longer host the thousands of visitors who attended these shows. The move comes with a huge price tag – a loss of annual revenue exceeding $90 million; for the next five years, the shows will be held in Denver, Colorado.[25]

When we look back in history, 2019 is likely to stand out as a pivotal time when more Americans began to comprehend the reality of climate change. After numerous climate-related disasters including the devastating floods in the Midwest, July was the hottest month ever recorded on Earth replacing July of 2016.[26] Meanwhile, as an intensive heat wave swept across Europe, previous high temperature records across the continent were smashed. Paris, France recorded its all-time highest temperature at nearly 109 degrees; Germany, Belgium, the Netherlands and at least nine other countries also set all-time highs.[27] When 2019 finally ended, it was the second hottest year ever recorded just behind 2016; it should be noted the top ten hottest years have all occurred since 2005.[28]

Back in the U.S., the Trump administration is moving to erase Obama-era rules on methane emissions from the oil-and-gas industry. Flaring is a process where the excess methane is burned off at the site. Even though scientists say methane is a significant contributor to climate change, the Trump White House claims the federal government overstepped its authority when it set limits on its release. On August 29, 2019, EPA "proposed a new rule that would lessen federal requirements for technology that monitors methane leaks from the oil and gas industry...which will save the oil and gas industry $17 to $19 million a year."[29]

In frack-happy states like Texas, this is welcome news to local regulators. Fortunately, Shell and other major oil and natural gas companies have indicated they support the regulation of methane emissions – further evidence how out-of-step President Trump and his EPA are with the rest of the world.

Gretchen Watkins, President U.S. Shell, told *The Washington Post* that the company will stick to its own plan to lessen methane leaks. "Despite the administration's proposal to no longer regulate methane, Shell U.S.'s assets will continue to contribute to that global target."[30] These companies make billions of dollars annually and they understand the savings from this rule change are miniscule in comparison to the scope of the challenge posed by climate change.

When scientists talk about "representative concentration pathways" or RCPs, not a lot of people are going to listen. RCPs are future emissions scenarios used to model what will happen if we continue to burn fossil fuels at a certain rate. They represent assumptions about how carbon emissions in the atmosphere will change in the future because of human activities. In other words, think of it as an "if this occurs, then this will happen" scenario for global warming.[31] How many of our political leaders understand the term? Yet, they are responsible for setting our nation's energy policy.

Even when confronted with overwhelming evidence, some people choose to ignore the truth. It is what one Canadian activist calls "climate nihilism" – extreme skepticism maintaining that nothing has a real existence.[32] So what will be the spark to finally commit the nation to a more sustainable future? America's outdoor retailers are not about to surrender our public lands to the big energy companies with their huge tax breaks. Like President Trump, Utah's public officials fail to grasp that fossil fuels and nuclear plants are no longer a viable option. The future of coal is as dark as the mines from which it comes from.

The proponents of these dying industries can echo their beliefs to their final days. Perhaps achieving a 99 percent renewable energy goal like Costa Rica is out of our reach. Nonetheless, there is plenty of momentum pushing us in that direction. For the sake of argument, even if climate change is a "hoax," we will be left with a healthier country and a more vibrant economy. Just don't tell the former residents of Mexico Beach, Florida and Paradise, California that climate change is not real; one was destroyed by Hurricane Michael and the other by a massive wildfire. Perhaps the proposed Green New Deal is not such a bad deal after all.

Is Netflix Bad for the Environment? How Streaming Video Contributes to Climate Change

EcoWatch, July 13, 2019: Sending dozens of emails a day, making a quick call on WhatsApp, uploading some photos to the cloud, watching a short viral clip on YouTube are all part of the digital daily life around the world. For the individual, it may be "just one photo" or "just a few minutes of video," but, taken together, our collective Internet traffic contributes enormously to climate change. Everything a computer, tablet or smartphone does requires electricity. And, to generate that electricity, the world still predominantly uses fossil fuels.

Digital technologies have even surpassed the aerospace industry in terms of carbon emissions. While aviation's share of global CO_2 emissions is estimated to be around 2.5 percent and rising, nearly 4 percent of all CO_2 emissions can now be attributed to global data transfer and the necessary infrastructure. The calculations include both the energy costs of creating IT infrastructure and the actual use of that infrastructure, with the latter consuming 10 percentage points more electricity than the production of all equipment and technology combined.

According to a projection by tech giant Cisco, by 2022 around 60 percent of the world's population will be online, with video making up more than 80 percent of all Internet traffic. Maxime Efoui-Hess, an energy and environmental expert at The Shift Project and author of the study, said we need to urgently reconsider the future of Internet use and think about cutting back.

"We have limited energy resources and even if we make the shift to renewables now, the Internet is a worldwide thing, so it would require every country in the world to be powered by renewable energy." But he said, "that goal remains impossible in such a short time, meaning we can't let Internet usage grow as rapidly as in the past."[33]

The Times They Are A-Changin'

Courier Journal, April 7, 217: If there is one building in eastern Kentucky that you would not expect to have a solar-power system, it most likely would be a coal museum. But that is exactly what visitors to the Kentucky Coal Museum will find on the building's roof – 80 solar panels.

Inside the Kentucky Coal Museum, visitors can peruse plenty of memorabilia on mining and the commonwealth's coal camps, but – in a cost-saving move – the museum is embracing the sun as a source of affordable energy. Located in the small town of Benham, the museum expects to save up to $10,000 per month. Generating up to 60 kilowatts at full capacity, any surplus power will be shared with a local college. The system was installed in 2017 and was fully funded by private donations. As Bob Dylan said, "The times they are a-changin."[34]

Chapter Twenty-Seven
Changing the Rules of Capitalism

"Humanity is called to recognize the need for changes of lifestyle, production and consumption, in order to combat this warming and highly polluting fossil fuels need to be progressively replaced without delay."

- Pope Francis –

America's rise as an economic powerhouse is unprecedented. but it does not change the fact that American Capitalism is not in balance with nature. We have sought to overpower nature and in doing so, we have forever altered the landscape. We believed by conquering nature, we can control the natural world. Despite the efforts of many, little has changed and big business remains focused on short-term profits while forsaking the climate and producing unmanageable amounts of waste.

During the first decade of the 21st century, 80 percent of Americans believed that a free market economy was the optimum economic structure. Today, that number is 60 percent with one poll showing that only 42 percent of millennials support capitalism as currently practiced. This decline is happening as the nation continues to enjoy an economic recovery following the Great Recession that began in 2008 after credit markets had failed the previous year.[1]

The recovery that started in 2009 has only widened the gap between the haves and have-nots and it is rupturing the traditional views of our economic system.

At the same time, we are facing an unprecedented environmental crisis that is leading to mass extinctions and overwhelming climate disruption while our politicians do little to seek solutions or change the nation's trajectory.

To show how far our current politics and national priorities have strayed since the birth of the environmental movement in 1970, here is what President Richard Nixon said that same year as part of his State of the Union address:

> "Restoring nature to its natural state is a cause beyond party and beyond factions. It has become a common cause of all the people of this country. It is a cause of particular concern to young Americans, because they, more than we, will reap the grim consequences of our failure to act on programs which are needed now if we are to prevent disaster later...We can no longer afford to consider air and water common property, free to be abused by anyone without regard to the consequences. Instead, we should begin now to treat them as scarce resources, which we are no freer to contaminate than we are free to throw garbage into our neighbor's yard.
>
> This requires comprehensive new regulations. It also requires that, to the extent possible, the price of goods should be made to include the costs of producing and disposing of them without damage to the environment. The answer is not to abandon growth, but to redirect it. For example, we should turn toward ending congestion and eliminating smog with the same reservoir of inventive genius that created them in the first place."[2]

President Nixon went on to espouse the benefits of abolishing hunger in America, providing a minimum income for families, and placing a priority on "better housing, faster transportation, improved health and superior education." These are the same virtues of the Green New Deal, yet its proponents are called socialists. President Nixon – the most disgraced president in the nation's history – was many things, but he was not a socialist.

This does not mean it is time to throw capitalism out the window. When the system is rigged to favor the fossil fuel industry, it comes at the expense of developing clean and renewable energy. And when companies freely pollute our natural resources, the U.S. taxpayer gets stuck with the clean-up bill giving polluters an unwarranted subsidy. To chart a new course, American Capitalism needs to change course and reinvent itself.

In his 2018 book, *Can American Capitalism Survive?* award-winning author Steven Pearlstein "chronicles the excesses of capitalism and shows how its ethical foundations have been shattered by a radical free market ideology – often referred to as 'neoliberalism'." Pearlstein believes that capitalism is not dead, it just needs to be saved before it is too late.[3]

> "My answer has to do with something called social capital, which is a social science term that generally refers to the amount of trust that we all have in each other and in our institutions. And when things get so unfair that that trust becomes eroded, that's when you know you've gone too far. That's when you know that things have become too unequal. Another way that you would know it is when you see class mobility, intergenerational class mobility, start to decline."[4]

A robust economy or a healthy environment is not a binary choice. There is always a right way to do things but the singular goal to maximize profit, especially short-term profit, usually comes at the expense of the public interest. To create a more just society and economic system that benefits everyone equally, we need a reset of the nation's values and priorities. Standing in the way are the wealthy and powerful who would prefer to protect their sizeable slice of the pie; because of their ability to purchase the influence of politicians, conflict is inevitable.

But things are changing slowly as a new age of corporate responsibility is on the horizon. The Business Roundtable is comprised of the CEOs from the nation's largest companies, private and public, that has been creating for the past forty years what it calls "Principles of Governance." In August 2019, 181 U.S. companies signed a statement saying that "corporations need to focus on fair trading, ethics and responsibility instead of solely on shareholder returns." The list of signatories included Apple, Amazon, Dell and General Motors. In a prepared statement, the Business Roundtable said:

> "Businesses play a vital role in the economy by creating jobs, fostering innovation and providing essential goods and services. If companies fail to recognize that the success of our system is dependent on inclusive long-term growth, many will raise legitimate questions about the role of large employers in our society."[5]

What they say or do on the front end is one thing, but it is the practices behind the curtain that matter. A business may appear to be "green" but belongs to a trade association that vigorously opposes any environmental or climate-related regulations; corporations contribute millions to these trade associations that lobby indirectly on their behalf.

A 2018 study by a U.K. based think tank examined the links between 200 of the world's biggest companies and 75 of the most powerful trade groups. It found most of them have opposed climate policy since the landmark Paris Agreement was signed three years earlier; at least 90 percent also retain membership in trade associations which have actively opposed climate policy around the world.[6]

In the U.S., the Chamber of Commerce lobbies on behalf of the fossil fuel industry and has spent more than $1.5 billion on federal lobbying since 1998.[7] Opposing any federal legislation that is a potential threat to energy development, they exert enormous influence on our representatives. Here is a Chamber vote alert from September 2019:

> "The U.S. Chamber of Commerce strongly opposes H.R. 205, the 'Protecting and Securing Florida's Coastline Act of 2019,' and H.R. 1941, the 'Coastal and Marine Economies Protection Act,' which would permanently ban energy leasing in the Eastern Gulf of Mexico, and the Atlantic and Pacific planning areas respectively. The Chamber also opposes H.R. 1146, the 'Arctic Cultural and Coastal Plain Protection Act,' which would prohibit energy development in the 1002 area of the Arctic National Wildlife Refuge (ANWR). The Chamber will consider including votes on these bills in our annual How They Voted scorecard."[8]

Often these actions are in direct opposition to local and state aspirations to limit energy exploration and protect the environment. H.R. 205 and H.R. 1941 were supported by every West and East Coast governor along with more than 2,100 elected officials from both parties and from all levels of government along with some 369 municipalities; more than 50,000 business interests and 500,000 fishing families were also in favor of the legislation. On September 11, 2019, the House passed both bills; whether the Senate will do the same is unknown.[9]

Companies are also often guilty of having it both ways – promoting their green products while continuing their traditional business practices. ExxonMobil proudly promotes their research into converting algae to biodiesel fuel and supporting a project that can efficiently adsorb carbon dioxide from emission sources using small pellets.[10]

But in the eye of some shareholders, these ventures are not enough to offset ExxonMobil's responsibility in the impending climate crisis, and they are demanding more accountability. ExxonMobil spends millions of dollars each year on federal lobbying and is a member of numerous trade associations that do the same. To promote greater transparency, the United Steelworkers and 20 other co-sponsors filed a resolution to be voted on by all ExxonMobil stockholders. This is part of an "ongoing investor campaign to expose corporate lobbying expenditures designed to influence legislation and regulation."[11]

Although ExxonMobil provides the basic lobbying disclosures required by law, the critical kind of information sought by shareholders is not available. The Resolution sought by the United Steelworkers and others would change that and be more in line with other companies like Walmart. Their proposal was presented at ExxonMobil's 2019 annual meeting. Listed as Item 10, it called on ExxonMobil to prepare an annually updated report, disclosing:

1) ExxonMobil's policies and procedures governing lobbying, both direct and indirect, and grassroots lobbying communications;

2) The Company's payments for direct and indirect lobbying, or grassroots lobbying communications, including amounts and recipients; and

3) The management's and Board's decision - making process and supervision for making such lobbying payments.[12]

The resolution passed on May 31, 2019 with 62.3 percent of the votes; a similar initiative lost in 2018 garnering only a 38 percent approval. Although non-binding and opposed by ExxonMobil, the latest vote should force the company to re-examine its disclosures guidelines. As the pressure grows around the fossil fuel industry, activist-led proposals are likely to increase.

> "The stakes have gotten higher since the last vote. The business-impact issue is central to lawsuits by two state attorneys general alleging Exxon soft-peddled the risks to consumers and shareholders. Wall Street support of similar measures also has convinced energy companies including Occidental Petroleum to address the Paris climate accord's goal of keeping global temperature increases under 2-degrees Celsius."[13]

The strength of capitalism is its ability to create wealth. The time has come to redirect some of that capital toward cleaning up the planet and positioning the country on a path of sustainability. While many believe that a complete overhaul of our economic system is overdue – what some call base structural changes – small incremental steps can help point us in the right direction.

As more people rely on online shopping, companies like Amazon are expanding their next-day shipping services which are not compatible with reducing the impacts of climate change. Rather than ban one-day shipping, we should tax it. Just as fliers pay a TSA 9/11 security fee, there should be a carbon tax on these shipments – an "Earth security fee."

Amazon has justified the increase in next-day shipping by claiming its new business model means smaller distribution centers closer to the consumer, i.e. a place where goods are kept and then delivered – an explanation that sounds strikingly like the traditional concept of stores with the only difference being Amazon brings the goods to the consumer rather than the other way around. On the plus side, Amazon has already committed as part of their climate pledge to purchase 100,000 electric, zero-emission delivery trucks from Rivian, a U.S. based manufacturer. The United Parcel Service also plans to invest in electric delivery trucks.[14]

Time will tell if Amazon's new delivery plan will lessen greenhouse gas emissions. The most effective way to favorably alter consumer behavior is to target business practices that are potentially harmful by giving people options. A value-added fee to next-day delivery gives the consumer the choice to wait two or more days for their package or pay for the faster delivery. A $2.00 fee per package would be a reasonable cost to the consumer. The funds generated could then be used to support green energy projects such as providing grants to public school districts to purchase school buses that run on cleaner fuels.

New York City has been converting its fleet of 6,000 plus buses from diesel to natural gas and hybrids; Los Angeles has declared they will only buy fully electric buses beginning in 2025.[15] In 2003, Iceland began using commercial hydrogen-fueled buses in Reykjavik, its capital city. While these cleaner buses can cost up to three to four times more than one with a diesel engine, the federal government could reimburse schools for the additional cost with the fee revenue.[16]

There are simpler solutions to solving some of our problems; switching over the nation's school buses to cleaner fuels not only helps to reduce emissions and air pollution, it also provides a positive vision of the future for schoolchildren. Only Congress can impose this type of fee but to date have shown little interest to tether the economic forces affecting the climate.

As for the more structural changes, one place to start is the chemical industry. In the 1970s, Congress passed a chemical "safety" law that exempted over 62,000 chemicals from testing; only about 250 have been tested since the law's passage. One of those exempt chemicals was formaldehyde. Much to the relief of manufacturers, they then proceeded to use formaldehyde in everything from carpets and cigarettes to makeup and medicines. Only years later did researchers discover the chemical leads to cancer.[17]

Representing the largest chemical companies such as Dow, Dupont and Proctor & Gamble, the American Chemistry Council has for decades lobbied against stricter testing rules. A complete overhaul of the laws related to toxic substances is required. This would represent a structural change to the products companies can bring to market and it would put the emphasis on public health over profit.[18]

"Greenwashing" is defined as disinformation disseminated by an organization to present an environmentally responsible public image. As Americans become better educated about the environment, greenwashing will go by the wayside and companies will have no choice but to become more transparent. Amazon is starting to send its unsold inventory to charities just as some supermarkets give their leftover products to food banks. Our tax laws need to encourage the redistribution of goods rather than their disposal; companies should also be required to publicly disclose how they get rid of excess inventory.

Cultural preferences often drive what stores offer and can lead to unanticipated consequences. Supermarkets now provide boundless options of prepared foods but there is a price for this convenience. When capitalism responds to what the consumer demands, everyone is to blame.

> "One group that aims to rescue food from the rubbish bin to better purpose is Indiana-based Food Finders. The group redistributes unsellable food from supermarkets and restaurants to food banks. But the group's biggest challenge is finding a useful afterlife for the ready-made meals. The biggest amount of wasted food is prepared food as it cannot be repackaged, stored in a freezer or held for redistribution through their mobile pantry the next day. In some states, the law requires that food that's been cooked be served right away."[19]

We can no longer tolerate corporations pleading ignorance when it comes to climate issues and lowering carbon emissions. Corporate responsibility starts at the top and as witnessed during Climate Week New York City 2019, corporations are beginning to get the message.

At the September summit, "87 multinational companies with a combined worth of $ 2.3 trillion, announced they would set climate targets for their entire value chains aligned with limiting global temperature rise to 1.5 C and reaching net-zero by no later than 2050." The emissions from these companies is estimated to equal 73 coal-fired plants. While this is significant, not enough energy or U.S.-based corporations made this commitment.[20]

One way to get more U.S. corporations on board is through investor-driven initiatives like the one brought by the United Steelworkers. But just as important is the role of anyone who owns stock in a company, including Universities and retirement funds, when it comes to investments. Known as "Stakeholder Capitalism," we can no longer be silent when it comes to the flow of money. Only when the nation stops building fossil fuel infrastructure will real progress be achieved, and this can most effectively be done but cutting off the supply of capital.

ESG – which stands for environmental, social and governance – is a term used in capital markets to describe "sustainable investing." Investors evaluate companies on their behavior as well as financial performance. The critical non-financial performance indicators include "managing a company's carbon footprint and ensuring there are systems in place to ensure accountability."[21]

With this in mind, investors can better determine the risk and benefit of investing in a company; it also points out the need for full corporate disclosures in their annual reports. Many colleges and universities have already taken the step of divesting from stocks they deem undeserving of their financial support.

Ending our dependence on fossil fuels can occur in incremental steps and U.S. companies could help decarbonize the economy through what are called value chains – Renewable Value Chain Initiatives. According to the American Council on Renewable Energy, some large corporate interests have begun to implement business-to-business market incentives that encourage renewable energy procurement throughout their business model. Called a "value chain," the process examines the full range of activities needed to create a product or service and determines what are the corresponding environmental impacts.[22]

Efforts are underway to replicate the tools corporations need to embrace renewable energy and to share their experience with others throughout their entire supply chain; to date more than two-thirds of the Fortune 100 companies have committed to move in this direction. The same strategies can also be employed to decarbonize the retail chain.[23]

What cannot be tolerated is climate greed. As the earth's ice sheets melt away, many fossil fuel companies see it as an opportunity to drill for more gas and oil such as in Alaska's National Wildlife Refuge; the same goes for mining operations. Public pressure is required to prevent these types of activities. No company wants to be viewed as the most odious climate abuser once there is a shift in public sentiment. Corporate leaders will be judged on how they respond to the climate crisis. We also need to hold corporations accountable when things go badly.

In November 2018, the deadly Camp Fire in California destroyed the Town of Paradise and killed 85 people. Although no final determination as to the cause has been made, early winds that morning snapped a powerline that ignited a fire under it, which was spotted by a Pacific Gas and Electric (PG&E) worker. The company has since disclosed it "repeatedly delayed a safety overhaul of a century-old high-voltage transmission line that is a prime suspect behind the fire" despite the fact they told state regulators in 2013 – and every year thereafter – it planned to complete the work. The upgrades never happened.[24]

Even though the company had received rate hikes to pay for maintenance projects, there has been no accountability for the funds. California's regulators failed to provide the necessary oversight to its citizens and now PG&E is on the verge of bankruptcy. Whether this was corporate maleficence may never be known. The tragedy of the Camp Fire instead speaks to why corporate responsibility and the government must work hand in hand, and the need for stricter regulations that are enforced impartially.[25]

Capitalism should embrace the new green economy with the goal of achieving a net-positive impact on the environment that allows companies to still make a profit. While things are changing, is it happening fast enough to make a difference? To capture the hearts and minds of Americans, companies must do more to rebuild the nation's distressed neighborhoods and cities as well as tackle climate change head on. Congress also needs to change the bankruptcy laws so when a company causes harm to the environment, it is not able to simply walk away from the damage it has left behind.

Microsoft plans to be carbon negative by 2030. In addition to establishing a one-billion-dollar climate innovation fund, it will also by 2050 remove from the environment all the carbon the company has emitted since it was founded in 1975.[26] Other companies are more resistant to changing their business model. Coca-Cola has announced it will not be phasing out its single-use plastic bottles anytime soon for one single reason. They claim their customers prefer the plastic containers and getting rid of them would hurt business.[27]

If corporations refuse to accept their new responsibility in an increasingly polluted and climate-stressed world, then they will be forced to do so through regulation and public pressure on our lawmakers. All the naysayers who say going green will spell the end of American Capitalism are right about one thing. The green economy will transfer wealth from the powerful to thousands of new and likely smaller businesses. And the rich and powerful are scared.

Promoting Social Responsibility

Business News Daily, April 22, 2919: In today's socially conscious environment, employees and customers that have the luxury of doing so place a premium on working for and spending their money with businesses that prioritize corporate social responsibility (CSR).

CSR is an evolving business practice that incorporates sustainable development into a company's business model. It has a positive impact on social, economic and environmental factors.

As the use of corporate responsibility expands, it is becoming extremely important to have a socially conscious image. Consumers, employees and stakeholders are beginning to prioritize CSR when choosing a brand or company. They are holding corporations accountable for effecting social change with their business goals, practices and profits.

"A robust CSR program is an opportunity for companies to demonstrate their good corporate citizenship...and protect the company from outsized risk by looking at the whole social and environmental sphere that surrounds the company," said Jen Boynton, CEO of B Targeted Marketing Co.

To illustrate how critical social responsibility has become, previous research by Cone Communications found that more than 60 percent of Americans hope businesses will drive social and environmental change in the absence of government regulation.[28] Unfortunately, hope will not save the planet. It will take a commitment by businesses and the consumers who purchase and use their products to implement the change required. In the absence of full transparency, it will be difficult to measure how much progress is being made.

A Common Weed Killer Found to Cause Cancer Goes On Trial

Associated Press, March 19, 2019: A U.S. jury on Tuesday found Bayer AG's glyphosate-based weed killer to be a "substantial factor" in causing a man's non-

Hodgkin's lymphoma, allowing the trial to proceed into a second phase on liability and damages.

The jury in San Francisco federal court in a unanimous ruling found Roundup, one of the world's most widely-used weed killers, to be responsible for the cancer of California resident Edwin Hardeman. It was not yet a finding of liability against Bayer, however.

The case will proceed into a second trial phase before the same jury on Wednesday to determine Bayer's liability and potential damages. During that phase, Hardeman's lawyers can present evidence allegedly showing the company's efforts to influence scientists, regulators and the public about the safety of its products, which they were not allowed to in the initial phase.

In a statement on Tuesday, Bayer said it was disappointed with the jury's initial decision. "We are confident the evidence in phase two will show that Monsanto's conduct has been appropriate and the company should not be liable for Mr. Hardeman's cancer," the company said. Bayer had previously acquired Monsanto, which makes Roundup. The case was only the second of some 11,200 Roundup lawsuits to go to trial in the United States. Another California man was awarded $289 million in August after a state court jury found Roundup caused his cancer, sending Bayer shares plunging at the time. That award was later reduced to $78 million and is on appeal.

Associated Press, March 28, 2019: – The jury decided Wednesday to award Hardeman $200,000 for medical expenses, $5,600,000 in compensatory damages and $75,000,000 in punitive damages. In July, the judge reduced the punitive damages to $25,270,000 based on several factors including the legal ratio of punitive to compensatory per federal law.[29] Bayer is now appealing the verdict.

Chapter Twenty-Eight
Avoiding Climate Chaos

"We must get to one hundred percent renewable energy in ten years. There is no other option."

- Alexandria Ocasio-Cortez -

The main premise of this book is that we live in a society where profit takes precedent over the environment and we are ill-prepared to deal with the climate disruptions sitting on our doorstep. We need to move past a world run on fuel sources that originated when there were no other alternatives. For the sake of our grandchildren, a climate catastrophe can only be avoided if we are willing to adopt a lifestyle that is in harmony with nature. The choices before us come in many sizes, but fit under a single banner.

We need to advance what has been called the "New Growth Economy." Its basic principle is simple: We can "restructure the fundamentals of our global cultural and economic systems to cultivate an ecological civilization: one that prioritizes the health of living systems over short-term wealth production."[1]

Those who promote a new worldview are exploring how government and other public institutions can lead the transition to this new economy:

> "Humanity has everything it needs to build that world in a single generation: billions of creative, hardworking people, technology that already can allow us to make a comfortable living safely and sustainably, and unlimited energy from the sun that we can now harness to power that technology. The obstacles to getting there are

political, not technical.   Entrenched political
elites fight to keep the world as it is."[2]

At some point, the world's industrialized nations and
largest economies will need to heed these words. This
includes Brazil who, under its recently elected President,
is trying to go back to the economics of the past by once
again reopening the Amazon rainforest to support
agriculture, logging and mining. Serving as the world's
"lungs" consuming large amounts of carbon dioxide and
releasing twenty percent of the world's oxygen, the
forest must be protected at all costs. The nations of the
world occupy the same lifeboat and all will suffer if the
rainforest is lost.

While many countries are already headed toward
accepting the tenets of the new growth economy, the
U.S. lags far behind at least on the federal level or our
society's ability to make significant change. Like the rest
of the world, we will have no choice but to adopt the new
growth economy. It is only a question of when.

But this lack of a large-scale transformation has not
immobilized many of our states on implementing
strategies to become more sustainable; many larger
urban areas are doing the same as well as a growing
number of smaller communities. As the only state made
up of islands, Hawaii, a state that, in the past, relied on
oil to meet its energy needs, it now has embarked on an
ambitious energy independence plan. Babcock Ranch, a
newly-built community in Southwest Florida, is the first
solar-powered town in the country; with 343,000 solar
panels, enough power is generated for the entire town
and surrounding area.[3]

Sometimes it takes a catastrophic event to force
change. On the evening of May 4, 2007, Greensburg,
Kansas was devastated by a tornado that leveled over 95
percent of the town and killed eleven people. Today,
Greensburg stands as a model town, what some have
described as the "greenest" in America. The hospital,
city hall and school have all been built to the highest
certification level issued by Leadership in Energy and
Environmental Design (LEED).[4]

Not every community can rebuild itself so quickly in the right way; the larger the population, the longer it takes to recover from any type of disaster. As tornadoes, hurricanes and wildfires become more intense there will be many more places facing difficult choices. While these states and local efforts are laudable, the federal government is the only one who can provide the regulatory path and financial resources to steer the economy away from fossil fuels.

The solution most favored by many economists is carbon pricing through emissions trading systems (ETS) or carbon taxes as described here:

- An ETS or cap-and-trade system limits the total level of greenhouse gas emissions and allows those industries with low emissions to sell their extra allowances to larger emitters. By creating supply and demand for emissions allowances, an ETS establishes a market price for greenhouse gas emissions. The cap helps ensure that the required emission reductions will take place to keep the emitters (in aggregate) within their pre-allocated carbon budget.

- A carbon tax directly sets a price on carbon by defining a tax rate on greenhouse gas emissions or – more commonly – on the carbon content of fossil fuels. It is different from an ETS in that the emission reduction outcome of a carbon tax is not pre-defined, only the cost.[5]

The purpose of carbon pricing is to decouple economic growth from fossil fuels while reducing the carbon intensity of all energy sources. Some 40 countries already use carbon pricing mechanisms with varying degrees of success in lowering greenhouse gas emissions.[6]

Numerous European countries have passed some form of carbon pricing. In 1997, Costa Rica – a leader in renewable energy – imposed a 3.5 percent carbon tax on hydrocarbon fuels. The funds are used to encourage property owners to practice sustainable development and forest conservation. Mexico introduced a carbon tax in 2014 that applies to the use of fossil fuels. British Columbia, Canada passed their tax in 2008.[7]

At the end of 2017, China launched the world's largest carbon marketplace. As the world's biggest emitter of greenhouse gases, the government hopes to achieve the emissions goal set by the Paris Accord.[8] In 2019, Singapore implemented Southeast Asia's first carbon tax targeting more than 30 of its biggest polluters such as power plants. The revenue will be used to fund industry measures to reduce future emissions and create jobs in the clean energy sector.[9]

In the U.S., California passed Assembly Bill (HB32) known as the California Global Warming Solutions Act of 2006. It was the first program in the country to take a comprehensive, long-term approach to addressing climate change. The law requires California to return to 1990 levels of greenhouse gas emissions by 2020 and maintain a robust economy by implementing a cap-and-trade program; it sets a statewide limit on sources responsible for 85 percent of the carbon emissions.[10] Not everyone was in favor of the law.

> "In 2013, the California Chamber of Commerce launched the first industry lawsuit against the auction portion of California's cap-and-trade program on the basis that auctioning off allowances constitutes an unauthorized, unconstitutional tax. However, California superior court has rejected the challenges to the state's cap-and-trade program, upholding a significant element of California's suite of programs to comply with AB 32 and to reduce the state's greenhouse gas emissions."[11]

There are also several regional cap-and-trade initiatives such as the Midwestern Regional Greenhouse Gas Reduction Accord and the Western Climate

Initiative which includes seven western states and four Canadian provinces.[12]   The Northeast Regional Greenhouse Gas Initiative (RGGI) is the first mandatory market-based program in the U.S. to reduce greenhouse gas emissions; it includes six New England states along with New York, Delaware and Maryland.[13]

RGGI establishes a regional CO_2 cap of emissions from the power sector and the states sell most of the emission allowances through quarterly auctions. The revenue is then invested in energy efficiency and renewable energy to encourage innovation and create green jobs.   After a long public process, New Jersey finalized regulations that follow the RGGI Model Rule and will participate in the group effective January 1, 2020.[14]

The effectiveness of RGGI and similar programs has yet to be determined. Meanwhile, no U.S. state has a carbon tax (Washington's proposed carbon tax failed at the ballot box in 2016). At least six other states as well as Washington, D.C. are considering enacting carbon taxes; Oregon has gone so far as to do a detailed study on the potential impacts of the tax on their economy.[15]

The first municipality in the U.S. to impose a voter-approved tax on carbon emissions generated from electricity occurred in Colorado.   Passed in 2006, Boulder's Climate Action Plan – often referred to as CAP – allows for climate-related programs and services that are paid for by a tax levy on city residents and businesses based on the amount of electricity they consume. The program generates about $1.8 million per year and the annual residential cost is less than $25. Boulder hopes to provide 100 percent of its electricity with renewable energy by 2030.[16]

Deciding whether to employ a national carbon tax or cap-and-trade system is not currently a top priority for our political leaders and the fossil fuel industry has already demonstrated its willingness to push back against any program that could impact their bottom line. The lobbying influence of the big energy companies should never be underestimated and there are other less overt ways of discouraging the use of fossil fuels. Raising the federal gasoline tax is one possibility. However, not only does this type of tax discriminate against the poor, the revenue generated is better suited for infrastructure improvements under the pretext that the users of the roads pay for the upkeep.

The failure of the American Clean Energy and Security Act of 2009 (ACES) shows how hard it is to pass major climate-related legislation. The bill – a cap-and-trade system that would have required a 42 percent reduction in greenhouse gas emissions by 2040 – narrowly passed in the House of Representatives making it the "first time either house of Congress had approved a bill meant to curb the heat-trapping gases scientists have linked to climate change." It never made it to the Senate floor for a vote despite President Obama's support.[17]

One noteworthy casualty of the House vote was Republican Congressman Bob Inglis of South Carolina. It is generally believed he lost a 2010 primary race to retain his seat in part because of his support for climate legislation. In 2012, Inglis launched the Energy and Enterprise Initiative, a nationwide public engagement campaign promoting conservative and free-enterprise solutions to energy and climate challenges.[18]

> "On climate change, Inglis said that conservatives should go with the facts, and the science, and accept the National Academy of Science's conclusion that climate change is caused by human activities and poses significant risks, which 97 percent of climate scientists agree with. Studies conclude that coal power plants are responsible for 23,600 premature deaths in the U.S. per year, and conservatives should hold them accountable, he said, perhaps with a carbon tax on their emissions."[19]

When Republicans are defeated at the polls for addressing the issue of climate change, other Republicans are likely to think twice about supporting future climate legislation. This becomes problematic as we are running out of time to achieve the emissions goal initially proposed in ACES – a bill opposed by some environmental groups as not being robust enough.

Unlike the EPA's phasedown of leaded gasoline in the 1980s, establishing a comprehensive cap-and-trade program that works may be out of reach. "When there are ongoing changes in the economic factors affecting the magnitude of emissions, the technology for reducing emissions and the scientific evidence about the cost of emissions, setting a specific limit on the quantity of pollution allowed may be even harder than it looks."[20]

Although trading carbon credits can help reduce the amount of greenhouse gas emissions, it does not eliminate the use of fossil fuels. For the past decade, Tesla (which is based in California that has a cap-and-trade program) has been selling credits to General Motors to offset sales of its SUVs and gas-guzzling trucks; Fiat Chrysler has been purchasing credits as well. Since 2010, Tesla has taken in nearly two billion dollars in selling regulatory credits.[21]

Selling these credits may be good for Tesla's bottom line, but it provides an escape hatch for carmakers to make vehicles that are the most harmful to the environment. In the end, a targeted carbon tax may prove to be more effective as the funds can be immediately directed to subsidies for cleaner sources of energy; just like a sales tax, the user pays directly for the privilege of getting something in return. If Congress fails to act, it might be more plausible for states to pass their own carbon tax

Since Congress controls the purse strings, the federal government could provide incentives to states that adopt some stringent form of a carbon tax and/or develop realistic renewable energy goals. Hawaii's energy independence plan provides an excellent model for other states to follow. Whereas if Kentucky, West Virginia and Virginia continue to subsidize their state's coal operations, they would have to pay a phased-in penalty to the government; for years Virginia granted tax credits to its power plants just to burn coal from Virginia.[22]

There are other potentially effective solutions the federal government can employ:

1. Stop federal subsidies to the gas, oil, coal and nuclear industries, and redirect these funds to create a clean-vehicle infrastructure bank program to fund the transition.

2. Convert the entire fleet of federal cars, vans and buses to zero-emission vehicles.

3. Shut down all the coal-fired plants generating electricity within five years and ban the shipment of coal to other countries.

4. Permanently end offshore leasing permits for oil and gas exploration.

5. End fossil fuel production – coal, oil, gas, oil shale and tar sands – on public lands and limit new mining activities by creating reasonable targets for reduction based on approved carbon targets.

6. Withdraw federal approval of the Keystone XL and expansion of the Dakota Access pipeline and only approve the replacement of existing pipelines.

7. Repeal EPA's 2019 Affordable Clean Energy Rule (ACE) and restore Obama's more stringent Clean Power Plan.

These initial measures are needed to level the playing field when it comes to energy production. If enacted quickly, it will raise the price on fossil fuels and accelerate the transition to renewables like wind and solar. The challenge will be to get these measures through Congress without meaningful campaign finance reform to control the flow of money to political campaigns; at the same time, we should aspire to elect a pro-climate Congress.

The landmark case that opened the door to unlimited "dark money" in politics was *Citizens United v. FEC.* Decided in 2010, the U.S. Supreme Court ruled "that the federal government cannot limit corporations – or, for that matter, unions, associations or individuals – from spending money to influence the outcome of elections." Their decision led to the creation of super PACs and eliminated the constraints imposed by the McCain-Feingold law – commonly known as the Bipartisan Campaign Reform Act of 2002.[23]

If powerful super PACs can spend unlimited amounts of money on political campaigns, the fossil fuel industry will continue to hold sway with politicians. The four dissenting justices described the majority opinion as a "rejection of the common sense of the American people, who have recognized a need to prevent corporations from undermining self-government since the founding, and who have fought against the distinctive corrupting potential of corporate electioneering since the days of Theodore Roosevelt."[24]

With or without support from our political leaders and undue influence from lobbyists, the future of energy will look radically different from today. Far more buildings will be heated and cooled by using the natural power of geothermal energy. Solar and wind energy are inevitable; solar PV – which converts sunlight directly into electricity – can be easily distributed. Unlike nuclear power that is highly centralized, many of these new sources of power will be in everyone's backyard or on their rooftops. Whereas today's electrical grid can be brought down by a single point of failure, the electrical system of tomorrow will feature a structure where power is constantly being produced and consumed or shared with others.[25]

The cornerstone of this new electrical network is the "smart grid." It will be based on digital technology that includes smart meters and appliances; it will be able to monitor and analyze the efficiency of the electrical supply chain and make the necessary adjustments. Energy efficiency values will soar and lead to a far more resilient energy system that will benefit everyone. It will change the focus from always needing to produce more energy and shift it to conservation and wise energy use.[26]

And the benefits to society do not end there. While there is some pollution related to the manufacturing and disposal of these new power sources, they produce no operational pollution. Ending our dependence on fossil fuels will help clean up the air and prevent thousands of new cases of asthma and other respiratory diseases. Closing the coal mines will put an end to Black Lung Disease; in all, the health cost savings will run into the billions of dollars. Outlawing strip mining and mountain top removal will preserve the landscape and protect our waterways.

More ambitious policies are also possible. On February 7, 2019, Representative Alexandria Ocasio-Cortez (D-NY) introduced her Green New Deal; a companion resolution was introduced in the Senate by Senator Ed Markey (D-MA). Modeled in part after President Franklin D. Roosevelt's New Deal which helped America recover from the Great Depression, the Green New Deal seeks to transform American society by creating an ecologically-based and socially- responsible economy. Senator Markey put it this way:

> "Five decades ago, President Kennedy announced the ambitious goal of sending an American safely to the moon. He didn't say how it would be done but that we would do it. We would need a giant rocket made of new metal alloys that had not been invented yet, and it would have to be returned safely to Earth within ten years. He urged us to be bold. I say today that it is time for us to be bold once again."[27]

If the country wants to reach net-zero emissions by 2030, massive emissions reductions will need to be achieved in the transportation sector – now the largest contributor of U.S. emissions at around 28 percent. This will mean more EVs on the road. One of the most ambitious goals of the Green New Deal is to meet 100 percent of the power demand in the U.S. through clean, renewable and zero-emission energy sources. Once the country has switched over to renewable sources for electricity, the benefits of EVs will increase dramatically. The Green New Deal also moves the U.S. toward cleaner and affordable public transit, and high-speed rail.[28]

For society to fully adopt EVs (both hybrids and plug-ins), it will take more than tax incentives. Just as U.S. consumers evaluate fuel efficiency when purchasing a gasoline-powered vehicle, Plug-in EVs – known as PEVs – are judged by how they can travel when fully charged. The new Tesla Model S has a range of up to 370 miles; it also costs over $78,000. The far more affordable Chevy Bolt has a range well over 200 miles; most other PEVs currently on the market are closer to 100 miles.[29]

To get Americans excited about EVs, most experts believe a minimum of 350 to 400 miles is the tipping point. To make this happen, the U.S. needs to invest in battery technology. The Tesla Giga Factory in Nevada is currently the largest producer in the world of lithium-ion batteries for vehicles; the other leading manufacturers are based in China, Japan and South Korea.[30] If the U.S. wants to retain its status as an economic power, more plants like the one in Nevada must be constructed; the country does not want to go from importing oil to importing batteries.

While hybrid vehicles either don't need to be charged or can be done so at home, PEVs need access to public charging stations; the more PEVs on the road, the more stations required. At the beginning of 2018, there were over 48,000 public stations with an average of 2.75 outlets per location; only twenty percent of these are considered Level 1 – the fastest of the three levels; also in development are super charging stations that can handle multiple vehicles.[31]

If the U.S. market grew to 15 million PEVs on the road, the number of public charging stations needed according to the U.S. Department of Energy's National

Renewable Energy Laboratory ranges from 100,000 to more than 1.2 million. The large discrepancy is based on consumer preference and driving behavior; once Americans want their electric vehicles for long-range travel, the greater the need for more charging stations.[32]

Right now, the projected number of PEVs in the U.S. in the year 2026 is less than 4.3 million based on an annual growth rate of fifteen percent; at a five percent growth rate, the number of vehicles drops to 2.7 million.[33] Without the proper infrastructure, Americans will be slow to switch to PEVs. It is the same challenge California faces with its futuristic hydrogen highway. It is also another example of the green jobs that will be created once we make the switch.

At the turn of the nineteenth century, the U.S. successfully transitioned from the horse to the automobile. Many civilizations in the past have collapsed because they were unable to adapt to changing conditions. Lots of saddle makers and horse-drawn carriage manufacturers were put out of business thanks to Henry Ford's invention of the assembly line, but this led to the growth of numerous new industries still in existence today.

This transition to a green economy is already happening. About 40 percent of the nation's coal comes from Wyoming's Powder River Basin; the quality of coal found in the surface mines here meant mine closures were unlikely despite the nation's shift toward cheaper and cleaner natural gas. But that all changed on July 1, 2019, when two of the area's twelve coal mines abruptly closed and nearly 600 workers lost their jobs. Revenue from the fossil fuel industry traditionally accounts for over 50 percent of Wyoming's revenue and the mine closures sent shock waves through the area, which proudly dubs itself the "Energy Capital of the Nation."[34]

Instead of accepting that the coal industry will continue to decline, Wyoming is spending state dollars to find "new uses for coal." There is no future for coal and the state would be better served investigating ways to diversify their economy. The New Growth Economy will present endless opportunities for emerging new industries. The first batches of batteries from EVs are nearing retirement, but that does not mean they will be discarded. It is estimated many of these batteries can be converted to other uses for up to ten more years; potential applications include powering residential automobile charging stations or storing energy for homes. As reported by *Bloomberg Businessweek*:

> "Finding ways to reuse the technology is becoming more urgent as the global stockpile of EV batteries is forecast to exceed the equivalent of about 3.4 million packs by 2025, compared with about 55,000 this year. China, where about half the world's EVs are sold, is implementing rules to make carmakers responsible for expired batteries and to keep them out of landfills; the European Union has similar regulations as well."[35]

This is projected to be a multi-billion-dollar industry in the coming years and a superior investment in comparison to propping up the coal industry. It is up to the citizens of Wyoming to choose their own future. Their political leaders might decide to push for national legislation that requires vehicle batteries be produced in the U.S. and remain here forever. The state could then become a leader in battery production, reuse and recycling.

Wyoming is not alone. As the world's glaciers are melting away, the nation faces the same predicament – move quickly toward a green economy or continue to do business as usual. The clock is running out as the melting of ice sheets far exceeds earlier climate models; between the years 2011 and 2014, the Greenland ice sheet lost an astounding one trillion tons of ice and the planet is only getter hotter.[36]

To attain a more sustainable society and reduce the risks posed by climate change, we must think of it as a marathon, not a sprint. As any_triumphant, long-distance runner knows, it takes months of training before entering the race. The transition to a green economy will take years. States like California and Hawaii have been making the transition for a long time. Wyoming, the Trump Administration and many members of Congress have failed to grasp the exigency of providing the leadership to guide a nation that is adrift. By withdrawing from the Paris Agreement, the U.S. has no climate standing on the world stage. This only serves to underscore the importance of the 2020 national election.

Ultimately, the nation needs to move toward the goals set forth in the New Green Deal. The plan starts with a net-zero gas emissions economy that will create millions of good, high-wage jobs and it invests in suitable infrastructure to support a greener transportation sector. But it is also about addressing the economic inequities in our country. The plan seeks to ensure a fair and just transition to the new economy for U.S. workers and communities; the jobs that are created will make future economic growth more inclusive. It promises clean air and water, healthy food and a sustainable environment for our grandchildren and future generations.

Perhaps the most controversial component of the plan centers around closing the gap between the wealthy and the disadvantaged.   Historically, poorer communities have suffered greater environmental harm than wealthier towns and neighborhoods. The Green New Deal strives to end this practice in order to "promote justice and equity by stopping current, preventing future, and repairing historic oppression of frontline and vulnerable communities."[37]

To this end, Senator Kamala Harris (D-CA) and Representative Alexandria Ocasio-Cortez (D-NY) introduced the "Climate Equity Act of 2019" which targets the inequities posed by climate change. Low-income communities are often located in easily flooded areas or near oil and gas refineries and other pollution-causing industries. The legislation is designed to protect vulnerable communities from the perils posed by their proximity to natural and man-made hazards.

"This bill would require congressional climate and environmental bills to have an equity score and require additional review for 'climate equity' in federal regulations. The bill would additionally require all major federal climate and environmental investments to consider front-line groups, including low-income communities, indigenous communities, and communities of color. It would create an office of Climate and Environmental Justice Accountability to handle new responsibilities created by the bill."[38]

America's progress-at-any-cost economy has run its course. Devastating hurricanes and massive wildfires do not discriminate between rich and poor homes. Climate disruption puts all communities at risk and if we are to survive as a vibrant nation, it will be a collective effort. But we need to act decisively.   Unlike Franklin Roosevelt's New Deal, we cannot count on the federal government to lead the way.

If the New Green Deal is to achieve environmental justice and the end of destructive energy practices, new leadership is required absent of greed and corruption. Even well-intentioned projects such as mass transit improvements are fraught with long delays and cost overruns; these breakdowns further undermine people's faith in government. The Green New Deal will only take root if a groundswell of activists can convince a passive citizenry that it is time to save the planet.

A Sunnier Future

Business Wire, November 19, 2019: Heliogen, the clean energy company that is transforming sunlight to create and replace fuels, today announced it has – for the first time commercially – concentrated solar energy to exceed temperatures greater than 1,000 degrees Celsius. At that temperature, Heliogen can replace the use of fossil fuels in critical industrial processes, including the production of cement, steel, and petrochemicals, dramatically reducing greenhouse gas emissions from these activities. This singular scientific achievement was accomplished at Heliogen's commercial facility in Lancaster, California.

Heliogen's mission is to create the world's first technology that can commercially replace fossil fuels with carbon-free, ultra-high temperature heat from the sun and transform sunlight into fuels at scale – taking a major step towards solving climate change. Its heat technology represents a key technical breakthrough for concentrated solar thermal.

Previous commercial concentrating solar thermal systems have been designed to reach temperatures of up to only 565 degrees Celsius – useful for power generation, but insufficient for many industrial processes. Many of these processes require much higher temperatures, which have traditionally been reached through the burning of fossil fuels.

The potential impact of Heliogen's patented technology is massive. With temperatures from its concentrating solar thermal technology exceeding 1,000 degrees Celsius, Heliogen will be able to replace the fuel that generates greenhouse gas emissions from industrial processes with solar energy for the first time. For instance, cement production – one of the industrial processes well suited to Heliogen's technology – alone accounts for more than 7 percent of global CO_2 emissions.

In addition to industrial process heat, Heliogen's technology roadmap calls for temperatures up to 1,500 degrees Celsius. At that temperature, Heliogen can perform CO_2-splitting and water-splitting to make 100 percent fossil-free fuels such as hydrogen or syngas.

"Today, industrial processes like those used to make cement, steel, and other materials are responsible for more than a fifth of all emissions," said Microsoft's Bill Gates, Heliogen's CEO and Founder. "These materials are everywhere in our lives but we don't have any proven breakthroughs that will give us affordable, zero-carbon versions of them. If we're going to get to zero-carbon emissions overall, we have a lot of inventing to do."[39]

End Fossil Fuel Development on Our Federal Lands

Center for Biological Diversity, September 2015: According to a recent report, from 2003 - 2014 approximately 25 percent of all U.S. fossil fuel greenhouse gas emissions are attributable to federal fossil fuel production. More than 67 million acres of public land and oceans – an area 55 times larger than Grand Canyon National Park – are already leased to the fossil fuel industry. Those leases contain up to 43 billion tons of potential carbon dioxide pollution.

The Mineral Leasing Act of 1920 governs leasing of federal onshore oil, gas, coal, oil shale and tar sands, and affords the president's interior secretary discretion to offer federal fossil fuel leases. The Outer Continental Shelf Lands Act of 1953 gives the president the same authority to restrict the leasing of any land of the Outer Continental Shelf.[40]

Congress has vested the president with authority to control new federal fossil fuel leasing. By taking this singular step, we can begin to end our dependence on fossil fuels.

Chapter Twenty-Nine
Greenprint – A Path Forward

**"The greatest threat to our planet is the belief
that someone else will save it."**

- Robert Swan -

America has always been known as the "Can-Do Nation."
It is time to show the world that collectively we can
survive the evolving climate crisis. The process starts
with changing our politics. This means overturning the
Citizens United v. FEC decision; dark money can no
longer dominate the political landscape. It will require
the political will to take on the corporate giants that
control our economy.

At the other end of the spectrum, all of us will be
pressed into action. This means ending our mindless
addiction to shopping. More than two decades ago when
shopping malls still reigned supreme and Amazon only
sold books, work began on a mega entertainment and
shopping complex on a vast expanse of swamp land in
New Jersey known as the Meadowlands. It is called the
American Dream.

After endless delays and billions of dollars, the
mammoth complex opened its doors on October 25,
2019. When fully completed, it will be the second
largest mall in America, the largest being the Mall of
America in Minnesota. It will feature an eye-popping
three million square feet of leasable space that will
include some 450 retail shops; the mall also includes an
indoor ski slope, rollercoaster and waterpark.

What is unknown is the financial vitality of the mall.
Does the American Dream represent capitalism's last
stand and that wasteful consumerism knows no bounds
or will shoppers simply stay home and order what they
desire through Amazon Prime? Neither option will do

anything to protect the country from the ravages of climate disruption. Some communities in the Meadowlands are already suffering from periodic flooding due to sea level rise; in less than twenty years, the mall might one day become a natural "waterpark."

There is nostalgia for the way things have always been done and rapid change can lead to societal stress and fear of the future. It is difficult to give up a way of life. But during the Great Depression in the 1930s, there was no throw-away culture. It was just the opposite – people hoarded goods and resources. And this is the big advantage of today's advanced technological society. Innovation can help solve many of our problems. Creating a better world that benefits everyone is within our grasp if we have the courage to reach for it.

A step in the right direction would be to end the plastic waste stream. Plastic has thousands of great uses; single-use packaging is not one of them. As communities and states are coming to terms with the amount of waste being generated, there is a movement to reinvent the packaging industry but one would never know it judging by the actions of the fossil fuel industry.

In Monaca, Pennsylvania on the Ohio River near Pittsburgh, Royal Dutch Shell is building a facility that will produce a million tons annually of the last thing the world needs – more plastic. Once operational, the tiny plastic pellets will be transported via a new rail system to be turned into everything from children's toys to single-use packaging. If we eliminate the latter, this mega plastic manufacturing plant could quickly turn into a relic of the past.

The European Union is moving toward what is called a circular economy. This is a system based on eliminating waste and the continual reuse of materials. By creating a closed-loop platform, the manufacturer retains ownership of the packaging. If a bottle was used, the company is responsible to collect and reuse it. This would minimize the need for single-use plastic resulting in less waste, pollution and carbon emissions.

How do we further tip the balance away from disposable plastic? Voluntary compliance has been shown not to work while regulation creates new bureaucracies and is generally despised by industry. What fits best under capitalism are economic incentives and, in the case of plastics, this means taxing its most basic element – carbon. Plastics are made from oil, gas and coal that are transformed to what are called monomers. If we want to move markets from using plastics to something else, taxation is the quickest way to do it.

A carbon tax will result in multiple benefits besides reducing the amount of plastic. Higher gas prices will encourage greater fuel efficiency for gas-powered vehicles and increase the demand for affordable EVs. The revenue generated can be used to support green infrastructure. The tax can be phased in over several years to avoid market disruptions and to provide ample time for replacement products to take hold. By "decarbonizing" the tax code, it will ignite a massive shift toward renewable energy sources.

While some companies will likely use their considerable influence to prevent such a tax from seeing the light of day, there's growing momentum to put a price on carbon emissions. Many U.S. businesses in response to the growing public awareness of climate change are pushing for a price on carbon as an alternative to regulation. Others, like Unilever – a British-Dutch company that owns several large U.S. brands – have already embraced the new circular economy. Unilever has pledged that all their plastic packaging will be reused, recycled or composted by 2025. We do not need to eliminate plastic packaging, just use it more wisely.

"Loop" is a new purchasing system that's circular by design. Under this waste-free shopping and delivery model, products are shipped directly to consumers and are then returned to be refilled. The system brings together major brands and retailers with the idea of shifting from a model that is disposable to one that is durable where packaging is reused or easily recycled.

PET is the type of plastic labeled with the #1 code. Because of its strength, thermo-stability and transparency, this soft plastic is most commonly used to package soft drinks, water, juice and other popular food items. And that is the problem. Americans consume large amounts of plastic water bottles which are often needed during natural disasters or when public water supplies are shown to be contaminated. Hard plastic bottles that can be more easily recycled are a better choice; reusable water bottles are the preferred option.

To make the recycling of plastic more efficient, hybrid plastics and mixed containers that include other materials should be banned along with things like plastic straws. More uniform plastic containers for certain products like yogurt are needed as well; Americans prefer diversity and with a little creativity, companies could use a standard container which comes with removable and recyclable paper wrapping.

If we can solve the plastic mess, the recycling industry can concentrate on the other recyclables like paper, glass and aluminum. Of course, recycling requires collecting and transporting bulk materials which is why renewable fuels for trucks is so critical. This is where American ingenuity comes into play. As referenced in Chapter Twelve, Xyleco has developed a process to convert biomass to a material that contains sugars which can be used to make plastics and fuel.

States also need to do their part. Under current interstate commerce laws, it is illegal to prevent the transport of trash from one state to the next. But what if the law was changed and states could charge a tipping fee to haulers who transport garbage across state lines? What is clear, states, municipalities and towns need to be more responsible for dealing with their own waste and not ship it miles away.

Regulation – state and federal – plays a significant role in cleaning up the environment and reducing waste. We need to ban Styrofoam as Maine and six other states have already accomplished. We need to improve the reparability and service life of devices, implement product standards that encourage alternate forms of packaging which can be easily recycled, and power cords should be universal and labeled to match up with the right device.

Waste comes in many forms and tons of new goods that are dumped in landfills every year in the U.S. simply to get it off the books. These are perfectly good products that did not sell and could be given away with better tax incentives. As the country moves toward an online yard-sale economy, it will lead to products made to be resold and not thrown away. This will encourage consumers to demand safer products that protect public health from unknown chemical hazards. And if companies fail to join the new green economy, they should be forced to shoulder a large share of the costs associated with waste disposal, recycling and litter removal.

There are much broader issues to tackle than getting rid of plastics, but understanding a person's role in creating a new environmental ethic begins at home. If we fail to address our daily wasteful habits, it becomes harder to convince someone to purchase an electric vehicle, pay more for one-day shipping, or give up coupons sent via third-class mail. Americans would be better served to live by the ethic, "what I do affects others."

The Green New Deal provides a road map for dealing with the climate crisis and while the details are still a work in progress, the core tenets are clearly quantified. As with any large undertaking, it begins with planning; according to the most recent U.S. National Climate Assessment, climate change is far outpacing our ability to deal with this new reality. By adopting strict climate adaptation measures along the coasts, we can reduce the future costs due to climate-related disasters. This means restoring our coastal marshes and increasing the flood-preparedness of residential and commercial buildings while ceasing all new construction in flood-prone areas. And if we want to reduce the risks from wildfires, we need to stop building in every nook and cranny of undeveloped land.

With the privilege of owning public lands comes the responsibility of protecting the natural wonders of the

U.S. as well as preserving the vast open spaces that still exist. In addition to ending fossil fuel exploitation of these special places, it means repealing the General Mining Law of 1872 and its massive subsidies to mining companies. The U.S. population was less than 40 million when this antiquated act became law and it no longer reflects the needs of a nation facing dwindling natural resources. These lands are part of our heritage acquired by our ancestors to be passed on to future generations.

Cattle, sheep and other livestock graze on millions of federally-owned acres. Overgrazing causes soil erosion, damaging wetlands and destroying wildlife habitat while the low grazing fees do not begin to cover the environmental costs. American taxpayers should not be subsidizing ranchers any more than corporate farmers. Those who want to utilize our federal lands must cause no harm or pay for the damage done. Opponents will say this will lead to higher meat prices and they are probably right; a small price to pay to protect our public lands.

We must also protect the nation's vital infrastructure. This means preparing a priority list of those facilities most vulnerable to wildlfires, storm damage and sea level rise such as military installations, nuclear plants, oil refineries and wastewater treatment plants. According to the Government Accounting Office, the climate crisis has put nearly 950 designated toxic sites at severe risk. It is up to industry to climate-proof privately-owned facilities and for Congress to establish a climate fund to help cover the costs for publicly-owned infrastructure.

Following World War II, the U.S. launched the Marshall Plan to rebuild Europe. Access to federal financing to fund green-building retrofits and new construction will help spur redevelopment of our urban areas and provide high-quality jobs. This in turn will drive new private capital investment for clean energy projects such as turning garbage into methanol and other flex-fuels; research dollars are also needed to fund efforts like carbon sequestration.

Past efforts by Congress to set aside funds for these greener endeavors have failed. But creating a "climate bank" remains a top priority. Senator Michael Bennet

(D-CO) has put forward a plan to spend one trillion in federal dollars to catalyze ten trillion in private spending with the goal of net-zero emissions by 2050; others have proposed similar plans to generate the funding required. Regardless of what plan is agreed upon, a bond market for green infrastructure is a prerequisite for the transition to a green economy. For example, the solar industry is developing a wide array of new products. These include floating solar farms (aka floatovoltaics), solar films for windows, and photovoltaic solar noise barriers to be used on the nation's 3,000 miles of traffic noise barriers. This type of innovation requires financial backing.

On the housing front, Congress should adopt a national zero-carbon building standard. By partnering with states and cities to pass new building codes, it will help propel the transition to renewable energy to power America's homes as well as businesses. Countries like Norway have already embraced this type of climate-conscious architecture where recycled materials are preferred and new ones are traced to their place of origin to make sure they come from a sustainable source. The emphasis is on design and using long-lasting materials rather than maximizing profit and getting the work done quickly. This same ethic can then be carried over to products used in the home. By adopting a lifestyle based on durability rather than cost, consumers can lessen their carbon footprint and reduce waste. This means educating the public that if something lasts longer, it is a better value than a lower cost item with a shorter lifespan.

The same approach should apply to all new construction projects. States should adopt stricter land use and development guidelines like Vermont's Act 250. Established in 1970, the law covers any project more than ten acres or ten housing units and is designed to safeguard the environment, community life, and aesthetic character of the state. In 2020, New Jersey will become the first state in the U.S. to require builders to consider the impacts of climate change before seeking a building permit. The process will also look at the potential release of greenhouse emissions. With 130 miles of coastline, New Jersey is especially vulnerable to sea level rise. All states need to adopt similar guidelines.

To address the larger issues related to reshaping the economy, EPA must return to its prior regulatory role and be fully funded. A reinvigorated EPA can reestablish the protections that the Trump Administration has rolled back such as Obama's Clean Power Plan. Restrictions on methane emissions and revealing the chemicals used during the fracking process are critical as the nation transitions to renewable energy. And when companies vacate obsolete coal and uranium mine sites, they will be on the hook for the clean-up and restoration costs. To protect our health, there must be much stricter regulations on the testing and development of chemicals.

Land that no one wants can prove suitable for solar installations. Many states have in place renewable energy standards for locating green energy installations; the federal government should pass complimentary guidelines and provide tax incentives to companies willing to invest in the reuse of abandoned lands.

This same type of oversight must be applied to the U.S. military as well. As the world's biggest polluter and a monolithic relic of the past industrial-military complex, its footprint dwarfs that of any corporation with thousands of installations that are spread across millions of acres. Many of these sites are contaminated and it will require a massive – and costly – restoration effort to clean them up. It also uses more oil than any other entity on the planet. The military should take a lead role in developing new fuels to operate its vast facilities and fleet of vehicles, jets and ships.

The future will be powered by a decentralized clean-energy system. It will run on wind and solar power and new technologies that utilize hydrogen and biogas. Congress should appoint a "Climate Czar" as an advisor to the president and federal agencies. It will take time to prepare the nation for this green revolution. We will need to take some if not all the following steps. While certainly not a complete list, it is a roadmap for moving forward.

Protecting Our Food Supply

Protecting our food supply begins with reassessing how federal agricultural subsidies are allocated. Instead of supporting the large industrial growers, farmers should be paid to sequester carbon by planting cover crops. We should put an end to large-scale ethanol production; once we switch to electric vehicles, ethanol will only be needed as an additive for various household products.

The benefits of preserving farmland and supporting local farms are well established and this means protecting the remaining prime farmland in every state. This will help support what are known as CSAs or "community-supported agriculture." Consumers pay local farmers a fee prior to the growing season in exchange for a weekly supply of fruits and vegetables in summer and fall which can be managed through a local food co-op.

As organic farming continues to blossom, Congress needs to update the Organic Foods Production Act that passed in 1990 and increase federal investments to enable communities to build healthier, more sustainable food systems. Consumers must do their part as well and support local farms while purchasing fewer imported products. This means understanding where foods come from and the source of ingredients such as palm oil which is often produced from cleared lands that replaced the existing rainforest.

Food labeling laws should compel manufacturers to list any additives so consumers can make informed decisions; nanotechnology is developing new food ingredients and additives which will require extensive studies of the effects on humans. In 2016, Chile implemented a new food labeling law with the intention of guiding consumers towards behavior patterns that promote public health. The U.S. should do the same. More research dollars should be allocated to our land-grant universities to develop innovative new products such as fertilizers not made from oil.

Water Resources

Protecting our nation's water supply will become even more critical as climate change affects existing sources of fresh water. The Clean Water Act currently is about managing pollution rather than eliminating sources. It needs to be revised with the long-term goal of net-zero discharges.   The nation needs tougher regulations regarding the disposal of hazardous materials and limiting the use of "forever chemicals" known as PFAS with the goal of protecting aquifers and groundwater recharge areas. Additional federal funding is needed to develop new technologies that will result in improved treatment systems.

The goal is to change how we think about water from something that comes out of the tap to a valuable commodity.   The definition of "covered waters" under the Clean Water Act also needs to be clarified as the Trump Administration replaces the Obama-era Waters of the United States rule, thus changing the protection provided to the nation's wetlands. The definition must be broad and the purpose should be to protect an unimpaired hydrologic cycle.

Once the focus is on prevention, new developments will be viewed in a different light. For homes, purple-pipe plumbing where grey wastewater is treated and returned to the user should be encouraged in addition to water conservation. It makes no sense to use potable water to wash our cars and to water our lawns, gardens, and golf courses.

For commercial projects, stormwater should be treated on-site, or the property owner would be charged a pollution fee managed as a stormwater utility. The fees would be used for public water improvement projects and pollution prevention. And when water lines are extended into rural areas, the developer must shoulder the cost.

The nexus between the fossil fuel industry and water is well documented. Green energy also requires water but the demand will be less and any industry that depletes water supplies should be more closely regulated. This will require more detailed reporting of water usage that documents not only consumption but the release of pollutants and greenhouse gas emissions.

The federal government needs to be much more effective in managing the nation's water supply. This means better coordination between the fragmented federal agencies that are charged with water-related programs and the integration of monitoring data from multiple locations. When federal funds are used, all new infrastructure must be designed to incorporate potential future impacts from water-related climate disruption.

America's Coasts and Oceans

We will never survive climate change until the nation's coastlines are protected. Barrier islands and associated wetlands are meant to protect the mainland from storm surges. The time has come to redirect government programs and subsidies away from harmful coastal development. We can no longer tolerate bad building decisions which means telling people, "You can't build here." Property rights advocates will demand compensation for the loss of development rights, but land that will soon be underwater has no value.

The Federal Emergency Management Agency (FEMA) is responsible for disaster relief no matter what the cause. When it comes to hurricanes, they have managed the National Flood Insurance Program with the aim of reducing the impact of flooding on private and public structures. They provide affordable flood insurance to property owners where it is mandatory to have coverage,
and encourage communities to adopt and enforce floodplain management regulations.

If your house was substantially damaged by flooding, you may be eligible for funds to help you pay for raising your home to minimize destruction from future storm events; there is also a Severe Repetitive Loss Program for buildings flooded multiple times. As sea level continues to rise, we will need to reevaluate the effectiveness of these programs and accept it is time to stop rebuilding in flood prone zones. Development on barrier islands and along the immediate coast needs to cease as we begin a slow retreat from vulnerable areas. FEMA's efforts should be on flood preparedness and restoration of lands that can best absorb storm surges and the rising ocean waters.

In the Netherlands, a low-lying country that does not require flood insurance, Dutch underwriters have developed an innovative online underwriting tool that allows homeowners to produce a risk assessment of their property by linking flood data with mapping technology. The U.S. should create its own state-of-the art platform; this includes updating flood maps every five to ten years.

The Coastal Zone Management Act (CZMA) under NOAA was first enacted in 1972 with the goal of protecting our fragile coastlines against development pressures. It accomplishes this through grants to states to develop and implement appropriate actions that balance economic activities with preserving an area's natural resources. The National Estuarine Research Reserve System (NERRS) is a program under CZMA and protects the nation's most valuable estuaries.

Congress has failed to reauthorize CZMA since the end of fiscal year 1999. While funding continues to be made available, it is time to strengthen the Act; its role is especially important when it comes to issues like offshore drilling and deep-sea mining. Future decisions about the industrialization of our marine resources should be based on what best serves the nation in the new green economy. Evaluating our coastlines for building windfarms and the placement of giant floating solar farms should be a high priority as well.

To ensure the protection of our oceans and estuaries, Congress should elevate NOAA to become its own agency separate of the Department of Commerce. NOAA should be given the authority to create a national ocean policy, to manage whole marine ecosystems and to develop a national aquaculture permitting system – a potentially critical future food source. Other Congressional priorities include passing the Law of the Sea Treaty under the United Nations which defines the rights and responsibilities of nations in their use of the world's oceans.

Investments in Urban Areas

As the nation turns toward sustainability, urban re-development is essential to keep people in our cities and to take advantage of existing infrastructure. The population of cities like St. Louis have plummeted since the 1950s while we continue to build in areas that should remain open such as the fire-prone foothills of California.

The Federal Opportunity Zones Program that was passed by Congress in 2017 is designed to be a catalyst for private financing and economic growth in low-income disadvantaged communities.

Dilapidated buildings and vacant shopping centers can be converted into affordable housing creating high-paying jobs. All it takes are public-private partnerships and generous tax incentives with assurance bonds that the work completed is climate friendly.

Cities of the future should include everything from greenways and community gardens to neighborhood-based wastewater treatment plants. The models to replicate across the country already exist; Detroit is turning vacant urban lots into productive green infrastructure and promoting vertical farming. By revitalizing America's abandoned urban neighborhoods, it will improve the quality of life for everyone living in and near our cities.

Climate Literacy and Climate-Ready Citizens

The science behind global warming is complex as it involves long-term trends which are obscured by multiple up and down fluctuations. This makes it difficult to convince most people to change their everyday habits. Since most governments take the short view, future potential problems are ignored. Addressing climate change suffers from the same type of bureaucratic indifference; denial is a much easier path than making difficult decisions.

Just as we need climate-ready crops, we need climate-ready citizens. We already have a weather channel. A climate channel that covers the crisis from around the world would go even further to keep the public informed. Relevant climate change imagery that shows the types of disruption we will face in the future is crucial; not just images of stranded polar bears but flooded roads and subways. The federal government also should play a role in educating the public and require the CEQ to release an annual report on the nation's progress in responding to the climate crisis.

As high school students across the nation rally against climate change, there is a whole generation that understands how climate change will affect the world they will inherit. But it is not enough to simply protest. We will need a highly educated citizenry to deal with a changing world and environmental education begins in childhood. This will require a revamping of school curriculums and a comprehensive framework for K-12 science education. The current STEM programs that emphasize math and engineering are a good model to follow. This also means teaching about environmental ethics, carrying capacities and steady-state economics.

In June 2020, the New Jersey Board of Education became the first state to require grade school students to learn about climate change and its impact on human society. The standards, which go into effect in September 2021, provide a template for other states to follow.

Climate science is full of terms like the Arctic Oscillation and high schools ahead of the curve could offer a standardized test on climate that must be passed in their senior year before a student receives his/her high school diploma. Federal grants through NOAA's Climate Office could assist schools in administering the test. Our colleges and universities should also play a lead role by developing standards for competency in climate science.

National Service

To prepare our youth for the planet they will inherit, the U.S. could learn a lesson from Israel's National Service program. Their mandatory conscription requires two years of military service. In the U.S., we should employ a more expansive program. Climate disruption could lead to a national emergency.

Just as local weather-related disasters force volunteers into action, America's youth should be trained to respond to areas impacted by climate-related events.

It was President Kennedy who envisioned a national service program to alleviate poverty. In 1965, Volunteers in Service to America – known as VISTA – was created and in 1993, it was incorporated into AmeriCorps as part of the Corporation for National and Community Service (NCC). As an independent federal agency, NCC engages more than five million Americans in community service under its various programs which also includes the Peace Corps.

While President Trump has proposed slashing NCC's funding in 2020, VISTA volunteers in Kentucky are training out-of-work coal miners computer skills and completing other worthwhile projects across all 50 states. In 2015, Senator John McCain introduced a bill to create a 21st Century Civilian Conservation Service Corps for young Americans and veterans to work in our National Parks and other public land. It was never approved by Congress.

Just as climate change presents the nation with new challenges, a mandatory service program is the kind of bold approach needed to prepare the nation's youth for what lies ahead. If one does not join the military, one would be enlisted to protect the nation in other ways. The most efficient way to sequester carbon is by planting trees or restoring natural forests through regeneration. For those who complete their service, they would be eligible for certain benefits like low-interest college loans and hiring priority for federal jobs. To honor former President Jimmy Carter's legacy of volunteerism, the program could be named after him.

Final Words

Climate deniers argue there is no urgency to deal with the climate crisis. Some people are skeptical of the science or believe climate change is good for us as longer summers will benefit our farmers. Others claim it will cost too much to fix which will lead to economic chaos or that other countries are to blame for the crisis ignoring our nation's role in the release of carbon emissions and our ability to find solutions. And when some spread fear saying Americans will be forced to live in the dark, they ignore the probability that Americans will generate their own electricity and share it with others through net metering.

For those who care about the world and how mankind responds to climate change, we cannot forget our evolutionary roots. Dan Gilbert, a psychologist at Harvard University, has written extensively about why people are not overly concerned about the environment. He contends that climate change lacks the fundamental features that typically trigger an immediate response in human behavior. Global warming is not an imminent threat that is trying to harm or kill us. It is something that will happen in the future. Miami will be flooded in 30 years, not tomorrow.

Fortunately, more of us are beginning to see the realities of climate disruption like the farmer whose crops are ruined due to extreme changes in the weather or insurance companies facing huge losses from increased storm damage. The U.S. Department of Defense is worried about the impact of flooding on our most critical military installations.

There are never easy solutions even when we decide to take action. For example, demand is soaring for the metal cobalt – an essential ingredient in batteries and abundant in rocks found on the ocean floor. When supplies on land dwindle, this would involve deep-sea mining.   As an emerging technology, it comes with unknown environmental risks.

Fighting climate change will require an international response. On May 7, 2019, the U.S. pulled out of the Arctic Accord after the Trump Administration would not accept an agreement that stated climate change seriously threatened the polar region.   While the remaining eight nations including Russia deal with the fallout, the destruction of the Arctic will prove catastrophic for Alaska and the rest of the planet.

When the U.S. turns its back on those nations seeking a greener world, one cannot forget what drives our lack of action. It is the power of money. When critics of the Green New Deal claim it will cost too much, what they are really saying is they are against the transfer of wealth from the multi-international fossil fuel corporations and other conglomerates that control our economy.

The challenge is to articulate a vision of the future equivalent to the scope of the impending crisis. By returning to the emission levels of 1990 – the base year of numerous climate agreements including the Kyoto Protocol – we can survive climate chaos if we act quickly.   While technology will play a key role in discovering potential solutions, there is no guarantee these will be timely or scalable. The world's ice is melting faster than our most preeminent climate scientists predicted just as environmental degradation continues to accelerate. America has faced many challenges in the past. We are now about to be tested like no other time in our history.

Epilogue
The Vanishing Window and Fearing the Future

"More than any time in history mankind faces a crossroads. One path leads to despair and utter hopelessness, the other to total extinction. Let us pray that we have the wisdom to choose correctly."

- Woody Allen -

In the television series Earth *2100,* that aired in 2009, there is a story about a frog. It goes like this. If one puts a frog in a pot of cold water and turns the heat on, the water warms so gradually that the frog does not notice and never realizes the precise moment it is cooked. It is becoming increasingly clear that we are the frog. While the world faces many challenges including nuclear proliferation and overpopulation, our collective failure to respond to the climate crisis could trigger social chaos and mass migrations of climate refugees, leading to civilization's collapse.

In March 2019, National Geographic Magazine published a story called, "Climate Study Warns of Vanishing Safety Window – Here's Why." A scientific analysis of over five million possible climate futures "found only a narrow window to keeping global warming at levels the international community has deemed safe. To save the world from rising sea and deadly heat waves, every country in the world must reach zero carbon emissions by 2030." That is a tall order. Everybody wants to make the right choice until it affects them.

Even as coal plants are closing, U.S. carbon emissions continue to be on the rise; the world's emissions gap is widening as well. This could not come at a worst time as climate impacts are outpacing our efforts to find solutions. Carbon capture and burial remain a technology of the distant future.

The Roman Empire collapsed due to its own self-indulgence. America is not immune from the same forces of ignorance. In President Trump's 2019 State of the Union Address, a speech of over 5,000 words, there was not a single mention of climate change. Later that October, White House Chief of Staff Mick Mulvaney announced that climate change would not be on the agenda of the next G7 summit in 2020. The most consequential issue of humankind and it will not be discussed by the most powerful democratic nations in the world.

On November 12, 2019, as Italy's Venice was experiencing the worst flooding in more than 50 years, the Veneto regional council rejected measures to combat climate change as part of their 2020 budget discussions. The council chamber, which is located on Venice's Grand Canal in the Ferro Fini Palace, was flooded a mere two minutes after the climate amendments were voted down. It was the first time the council's chambers have been flooded as the flood-proof bulkheads failed. As sea level rise threatens its very existence, the irony of the flooding was not lost on those concerned about Venice's future.

The decade that just concluded in 2019 – the hottest on record – did not end well. The world's oceans had their warmest year on record. Scientists warn the oceans are warming at a rate of five Hiroshima nukes every second. This is equivalent to every human alive today constantly pointing 100 hair dryers at the ocean. After enduring the Amazon fires of 2019, the new decade kicked off with the incredibly destructive fires in Australia. Some fear it will take more cataclysmic events before the world is forced to take action.

January 2020 was the hottest in 141 years of climate history. It marked the 44th consecutive January and the 421st consecutive month overall with world temperatures above the 20th century average. According to NOAA scientists, not a single land or water area set a record cold temperature during the month. In February, an island off Antarctica registered the continent's highest temperature ever recorded – 69 degrees F. Meanwhile, on February 10, the daily average of atmospheric CO_2 stood at 416.08 parts per million. The last time concentrations were this high was three million ago when sea levels were much higher.

Politically, the U.S. stumbled into the new decade. President Trump sought to undermine the National Environmental Policy Act (NEPA), the foundation on which our nation's environmental protection laws are built. His proposal (which he officially mandated in June 2020) will significantly limit enforcement of NEPA and exempt federal agencies from considering the climate impacts of pipelines and other infrastructure projects.

In January, at the World Economic Forum in Switzerland, he called climate activists "perennial prophets of doom." In February, against the advice of its own scientific advisory board, the Trump administration replaced the Obama-era Waters of the United States rule with the Navigable Waters Protection rule. By dismantling federal oversight of our water supply, pollution from fossil fuel development and mine waste is likely to substantially increase.

The President also announced a new trade deal with China that includes exporting coal to the Chinese. Instead of ending the use of coal, he wants to send more of it oversees.

These are the sort of stories that will continue to dominate national and world news around the climate crisis. New public surveys indicate Americans are becoming increasingly worried about the effects of climate change and it is likely to play a bigger role in 2020 than in past elections. As hundreds of homes are burned by out-of-control wildfires and entire towns are wiped out by ever-stronger hurricanes, it is not surprising public opinion has shifted. Recent polling shows Americans are now concerned about climate change more than ever before. For many, the Covid-19 pandemic has also exposed the weakness of our federal government in dealing with complex or unexpected dire issues. Fear can be a good thing in re-directing federal policy and our own thinking.

Unfortunately, the nation learned on January 20, 2020, that the *Juliana, et. al. v. United States* lawsuit had been thrown out by the courts. While the three-judge panel on the Ninth Circuit Court of Appeals agreed with the 21 young plaintiffs that the U.S. government had actively contributed to climate change by supporting a fossil-fuel-based economy and that the young people had been injured as a result, the courts were powerless to order government action. "Reluctantly, we conclude that such relief is beyond our constitutional power," Judge Andrew D. Hurwitz wrote in the court's opinion. As one environmental writer stated, "Where is the hope?"

For 10,000 years, human civilization has grown and flourished because of the Earth's climate stability and seemingly inexhaustible biological diversity. The systems that control life on the planet are intricately linked. If we destroy the rainforests, coral reefs and polar caps, we have no idea how to reconstruct these life-supporting ecosystems.

As we celebrate the 50th anniversary of Earth Day, we are making progress in moving away from fossil fuels. On April 22, 2020, the City of Houston – a major port of the oil and gas industry –

launched the community-driven Houston Climate Action Plan to reduce greenhouse gas emissions. They hope to meet the Paris Agreement goal of carbon neutrality by 2050 and lead the global energy transition.

The U.S. courts are also doing their part to relinquish our reliance our fossil fuels. In July 2020, the U.S. Court of Appeals ordered the shutdown of the Dakota Access pipeline over concerns about its potential environmental impact and the U.S. Supreme Court denied a request by the Trump Administration to allow TC Energy to build parts of the Keystone XL pipeline until the appeals process moves forward on a federal court order that blocked construction. At the same time, Duke Energy and Dominion Energy canceled their plans for the eight-billion-dollar Atlantic Coast Pipeline, citing a federal district court judge's decision that overturned federal permit authority for waterbody and wetland crossings. These are the kind of stories that give people hope.

Short of a nuclear holocaust, climate change does not mean the end of modern civilization, just as the Green New Deal is no guarantee we will achieve a green utopia. But as Johan Rockström, executive director of the Stockholm Resilience Center in Sweden, said, "People will look back on 2018 as the year when climate reality hit. This is the moment when people started to realize that global warming is not a problem for future generations, but for us now."

This view was echoed by Sweden's 16-year-old climate activist, Greta Thunberg. In her September 23, 2019, speech at the United Nations Climate Action Summit, she made a bold declaration to the nations of the world regarding their inability to deal with the impending climate chaos: "How dare you look away and come here saying that you're doing enough." Perhaps American business magnate and financier T. Boone Pickens, said it best, "I've been an oilman all my life, but this is one emergency we can't drill our way out of."

The Verdict Is In – Man Is Responsible for Global Warming

London, July 8, 2020: Climate deniers often argue "that global climate change is subject to natural cycles driven by astronomical forces and the Earth might be in one and that man is not responsible. In fact, they might claim, for the last 6,500 years the global mean surface of the planet has slowly and naturally been getting cooler due to lower levels of summer sunlight in the northern hemisphere."

But there is more to the story. Researchers from the U.S. and Europe report in the journal Scientific Data that they "used the most comprehensive collection of climate conditions from 679 sites worldwide to create 1,319 data sets." Going back 12,0000 years, they collected evidence from tree rings, fossil pollen samples, ice cores, etc.

The verdict is in. "The gradual cooling period that began 6,500 years ago came to a sudden and dramatic end in the 19th century as human cities and industries switched increasingly to coal, and then to oil and gas, to return ever-higher levels of ancient carbon to the atmosphere."

Once again, the past shows the role of greenhouse gases in climate change and why human beings are to blame. No longer can the skeptics claim man is not responsible. If humans have so single-mindedly caused the planet to overheat, we must now use that same single-mindedness to take action to repair it.

ABOUT THE AUTHOR

A native of Garden City, New York, Peter graduated from the University of New Hampshire with a Bachelor of Science degree where he studied Recreation and Parks Management with a minor in Sociology. He earned a Master of Science degree in Resource Management and Public Administration from Antioch New England Graduate School after completing a thesis on agricultural land protection.

For over twenty years, he was manager of the Great Bay National Estuarine Research Reserve – a federal/state partnership between National Oceanic and Atmospheric Administration (NOAA) and the State of New Hampshire, under the N.H. Fish and Game Department. His work included protecting over 10,000 acres of coastal lands in partnership with The Nature

Conservancy and other public and private entities. In 2008, he was the recipient of the Dr. Nancy Foster Habitat Conservation Award from NOAA Fisheries Office of Habitat Conservation. He also served as the first Great Bay/Piscataqua Waterkeeper and founded the Great Bay Stewards, a non-profit environmental group dedicated to protecting the Great Bay estuary.

Peter and his wife, Kathy, currently live on Long Island at the edge of the ever-expanding 'burbs and the once thriving pine barrens of Suffolk County. Their blended family includes four children and seven grandchildren.

Notes

Preface

Viper, Tom; *America's Most Affluent Neighborhoods*; *Forbes Magazine*; Feb. 13, 2012[1]

Wikipedia; *Hempstead Plains*; last edited Sept. 8, 2018[2]

Wikipedia; *Cradle of Aviation Museum*; last edited Oct. 31, 2018[3]

Introduction

Anderson, Monica; *Here's How Americans View Environmental Issues*; Pew Research Center; April 2017[1,3]

Benderev, Chris; *Millennials: We Help the Earth But Don't Call Us Environmentalists*; NPR's Weekend Edition Saturday; Oct. 11, 2014[2]

Henry J. Kaiser Family Foundation; *Health Care Ranks Among Voters' Top Issues for the 2018 Midterm Elections*; KFF Newsroom; Jan. 26, 2018[4]

International Energy Association; *Oil Market Report: Twin Peaks*; IEA website; Oct. 12, 2018[5]

Summary for Policymakers of IPCC Special Report on Global Warming of 1.5° C Approved by Governments; IPCC Press Release; Oct. 8, 2018[6]

Chow, Lorraine; *Oil Demand and Supply Reaches Landmark 100 Million Barrels a Day*; EcoWatch; Oct. 12, 2018[7]

Chapter One: How We Got It All Wrong from the Start

Mills, Kathy; *Ecological Trends of the Great Bay Estuary*; Great Bay NERR; 2009[1,19,20]

Wikipedia; *Portsmouth, New Hampshire*; last updated Oct. 15, 2018[2]

Audubon Society of New Hampshire; *The Great Bay Estuary Cultural History*; 1994[3,8,11]

Short, Fred and Webster, Monica; *The Ecology of the Great Bay Estuary, New Hampshire and Maine: An Estuarine Profile and Bibliography*; University of NH; Chapter 1, pgs. 5-6, 1992[4]

Berrill, Michael; *The Plundered Seas*; Greystone Books; 1997; pgs. 114-115[5]

Robinson, J.D.; *The Isle of Shoals: A Capsule History*; SeacoastNH.com; 1997[6]

Appelbaum, Diana; *Giants in the Land*; Houghton Mifflin Company; 1993; pg. 2[7]

Adams, John P.; *The Piscataqua River Basin*; University Press of New England; 1976; pg.134[9]

Roberge, Sheila; *The Legacy of Environmental Innocence*; *Great Bay Matters*; Winter 2019, Vol. 26, # 2; pgs. 2-3[10,18]

Bolster, Jeffrey A.; *The Mortal Sea*; Belknap Press, 2012, pgs. 158-59[12,13]

Great Bay NWR; *Great Bay National Wildlife Refuge Draft Comprehensive Conservation Plan and Environmental Assessment*; U.S. Fish and Wildlife; February 2012; pgs. 2-9[14]

Rare Historical Photos; *A Punt Gun, Used for Duck Hunting But Were Banned Because They Depleted Stocks of Wild Fowl, 1910-1920*; rarehistoricalphotos.com[15,16]

Whitehouse, Robert and Beaudoin, Cathleen; *Port of Dover: Two Centuries of Shipping on the Cocheco*; Peter Randall Publisher; 1988; pg. 17[17]

Piscataqua Region Estuaries Partnership; *Piscataqua Region Environmental Planning Assessment Grant Program Summary Report*; PREP; 2015-2016[21]

Waterview Consulting; *Rainbow Smelt: An Imperiled Fish in a Changing World*; NH Fish and Game Wildlife Journal reprint[22]

2018 Report to Congress on the Status of U.S. Fisheries; NOAA Fisheries[23]

Chapter Two: The Wildlife We Will Never Know

Virginia Department of Game and Inland Fisheries; *Our Wildlife Legacy*; *N.H. Wildlife Journal*; N.H. Fish and Game Department reprint; Sept./Oct. 2012[1,2]

Wikipedia, *American Bison*; last updated March 22, 2019[3]

Goldman, Laura; *10 Animals That Have Gone Extinct in the Last 100 Years*; care2.com; Sept. 30, 2018[4]

Wikipedia; *Heath Hen*; last edited on Aug. 28, 2018[5]

Wikipedia; *Eastern Elk*; last edited on Aug. 30, 2018[6]

Wikipedia; *Ivory-Billed Woodpecker*; last edited on Sept. 26, 2018[7]

Wikipedia, *Waterfowl Hunting*; last edited Oct. 4, 2018[8]

Wikipedia; *Punt Guns*; last edited Oct. 16, 218[9]
Field, Van; *Old Time Duck Hunting on Long Island*; Long Island Genealogy website[10]

Strauss, Bob; *Ten Recently Extinct Fish*; ThoughtCo website; Oct. 27, 2017[11]

Edmonds, Michael; *Taking Flight: A History of Birds and People in the Heart of America*;
Wisconsin Historical Society Press; May 23, 2018 excerpt[12]

Mitchell; Alanna; *The 1,300 Bird Species Facing Extinction Signal Threats to Human Health*; *Environmental Health News*; Aug. 6, 2014[13]

Three Billion Fewer Wild Birds Soar the Skies Than in 1970, Study Finds; PBS News Hour; Sept. 19, 2019[14]

Chapter Three: The Robber Barons

Josephson, Matthew; *The Robber Barons*; 1914, pg. 6[1]

Chernow, Ron; *Titan: The Life of John D. Rockefeller, Sr.*; Vintage Books; 1997[2]

Encyclopedia of U.S. History; *The Robber Barons*; Encyclopedia.com; 2006[3,4,5]

Wikipedia; *Andrew Mellon*; last edited Oct. 18, 2018[6,7]

Marshall, Gavin; *Robber Barons, Revolution, and Social Control*; March 10, 2011[8]

Chapter Four: The Potato Fields Came Calling and the Rise of Suburbia

Ruff, Joshua; *Levittown: The Archetype for Suburban Development*; American History Magazine; Oct. 4, 2007[1,4]

Galyean, Crystal; *Levittown: The Imperfect Rise of the American Suburbs*; U.S. History Scene[2,5]

Freeman, Tyson; *The 1950's: Post-War Hitches Up and Heads for the 'Burbs*; National Real Estate Investor; Sept. 30, 1999[3,8,14]

Weingroff, Richard F.; *Federal-Aid Highway Act of 1956: Creating the Interstate System*; Federal Highway Administration, Volume 60, No. 1; Summer 1996[6,7]

Melosi, Martin; *The Automobile Shapes the City*; The Automobile in American Life and Society Project, University of Michigan-Dearborn and Benson Ford Research Center; 2010[9,10,18]

Shmoop Editorial Team; *Society in the 1950s*; Shmoop University; Aug. 2012[11,15,16]

Meier, Peg; *The Shopping Center That Spawned a Community*; MN History Center.; Aug. 1981[12]

Loki, Reynard; *Eating Locally and in Season: Is It Really Better for the Environment*; Independent Media Institute; Oct. 23, 2018[13]

Mills, C. Wright; *Letter to the New Left; New Left Review, No. 5*; Sept.-Oct. 1960[17]

Downs, Anthony, et al; *Sprawl Costs: Economic Impacts of Unchecked Development*, Island Press; 2005[19,20]

Wikipedia; *Robert Moses*; last edited Oct. 30, 2018[21]

U.S. Census Bureau; *Percent of Workers 16 Years and Over Who Travelled to Work by Car, Truck or Van and Drove Alone*; American Community Survey; 2010 and 2017[22]

Ryan, Z.; *Stereotypes in Suburbia: 1950s and Today*; Rollins University ThirdSight photo essay; Nov. 20, 2016[23]

Hamer, Lauren; *This Is the Worst Suburb in America if You're Trying to Save Money*; Culture CheatSheet website; Dec. 17, 2017[24,25]

Main Street America; mainstreet.org[26]

How Many Malls Are There in America? reference.com[27]

Chapter Five: 1980's – The Decade of Greed

Kannan, Ashley; *How Did the Greed of the 1980's Affect the Political Climate?*; online enotes[1]

Wikipedia; *James G. Watt*; last edited Oct. 5, 2018[2]

On the Issues; *Ronald Reagan on Environment*; last updated Oct. 12, 2018[3,4]

The New York Times; Conviction of Ex-Official of E.P.A. Is Upheld; Jan. 19, 1985 archives[5]

Wikipedia; *Sagebrush Rebellion*; last edited May 1, 2018[6,7]

Wikipedia; *1970's Energy Crisis*; last edited Sept. 19, 2018[8]

On the Issues; *Ronald Reagan on Energy and Oil*; last updated Sept. 12, 2018[9]

Taylor, Bill; *Crime? Greed? Big Ideas? What Were the '80s About?*; Harvard Business Review; Jan.-Feb. 1992 issue[10]

Blodget, Henry; *The Truth About the Economy: In the 1980s, Greed Was Good... Then We Went Overboard*; Business Insider; June 26, 2012[11]

Kroll, Luisa and Dolan, Kerry; *Forbes Releases 36th Annual Forbes 400 Ranking of the Richest Americans*; Forbes Magazine; October 17, 2017[12]

French, Sally; *Warren Buffett Explains What's Wrong With the Economic System That Made Him Billions*; MarketWatch; Jan. 5, 2018[13]

Chapter Six: The Menace of Coal

U.S. Department of Energy; *Coal*; energy.gov website[1]

Adams, Patrick Sean; *The U.S. Coal Industry in the Nineteenth Century*; EH.net[2,3,4]

U.S. Department of Commerce; *Historical Statistics of the United States*; 1957; pg. 355[5]

Wikipedia; *Surface Mining*; last edited Oct. 1, 2018[6]

World Coal Association; *Where Is Coal Found?*; Retrieved June 28, 2011[7]

Gardner, J.S.; *Mountaintop Mining/Valley Fills in Appalachia: Final Programmatic EIS*; *Mining Engineering*; March 2007; pg. 48-55[8]

U.S. Environmental Protection Agency; *Mountaintop Mining/Valley Fills in Appalachia: Final Programmatic EIS*; EPA; retrieved Aug. 20, 2006[9]

Palmer, M.A. et al.; *Mountaintop Mining Consequences*; *Sci.* Vol. 327; pg. 148; Jan. 8, 2010[10]

Appalachian Voices; *Mountaintop Removal 101*; appvoices.org; 2017[11,13,15]

Ahern, Mellissa, et. al; *The Association Mountaintop Mining and Birth Defects Among Live Births in Central Appalachia, 1996-2003*; Vol. 111, Issue 6; Aug. 2011; pgs. 838-46[12]

Collins, Michael; *Feds Ban Mountaintop Mining in Tennessee*; *USA Today*; Dec. 7, 2016[14]

Wikipedia; *Mountaintop Removal Mining*; multiple references; last edited Oct. 12, 2018[16]

Negative Effects of Coal Mining: A Cheap But Dirty Fuel Source; theworldcounts.com; Aug. 5, 2014[17]

Wikipedia; *Coal-Seam Fire*; last edited Sept. 11, 2018[18]

SouthWings: Conservation Through Aviation; *Coal Slurry and Coal Ash*; southwings.com[19,20]

Jordan-Bloch, Chris; *Defending Uniontown, AL From Toxic Coal Ash*; earthjustice.org[21]

Gang, Duane; *Five Years After Coal-Ash Spill, Little Has Changed*; USA Today; Dec, 23, 2013[22]
Atkin, Emily; *EPA Will Not Declare Coal Ash a Hazardous Waste*; Think Progress website; Dec. 19, 2014[23,24,25]

Hunt, Max; *N.C. Residents Decry Lack of Progress in Coal Ash Cases Despite 2016 Legislation*; Mountain Xpress; July 1, 2017[26]

Wikipedia; *2014 Dan River Coal Ash Spill*; last updated Sept. 26, 2019[27]

Web Staff; *State Has Authority to Force Duke Energy to Excavate Remaining Coal Ash Basins in NC Judge Rules*; myfox8.com; August 2, 2019[28]

Appalachian Voices; *Coal Ash – Background*; appvoices.org; 2017[29]

U.S. Environmental Protection Agency; *EPA Finalizes First Amendments to the Coal Ash*[30]

Disposal Regulations Providing Flexibilities for States; EPA Press Office; July 18, 2018[31]

U.S. Energy Information Admin.; *Coal and the Environment*; EAI website; March 23, 2018[32]

Hurley, Lawrence; *U.S. Top Court Rebuffs Appeal of Kavanaugh Ruling Nixing Climate Rule*; Reuters; Oct. 9, 2018[33]

Wikipedia; *Coal Mining in the United States*; last edited Oct. 10, 2018[34]

U.S. Energy Information Admin.; *Today in Energy*; EIA website; Sept. 10, 2018[35]

U.S. Energy Information Admin.; *Today In Energy: U.S. Renewable Energy Consumption Surpasses Coal for the First Time In Over 130 Years*; EIA website; May 28, 2020[36]

U.S. Department of Energy; *Carbon Capture, Utilization and Storage*; energy.gov website[37]

Ingraham, Christopher; *The Entire Coal Industry Employs Fewer People Than Arby's*; The Washington Post; March 31, 2017[38,39]
Nutting, Rex; *Amazon is Going to Kill More American Jobs Than China Did*; MarketWatch; March 15, 2017[40]

Pearce, Joshua; *What If All U.S. Coal Workers Were Retrained to Work in Solar?*; Harvard Business Review; Aug. 8, 2016[41]

Butler, Tom and Wuerthner, George; *Energy*; Post Carbon Institute; 2012; pg. 37[42]

Hatcher, Margaret; *Life and Death in the Coal Mines*; Best of NPR; Jan. 24, 2019[43]

Englund, Will; *As Covid-19 Hits, Coal Companies Aim to Cut the Tax They Pay to Support Black-Lung Miners*; The Washington Post; April 8, 2020[44]

Chapter Seven: 1990's – The Decade of Missed Opportunities

Council on Environmental Quality; *Environmental Actions by President Clinton and Vice President Gore*; CEQ Earth Day 2000 Report; April 2000[1,2]

Royden, Amy; *U.S. Climate Change Policy Under President Clinton: A Look Back*; Golden Gate University Law Review; Jan. 22, 2002; Vol. 32, Article 3[3,4]

Berke, Richard; *Clinton Declares New U.S Policies for Environment*; The New York Times; April 22, 1993[5]

Wikipedia; *Climate Change Policy of the United States*; last edited Nov. 27, 2018[6,7]

Natoli, Nicole; *United States Problems with the Kyoto Treaty*; May 2, 2003[8]

Wikipedia; *Byrd-Hagel Resolution*; last edited July 31, 2017[9]

Merchant Brian; *The Only Nations That Haven't Signed 1997's Global Climate Treaty are Afghanistan, Sudan and the U.S.A.*; treehugger.com; Nov. 28, 2011[10,12]

Kyoto Protocol to the United Nations Framework on Climate Change; U.N. Depositary[11]

Chemnick, Jean; *Phone Call Transcripts Shine a Light on a Bygone Era of Climate Politics Including the Kyoto Protocol*; Scientific American Climate Wire; Jan. 11, 2016[13]

Wikipedia; *Kyoto Protocol*; last updated Dec. 3, 2018[14,15,16]

Wikipedia; *Climate Change Policy of the Bush Administration;* last updated June 29, 2018[17,19,20]

The White House; *Council on Environmental Quality*; CEQ web site[18]

Goldenberg, Suzanne; *The Worst of Times: Bush's Environmental Legacy Examined*; The Guardian; Jan. 16, 2009[21]

Wikipedia; *Christine Todd Whitman*; last edited Nov. 30, 2018[22]

Hertsgaard, Mark; *Obama's Record on Climate Change Provides Lessons for Taking on President Trump*; *The Nation*; Dec. 12, 2016[23,24]

Wikipedia; *Clean Power Plan*; last edited Oct. 31, 2018[25,27]

Davenport, Coral, et. al; *What is the Clean Power Plan and How Can Trump Repeal It?*; *The New York Times*; Oct. 10, 2017[26]

Wikipedia; *Paris Agreement*; last edited Nov. 29, 2018[28,29]

Wikipedia; *United States Withdrawal From the Paris Agreement*; last edited Dec. 2, 2018[30,33,34]

O'Donnell, Noreen; *Trump Stands With Pittsburgh, But Mayor Says He's With Paris*; Channel 10 News; June 1, 2017[31]

United Nations; *Paris Agreement U.S. Communication*; *UN* News; Aug. 4, 2017[32]

Reuters; *'Yellow Jacket' Protests in France Leave Gas Stations Running Dry*; Dec. 3, 2018[35]

Davenport, Coral and Friedman, Lisa; *How Trump Is Ensuring That Greenhouse Gas Emissions Will Rise*; *The New York Times*; Nov. 26, 2018[36]

Chapter Eight: How We Are Still Getting It All Wrong

Musser, George; *Crossroads for Planet Earth*; *Scientific American*; Sept. 2005, Vol. 293, #3[1]

Braden, Gregg; *Deep Truth*; Hay House Publishing;2011[2]

Union of Concerned Scientists; *What are Tar Sands?*; ucsusa.org; Feb. 23, 2016[3,5,6]

Wikipedia; *Oil Sands*; last edited Dec. 10, 2018[4]

Wikipedia; *Keystone Pipeline*; last edited Nov. 25, 2018[7,8]

Weidensaul, Scott and Wells, Jeffrey; *Saving Canada's Boreal Forest*; *The New York Times*; May 29, 2015[9]

Sylvester, Terry; *U.S. to Conduct Additional Keystone XL Review*; Reuters; Dec. 1, 2018[10]

Wikipedia; *Lac-Mégantic Rail Disaster*; last edited Oct. 24, 2018[11]

Nunez, Christina; *Switch to Natural Gas Won't Reduce Carbon Emissions Much, Study Finds*; National Geographic; Sept. 25, 2014[12,13]

Lallanilla, Marc; *Facts About Fracking*; LiveScience website; Feb. 9, 2018[14,15,17]

Oklahoma Earthquake Spike Likely Linked to Fracking Boom; rt.com; Feb. 20, 2014[16]

Miller, Justin; *Why It's So Hard to Regulate Fracking*; *American Prospect*; June 24, 2015[18,19]

Mooney, Chris; *To Round Out a Year of Rollbacks, the Trump Administration Just Repealed Key Regulations on Fracking*; *The Washington Post*; Dec. 29, 2017[20]

Documents Show Billions of Gallons of Oil Waste Fluid Dumped Into Gulf Waters; The Center for Biological Diversity; July 2, 2016[21]

Sakashita, Miyoko; *Administration Sued for Letting Oil Companies Dump Offshore Fracking Waste into the Gulf of Mexico*; Center for Biological Diversity; Feb. 13, 2018[22]

The National Academies of Science, Engineering, and Medicine; *What You Need to Know About Energy: CAFE Standards*; NASEM website[23]

Eisenstein, Paul; *Trump Rolls Back Obama-Era Fuel Economy Standards*; NBC News; March 16, 2017[24]

Knickmeyer, Ellen; *EPA Eases Obama-Era Rules on Climate-Changing Emissions From New Coal Plants*; Associated Press; Dec. 6, 2018[25]

O'Laughlin, Tamara and Sulakshana, Elena; *Op-Ed: Big Insurance is Climate's Quiet Killer*; Rolling Stone Magazine; April 20, 2020[26]

CNN; *Keystone Pipeline Leaks 383,000 Gals. of Oil in North Dakota*; cnn.com, Nov. 1, 2019[27]

Chapter Nine: Population Dynamics: Why Does Everyone Have to Live So Close Together

Woodford, Riley; *Lemming Suicide Myth Disney Film Faked Bogus Behavior*; Alaska Department of Fish and Game News; Sept. 2003[1]

Wikipedia, *Thomas Robert Malthas*: last edited Nov. 21, 2018[2]

U.S. Population, 1790-2000: Always Growing; United States History website[3]

Statista; *Population Projections for the U.S. From 2015 to 2060*; Statista website portal[4]

Rosenberg, Matt; *Population Density Information*; ThoughtCo website.; updated Feb. 8, 2018[5]

Wikipedia, *Carrying Capacity*; last edited Nov. 20, 2018[6]

Wikipedia; *List of United States Cities by Population Density*; last edited Nov. 16, 2018[7]

Rueb, Emily; *How New York City Gets Its Electricity*;; Feb. 10, 2017[8]

Where Does New York City Garbage Go? metrocosm.com; Oct. 27, 2016[9,10,12]

Wikipedia; *Fresh Kills landfill*; last edited Nov. 16, 2018[11]

New York City DEP; *New York City's Wastewater Treatment System*; nyc.gov; 2014[13,14,16]

Schlanger, Zoe; *If It's Raining, NYC's Raw Sewage is Probably Pouring Into the Waterways*; *Newsweek Magazine*; July 23, 2014[15]

NYC Ranked Worst Financial Condition in New Study; patch.com; last updated Nov. 17, 2016[17]

Wikipedia; *New York Metropolitan Area*; last edited Nov. 21, 2018[18]

Wikipedia; *Hurricane Sandy*; last edited Oct. 16, 2018[19]

Hunts Point Produce Market website[20]

These U.S. Cities Are Most Vulnerable to Coastal Flooding; climatecentral.org; Oct. 25, 2017[21,22]

Chapter Ten: Paradise No More

Hertsgaard, Mark; *Earth Odyssey*; 1998; pg. 10[1]

Funk, Cary and Kennedy, Brian; *Public Views on Climate Change and Climate Scientists*; Pew Research Center; Oct. 4, 2016[2,3]

Weather Trends; New York City Weather Data[4]

U.S. Environmental Protection Agency; *Climate Change Indicators*; epa.gov[5,7]

The 10 Hottest U.S. Years on Record; climatecentral.org; Dec. 5, 2018[6]

Geggel, Laura; *How Would Just Two Degrees of Warming Change the Planet?*; LiveScience; April 29, 2017[8]

Thead, Erin; *Sea Level Rise: Risk and Resilience in Coastal Cities*; Climate Institute; Oct. 2016[9]

McKie, Robin; *Miami is Drowning While the Powers That Be Look Away*; The Guardian; July 11, 2014[10,11]

National Oceanic and Atmospheric Administration; *Red Tide in Florida and Texas*; noaa.gov[12]

Hine, Albert; *Geology of Florida*; College of Marine Science, University of South Florida[13]

Southeast Florida Regional Climate Change Compact website[14]

Kusnetz, Nicholas and Banerjee, Neela; *Rising Seas Threaten Norfolk Naval Shipyard, Raising Fears of 'Catastrophic Damage'*; InsideClimate News, NBC News; Nov. 19, 2018[15,16,17]

Grey, Jennifer; *Visiting the Disappearing Tangier Island*; CNN; June 9, 2017[18]

Solomon, Libby; *Flash Floods Devastate Endicott City*; *Baltimore Sun*; May 27, 2018[19]

Dildine, Dave; Record Flooding – Just How Much Rain Fell When Ellicott City Flooded; WTOP News; July 9, 2018[20]

Wikipedia; *Hurricane Florence*; last edited Dec. 14, 2018[21,23]

Editorial Board; *Hurricane Florence Plus Man-Made Policies Leave a Toxic Legacy*; *USA Today*; Sept. 30, 2018[22,24]

Pydynowki, Kristina; *Florence-Ravaged Areas Face More River Flooding as Wilmington, North Carolina, Hits 100-inch Yearly Rain Total*; AccuWeather; Dec. 15, 2018[25]

Fountain, Henry; *Hurricanes, and Climate-Change Questions, Keep Coming: Yes, They're Linked*; *The New York Times*; Oct.10, 2018[26]

Hot, Dry Summer and Slow Start to Wet Season Primed California for November 2018 Fires; climate.gov, NOAA; Nov. 16, 2018[27]

Tedford, Daniel; *Over the Last 40 Years, There is a Surprising Trend with California Wildfires*; *The Orange County Register*; Sept. 14, 2017[28]

Sergent, Jim, et. al; *Three Startling Facts About the Camp Fire*; *USA Today*; Nov. 21, 2018[29]

Wikipedia; *Woolsey Fire*; last edited Dec. 20, 2019[30]

Corbett, Jessica; *'Hothouse Earth' Co-Author Says 'People Will Look Back on 2018 as the Year When Climate Reality Hit'*; EcoWatch; Aug. 20, 2018[31]

Carbone, Christopher; *'Largest Living Thing,' An 80,000-Year-Old Utah forest, Is Dying, Scientists Warn*; Fox News; Oct 18, 2018[32,33]

Salmon for All; *Columbia River Commercial Fishermen: Fishing for the General Public*[34]

Johnson, Miles; *Why Does Climate Change Matter to the Columbia River?*; Colombia Riverkeeper, Waterkeeper Alliance; July 5, 2018[35]

Geggel, Laura; *Mountain of Evidence Confirms: Climate Change Is Really, Really Bad for Human Health and Well-Being*; LiveScience; Dec. 14, 2018[36]

U.S. Environmental Protection Agency; *Climate Change* Indicators; epa.gov[37]

Leonhardt, David; *The Climate's Effect on Pregnancy*; The N.Y. Times, The Morning; June 19, 2020[38]

Funk, Cary and Kennedy, Brian; *Public Views on Climate Change and Climate Scientists*; Pew Research Center; Oct. 4, 2016[39]

Joyce, Christopher; *Climate Scientist Admits to Lying, Leaking Documents*; NPR's All Things Connected; Feb. 22, 2012[40]

Rmuse; *Earth's Climate Exceeded Its Tipping Point and Nobody Cares*; politicususa.com; Oct. 6, 2016[41]

Rosane, Olivia; *Flooding of Nebraska Air Force Base Illustrates Security Risk Posed by Climate Change*; EcoWatch; March 19, 2019[42]

Chapter Eleven: Where Has All the Water Gone?

Masters, Jeff; *Ten Civilizations or Nations That Collapsed From Drought*; Weather Underground; March 21, 2016[1,2]

Biggest U.S. Cities; *Phoenix, Arizona Population History 1950 – 2017*; Biggest U.S. Cities website; last updated July 2, 2018[3]

U.S. Global Change Research Program; *National Climate Assessment, 4th Report, Vol. I and II*; Global Change website; Nov. 2018[4]

The Causes and Effects of the Urban Heat Island Effect; thegreencity.com; March 11,2015[5]

Schultz, Colin; *Arizona Could Be Out of Water in Six Years*; Smithsonian website; June 20, 2014[6]

Arizona Department of Water Resources and the University of Arizona Water Resources Research Center; *Arizona's Water: Uses and Sources*; The Arizona Experience website[7,10]

U.S. Geological Survey and *National Geographic*; *The Colorado River*; The Arizona Experience website[8,9]

Wines, Michael; *Arizona Cities Could Face Cutbacks in Water From Colorado River, Officials Say*; *The New York Times*; June 17, 2014[11]

Lkeya, Deana and Cullom, Chuck; *Why the Colorado River Basin Snowpack is Important*; Central Arizona Project; March 8, 2017[12]

California Water Becomes Scarce and Energy Hungry; climatecentral.org; Feb. 18, 2015[13]

Southern Nevada Water Authority; *2018 Water Resource Plan and Water Budget*; 2018[14,18]

Fishman, Charles; *The Big Thirst*; Free Press; 2011; pgs.53-54,69 and 71[15,17,26]

Las Vegas Convention and Visitors Authority website[16]

McIntyre, Douglas and Sauter, Michael editors; *The 10 Biggest U.S. Cities That Risk Running Out of Water*; *Atlanta Business Chronicle*; Jan. 3, 2011[19]

Diamond, Mike; *Where Does LA Get Its Water?*; Mike Diamond Services blog; May 31, 2017[20]

Wikipedia; *Imperial Valley*; last edited Dec.13, 2018[21,22]

Manganiello, Chris; *Tri-State Conflict*; Chattahoochee Riverkeeper website[23]

Will Atlanta Run Out of Water? The U.S. Supreme Court is Set to Decide; Sustain Atlanta website; Sept. 25, 2016[24,25]

Pendero, David; *Will Atlanta Run Out of Water? The U.S. Supreme Court is Set to Decide*; Saporta Report website; May 21, 2018[27]

Southern Environmental Law Center; *Tri-State Water Wars (AL, GA, FL)*; SELC website[28]

Wikipedia; *Atlanta Metropolitan Area*; last edited Jan. 13, 2019[29]

Samuel, Molly; *Atlanta to Grow to 8 Million People By 2040*; WABE News; Sept. 11, 2015[30]

Alliance for Water Efficiency; *Golf Course Water Efficiency Introduction*; AFWE website[31]

Deford, Frank; *Water-Thirsty Golf Courses Need to Go Green*; NPR; June 11, 2008[32]

Wellenberger, Peter; *Lawn Tips for a Healthy Great Bay*; clf.org; July 18, 2012[33]

EPA; *How We Use Water*; EPA's WaterSense website[34]

Christian-Smith, Juliet Gleick, et al; *A Twenty-First Century U.S. Water Policy*; Oxford University Press; 2012; pgs. xvii-xvii[35,36]

Alexander, Kurtis; *California Water Wars: State Plans to Cut SF's Sierra Supply to Save Delta*; San Francisco Chronicle; Aug. 19, 2018[37,38]

Oaster, Bennett Courrier; *How Much Water Does a Water Leak Waste? (Because A Water Leak DOES Waste Water)* The WegoWire; April 16, 2015[39]

Barnett, Cynthia; *America, It's Time to Talk About the Price of Water*; ensia.com; Oct. 6, 2014[40]

Brodwin, Erin; *Here's Why Bottled Water Is One of the Biggest Scams of The Century*; Business Insider; May 3, 2017[41]

How Many Plastic Water Bottles Are Thrown Away Every Day?; pristineplanet.com[42]

The City of Flagstaff, Arizona; City of Flagstaff website, water conservation[43]

Center for Biological Diversity; *Massive Arizona Sprawl Development Threatens 'Oasis in the Desert'*; CFBD website; February 1, 2019[44,45]

Wikipedia; *Owens Lake*; last edited Nov. 11, 2018[46]

Cooley, Heather; *A Twenty-First Century U.S. Water Policy – Municipal Water Use*; Oxford University Press; 2012; pg. 181[47]

Osborne, Hannah; *Decades Without Rain: America Set For 'Megadroughts' Not Seen Since Medieval Times*; *Newsweek*; July 24, 2019[48]

Chapter Twelve: When the Cupboard is Bare

Wikipedia; *History of Agriculture in the United States*; last updated Jan. 24, 2019[1]

Statista; *Total Number of Farms in the United States From 2000 to 2017*; Statista website portal[2]

Farmland Information Center; *National Statistics*; farmlandinfo.org[3,4]

The Food Dialogues; *The Average Age of An American Farmer*; TFD website[5]

Loki, Reynard; *Eating Locally and In Season: Is It Really Better for the Environment*; Independent Media Institute; Oct. 23, 2018[6,7]

Leaman, Susan and Wetherington, Diane; *Where Do Our Fruits and Vegetables Come From?* Dirt-to-Dinner website; July 13, 2016[8,9]

Overton, Penelope; *Value of Maine Lobster Exports to China on Pace to Triple for 2016*; *Portland Press Herald*; Jan. 28, 2017[10]

Benson, Jonathan; *How America's Food Supply has been Hijacked by Multinational Corporations*; *Natural News* website; Nov. 24, 2015[11,12]

U.S. Dept. of Health and Human Services; *Arsenic*; U.S. Food and Drug Admin. Website[13]

Bearden, Caroline; *7 Most Common GMO Foods*; Builtlean website; Oct. 12, 2018[14]

Non-Gmo Project; *GMO Facts*; nongmoproject.org[15]

Samsel, Anthony and Seneff, Stephanie; *Glyphosate, Pathways to Modern Diseases II: Celiac Sprue and Gluten Intolerance*; *PubMed Central*; nlm.nih.gov; Dec. 2013[16]

Pollan, Michael; *The Omnivore's Dilemma*; Penguin Books; 2006; pgs. 36-37, pgs. 65-69[17,50,51]

Union of Concerned Scientists; *Industrial Agriculture: The Outdated, Unsustainable System that Dominates U.S. Food Production*; ucsusa.org, Food and Agriculture section[18]

Heid, Bill and Brawdy, Brian; *Food Shock: Dangerous New Trends that Change America Forever*; *Off the Grid News*; 2011[19]

Ostlind, Emilene; *The Big Four Meatpackers*; High Country News website; March 21, 2011[20]

Industrial Agriculture Threatens America's Food Supply; *Off the Grid News*; Sept. 12, 2018[21]

Dance, Scott; *As Chicken Industry Booms, Eastern Shore Farmers Face Not-In-My-Backyard Activism*; *The Baltimore Sun*; April 2, 2106[23]

Lam, Clarence K. and Hauter, Wenonah; *Let's Keep Big Chicken's Pollution Out of Our Bay*; *The Washington Post*; Feb. 12, 2016[24,25]

The Poultry Litter Management Act Factsheet; January 2016[26]

Wikipedia; *Ethanol Fuel in the United States*; last updated Jan. 25, 2019[27,30]

Center for Environment, Commerce and Energy; Energy Policy Act Summary[28]

Wikipedia; *Energy Independence and Security Act of 2007*; last updated Nov. 17, 2018[29]

Woodley, Kyle; *10 Things Disappearing From America*; InvestorPlace website; Nov. 20, 2013[31]

Kumar, Sandeep; *Biofuels; Renewable Energy Source for New Generation*; Indian Institute of Plantation Management; 2011; pgs. 7-9[32]

Xyleco website[33]

Wikipedia; *Colony Collapse Disorder*; last updated Feb. 14, 2019[34]

Wikipedia; *List of Crop Plants Pollinated by Bees*; last updated Feb. 11, 2019[35]

Freeman, Makia; *The Top Four Reasons for the Bees Dying Off*; The Freedom Articles; March 12, 2015[36,37]

Bienkowski, Brian; *Dow Wants to Bolster Use of a Pesticide Shown to Hurt Bees Reproduction*; Environmental Health News website[38,39]

Hill, Jay; *Working With Bees to Protect and Promote Pollination*; The Food Dialogues website[40]

Center for Disease Control; *Estimates of Foodborne Illness in the United States*; CDC website[41]

Rettner, Rachel; *Romaine to Honey Smacks Cereal: Why Were There So Many Foodborne Outbreaks in 2018?*; LiveScience website; Dec. 26, 2018[42,43]

Loki, Reynard; *Eating Locally and In Season: Is It Really Better for the Environment*; Independent Media Institute; Oct. 23, 2018[44,47]

Eller, Donnelle; *After Years of Catastrophic Losses, Dairy Farms are Increasingly Closing Their Barn Doors*; USA Today; Nov. 2, 2018[45]

U.S. Dairy Subsidies Equal 73 Percent of Producer Returns, Says Report; realagriculture.com; Feb. 9, 2018[46]

Hill, Catey; *This Chart Proves Americans Love Their Meat*; MarketWatch; Dec. 1, 2016[48]

McFetridge, Scott; *Tiny Nebraska Town Says No to 1,100 Jobs*; Associated Press; May 2, 2016[49]

Foley, Jonathan; *It's Time to Rethink America's Corn System*; Scientific American; March 5, 2013[52]

Spielmaker, D.M.; *Growing a Nation: The Story of American Agriculture*; agclassroom.org; March 21, 2018[53]

Jones, Nicola; *Redrawing the Map: How the World's Climate Zones Are Shifting*; Yale Environment 360, Yale School of Forestry and Environmental Studies; Oct. 23, 2018[54,55,56]

Choi, Candace and McFetridge, Scott; *'Ugly Produce' Trend May Have Limits, As Grocers End Tests*; Associated Press; Feb. 24, 2019[57]

Rossen, Jake; *The Real Reason Grocery Stores Spray Water on Their Produce*; mentalfloss.com; May 23, 2019[58]

Fast Forward; *The Problem of Food Waste in America*; Fast Forward website; Oct. 8, 2015[59]

Charles, Dan; *5 Major Crops in the Crosshairs of Climate Change*; NPR's The Salt; Oct. 25, 2018[60]

Chapter Thirteen: Our Waterways, Estuaries and Oceans in Peril

What Produces Most of the World's Oxygen? Reference website[1]

Mumby, Peter J; *D We Value Our Oceans*; The Conversation website; June 8, 2011[2]

Edwards, P. E. T. (ed.); *Summary Report: The Economic Value of U.S. Coral Reefs*; NOAA Coral Reef Conservation Program; 2013[3]

National Oceanic and Atmospheric Administration; *Understanding Ocean Acidification*; NOAA Fisheries website; June 28, 2017[4,5]

National Ocean Service; *What Percentage of the American Population Lives Near the Coast?* NOAA/NOS website[6]

Development: Are We Loving Our Coasts to Death?; *Mother Jones Magazine*; March 1, 2006[7]

Gellerman, Bruce; *Signs of Climate Change — Past, Present and Future — On Plum Island*; WBUR News website; July 19, 2017[8,9,10]

Wikipedia; *Intercoastal Waterway*; last edited Feb. 8, 2019[11]

U.S. Census Bureau; *Annual Estimates of the Resident Population: April 1, 2010 to July 1, 2016 U.S. Metropolitan and Micropolitan Statistical Area*; U.S. Census Bureau website[12]

Wikipedia; *Myrtle Beach, South Carolina*; last edited Feb. 18, 2019[13,14,15]

Wikipedia; *Mississippi River*; last edited March 1, 2019[16]

Royal Geographic Society; *Mississippi Erosion*; RGS website; pg. 65[17]

Charles, Dan; *The Gulf of Mexico's Dead Zone Is the Biggest Ever Seen*; NPR's Food for Thought; Aug. 3, 2017[18]

Manglik, Vrinda; *Ethanol's Contribution to a Record-Breaking Dead Zone in the Gulf of Mexico*; Aug. 3, 2017[19]

Milman, Oliver; *Meat Industry Blamed for Largest-Ever 'Dead Zone' in Gulf of Mexico*; *The Guardian*; Aug. 1, 2017[20]

Wikipedia; *Effects of Hurricane Katrina in New Orleans*; last edited Feb. 12, 2019[21]

Wikipedia; *Hurricane Katrina*; last edited, March 14, 2019[22]

Wikipedia; *Deepwater Horizon Oil Spill*; Last edited Feb. 21, 2019[23,24]

Exxon Valdez Oil Spill Trustee Council; *Questions and Answers about the Spill*; ARLIS website[25,26,27]

Weise, Elizabeth; *Damage of Exxon Valdez Endures*; Associated Press; retrieved Dec. 25, 2001[28]

International Wildlife Law; *Exxon Valdez Oil Spill Class Action*; IWL website[29,31]

Wikipedia; *Exxon Valdez Oil Spill*; last edited March 4, 2019[30,33]

Williams, Terrie; *Species Survival Depends on the Public's Voice*; USA Today; Nov. 15, 2005; pg. 13A[32]

Balliett, James; Oceans: Environmental Issues, Global Perspective; Routledge; 2014; pg. 51[34]

U.S. Environmental Protection Agency; *Addressing Nutrient Pollution in the Chesapeake Bay*; epa.gov[35,37]

Wikipedia; Chesapcake Bay; last edited Feb. 5, 2019[36]

U.S. Environmental Protection Agency; *Clean Water Act Section 303(d): Impaired Waters and Total Maximum Daily Loads (TMDLs)*; epa.gov[38]

2016 Chesapeake Bay Dead Zone Forecast; *Chesapeake News*; June 14, 2016[39]

Chesapeake Foundation; *2018 State of the Bay Report*; Chesapeake Foundation website[40,41]

Wikipedia; *Gulf of Maine*; last edited Feb. 4, 2019[42]

Wernick, Adam; *The Northern Right Whale, Already an Endangered Species, Is in Deep Trouble*; pri.com; April 1, 2018[43,44]

Wikipedia; *Tragedy of the Commons*; March 11, 2019[45]

Brown, Elizabeth, co-author; *Near Collapse of Gulf of Maine Cod Leads to Fishing Ban*; Huffpost website; Nov. 17, 2014[46,47]

Whittle, Patrick; *Cod Fishing Catches Plummet in Waters off New England*; Associated Press; March 24, 2017[48,49]

The Decline of Northwest Salmon; University of Oregon, no further citation available[50,51]

Ontario Ministry of the Environment and Climate Change; *Blue-Green Algae Blooms in the Great Lakes*; OMOECC website, State of Ontario's Biodiversity[52]

National Research Council; *Hormonally Active Agents in the Environment*; The National Academics Press; 1999; Chapter 5[53]

Great Lakes Environmental Assessment and Mapping Project; *PCBs in Great Lakes Sediments*; GLEAM website[54]

Riverkeeper; *Hudson River PCBs*; Riverkeeper website[55]

Nordhaus, Ted and Shellenberger, Michael; *Break Through, From the Death of Environmentalism to the Politics of Possibility*; Houghton Mifflin; 2007; pgs. 22-24[56,57,58]

U.S. Fish and Wildlife Service; *Digest of Federal Resource Laws*; USF&WS website[59,60,61]

Lyon, Greg and Stein, Eric; *How Effective Has the Clean Water Act Been At Reducing Pollutant Mass Emissions to the Southern California Bight Over the Past 35 Years? Environmental and Monitoring Assessment*; June 21, 2008[62]

Center for Effective Government; *Celebrating a Public Protections Milestone: The 40th Anniversary of the Clean Water Act*; Project on Government Oversight; Oct. 10, 2012[63,67]

U.S. Environmental Protection Agency; *Basic Information about NPS Pollution*; epa.gov[64,65]

U.S. Environmental Protection Agency; *National Water Quality Inventory: Report to Congress*; epa.gov; Aug. 2017[68]

Graczyk, Michael; *Oil Spill Cleanup Impedes Major Texas Ship Channel*; Associated Press; March 23, 2014[69]

Rowland, Robin; *"Very Low Levels" of Exxon Valdez Oil Threaten Salmon and Herring Survival 25 Years Later*; Northwest Coast Energy News; Sept. 8, 2015[70]

Rowland, Robin; *Gulf Oil Spill Caused Heart Defects in Fish Embryos New Study Finds*; Northwest Coast Energy News; March 24, 2014[71]

Chapter Fourteen: The Air We Breathe

Wikipedia; *Clean Air Act*; last updated Feb. 26, 2019[1,2]

Mackenzie, Jillian; *Air Pollution: Everything You Need to Know*; Natural Resources Defense Council website; Nov. 1, 2016[3]

U.S. Environmental Protection Agency; *Air Pollution: Current and Future Challenges*; epa.gov[4,5]

Ayre, James; *California Named U.S. State With Worst Air Quality, Yet Again*; Clean Technica website; June 21; 2017[6]

American Lung Association; *State of the Air Report 2018*; ALA website[7]

Tremble, Megan; *The 10 Cities With the Worst Traffic Congestion*; *U.S. News and World Report*; Feb. 6, 2018[8]

Schlichter, Sarah; *The Ten Cities With the Worst Traffic in the U.S.*; smartertravel.com; March 12, 2020[9]

California Air Resources Board; *Air Quality Standards*; ww2arb.ca.gov [10]
U.S. Environmental Protection Agency; *What Is Acid Rain?*; epa.gov[11]

Wikipedia; *Acid Rain*; last updated March 2, 2019[12,13]

U.S. Environmental Protection Agency; *Tools of the Trade: A Guide to Designing and Operating a Cap and Trade Program For Pollution Control*; EPA; June 2003; pgs. 1.1-1.2[14]

U.S. Environmental Protection Agency; *Cap and Trade Basics*; EPA, Clear Skies website; last updated March 18, 2016[15,16]

U.S. Environmental Protection Agency; *Clear Skies*; EPA, Clear Skies website; last updated March 18, 2016[17,18]

U.S. Environmental Protection Agency; *Wood Smoke and Your Health*; epa.gov[19]

Eilperin, Juliet; *Trump's Power Plant Plan Would Release Hundreds of Millions of Tons of CO_2*; *The Washington Post*; August 20, 2018[20,21,22]

Topf, Andrew; *24 States Line Up to Block Obama's Clean Power Plan*; mining.com; Oct. 25, 2015[23]

Pediatric Asthma Center; BronxCare Health System website[24]

Newbury, Joanne, et al; *Association of Air Pollution Exposure With Psychotic Experiences During Adolescence*; *JAMA Psychiatry* online; March 27, 2019[25]

McSweeney Robert; *Cutting Emissions Could Prevent Nearly 3000,000 U.S. Air Pollution Deaths*; CarbonBrief website; Feb. 22, 2016[26]

Craft, Elena; *Rejection of Post-Hurricane Harvey Air Pollution Monitoring "Part of a Disturbing Trend of Willful Ignorance"*; edf.org; March 5, 2019[27]

Chapter Fifteen: The Lawyer Economy

Clark, Josh; *Why Do Corporations Have the Same Rights as You?*; How Stuff Works website; April 1, 2008[1]

Wikipedia; *Corporate Personhood*; last updated March 8, 2019[2]

Zinn, Howard; *A People's History of the United States*; Harper Perennial; 2003; pgs. 260-261[3]

Wikipedia; *Sierra Club v. Morton*; last updated Sept. 15, 2019[4]

Community Environmental Legal Defense Fund; *Tamaqua Borough Pennsylvania*; celdf.org; Aug. 31, 2015[5,6]

Rights and Resources Initiative; *Ecuador Passes New Constitution Acknowledging Indigenous Rights*; rightsandresources.org; Oct. 23, 2008[7]

Wikipedia; *United States Antitrust Law*; last updated Feb. 15, 2019[8]

Wikipedia; *Standard Oil Co. of New Jersey v. United States*; last updated Dec. 1, 2019[9]

ExxonMobil; *Our History*; ExxonMobil website; Sept. 4, 2018[10]

Hertsgaard, Mark; *Earth Odyssey*; Penguin Random House Books; 1998; pg. 106[11,12]

Wikipedia; *National City Lines*; last updated Nov. 13, 2019[13]

Reiff, Nathan; *Top 7 Companies Owned by the Koch Brothers*; Investopedia website; March 4, 2019[14]

Osaka Shannon; *The Koch Brothers Hate Public Transit*; grist.org; Jan. 20, 2018[15]

Koch Brothers Fund Bogus Study Bashing Offshore Wind in New Jersey; thinkprogress.org; Aug. 17, 2011[16]

Editorial Board; *The Koch Attack on Solar Energy*; *The New York Times*; April 26, 2014[17]

Allessandra, Rikki; *2019 Renewable Energy Tax Credits in the U.S.*; solarfeeds.com; Sept. 12, 2019[18]

Negin, Elliott; *Will Koch Pull the Plug on Electric Cars?*; ucsusa.org; Dec. 5, 2018[19]

Restoring Citizens Authority Over Corporations; *Proposed Constitutional Amendments*; Reclaim Democracy! website[20]

Wikipedia; *Environmental Bill of Rights*; last updated Nov. 16, 2019[21]

Sigal, Samuel; *Lake Erie Now Has Legal Rights, Just Like You*; vox.com; Feb. 26, 2019[22]

Har, Janie; *U.S. Judge Scraps Oakland, California, Ban on Coal Shipments*; Associated Press; May 15, 2018[23]

Chapter Sixteen: Whose Side is God on Anyway?

Barooah, Jahnabi; *46 Percent of Americans Believe in Creationism According to Latest Gallup Poll*; HuffPost website; June 5, 2012[1,5]

Kehoe, Jacqueline; *Hike Through 500 Million Years in U.S. National Parks*; National Geographic; Nov. 29, 2018[2]

Sell, Jeremy; *Black Canyon of the Gunnison National Park*; The Life of Your Time website; April 14, 2013[3]

Wikipedia; *Young Earth Creationism*; last updated Feb. 9, 2019[4]

Swift, Art; *In U.S., Belief in Creationist View of Humans at New Low*; Gallup; May 22, 2017[6]

Nye, Bill; *Undeniable; Evolution and the Science of Creation*; St. Martin's Press; 2014; pgs. 5-7, 42[7,8,9]

Rankin, Terry; *Was Jefferson a Deist?*; Quora website; May 19, 2016[10]

Wikipedia, *Theistic Evolution*; last updated Jan. 12, 2020[11]

Wei-Haas, Maya; *Last Day of the Dinosaurs' Reign Captured in Stunning Detail*; National Geographic; Sept. 9, 2019[12]

National Human Genome Research Institute; *Background on Comparative Genomic Analysis*; nih.gov; Dec. 2002[13]

XXXV

Garrett-Hatfield, Lori; *Animals That Share Human DNA Sequences*; Seattepi.com[14]

Doherty, Shannon; *Human-Like Behaviors of Apes and Monkeys*; ourbeautifulplanet.net[15,16]

Lincoln Park Zoo; *Chimpanzees Have Five Universal Personality Dimensions*; Science Daily News website; June 3, 2013[17]

Niemela, Aina; *The Lost Gospel of the Earth*; *Amicus Journal*; Spring 1997; pgs. 42-44[18]

National Snow and Ice Data Center; *What Is an Ice Sheet?*; NSIDC website[19]

Sundstrom, Bob; *Pterodactyls and Birds*; BirdNote website[20]

Singer, Emily; *How Dinosaurs Shrank and Became Birds*; *Quanta Magazine*; June 12, 2015[21]

Wood, Frances; *Regal Great Blue Heron*; BirdNote website[22]

Fishman, Jason; *Eleven-Year-Old Girl Finds 475 Million-Year-Old Fossil in the Smoky Mountains*; visitmysmokies.com; May 11, 2018[23]

Haegele, Greg; *Creation Care – A Growing Movement*; treehugger.com; July 3, 2008[24]

Griffin, Paul; *Solar Light of the World: Evangelicals Launch Global Clean Energy Campaign*; *Christianity Today*; Dec. 11, 2019[25]

Chapter Seventeen: Biodiversity on the Brink

Lear, Linda; *The Life and Legacy of Rachel Carson*; Rachel Carson website[1]

'La Belle Dame Sans Merci': A Poem by John Keats; Interesting Literature website[2]

U.S. Environmental Protection Agency; *DDT - A Brief History and Status*; epa.gov[3,6,7]

Mitchell, Alanna; *The 1,300 Bird Species Facing Extinction Signal Threats to Human Health*; *Environmental Health News*; Aug. 26, 2014[4,8,9]

Wikipedia; *DDT*; last updated March 19, 2019[5]

Baumle Kylee; *The Monarch: Saving Our Most-Loved Butterfly*; St. Lynn's Press; April 2017[10]

Monarch Butterfly Could Get Endangered Species Protection; CBS News; Dec. 31, 2014[11]

Osborn, Liz; *Number of Native Species in United States*; CurrentResults.com[12]

Beaudry, Frederic; *Top States for Biodiversity*; ThoughtCo. website; Feb. 11, 2019[13,14]

Sen Nag, Oishimaya; *Why Are Species in Hawaii Going Extinct at Such A Rapid Rate?*; worldatlas.com; April 25, 2017[15,16]

Endangered Species in Hawaii; Pandaonline.com[17]

Wikipedia; *Endangered Species Act of 1973*; last updated March 27, 2019[18,19]

U.S. Fish and Wildlife Service; *Northern Spotted Owl*; Oregon Fish and Wildlife Service[20,21]

Oregon Forest Resources Institute; *Oregon's Old Treasures*; ORFI website[22]

Wikipedia; *Northern Spotted Owl*; last updated Feb. 9, 2019[23]

Migiro, Geoffrey; *Endangered Species in the U.S.?*; worldatalas.com; Aug. 1, 2018[24]

U.S. Fish and Wildlife Service; *Wetlands Losses in the United States: 1780's to 1980's Report*; National Wetlands Inventory website[25]

Manatee Facts; Save the Manatee website[26]

Brulliard, Karin; *A Tiny Endangered Deer Lives Only in the Florida Keys: Here's What We Know About Its Fate*; *The Washington Post*; Sept. 13, 2017[27]

U.S. National Park Service; *Wood Stork: Species Profile*; Everglades National Park website[28,30]

Wikipedia; *Everglades*; last updated Feb. 27, 2019[29]

Florida Fish and Wildlife Conservation Commission; Whooping Crane FAQ; FFWCC website[31]

Beyond Pesticides; *Impacts of Pesticides on Wildlife*; Beyond Pesticides website[32]

King, Andrew and Sumpter, David; *Murmurations*; *Current Biology*; Vol 22 No 4; 2012[33]

Nordhaus, Hannah; *What Trump's Shrinking of National Monuments Actually Means*; *National Geographic News*; Feb. 2, 2018[34,35]
Kolbert, Elizabeth; *The Sixth Extinction: An Unnatural History*; Henry Holt and Company; 2014; pgs. 165-168, intro.[36,37]

Friedman, Lisa; *U.S. Significantly Weakens ESA*; *The New York Times*; Aug. 12, 2019[38]

Wikipedia; *Snail Darter Controversy*; last updated Aug. 5, 2018[39]

Defenders of Wildlife; *Basic Facts About Red Knots*; defenders.org[40]

Chapter Eighteen: Invaders on the Loose

The National Wildlife Federation; *Invasive Species*; NWF website[1, 12,13,16]

U.S. Department of Agriculture; *Gypsy Moth in North America*; U.S. Forest Service website[2]

Walsh, Meredith; *Mute Swan*; Introduced Species Summary Project; Columbia University; last edited Nov. 21, 2004[3,4]

Allin, Charles and Hubbard, Thomas; *Mute Swan Impact on Submerged Aquatic Vegetation and Macroinvertebrates in Rhode Island*; *Northeaster Naturalist, Vol. 10*; Sept. 2003; pgs. 302-318[5,6]

Wikipedia; *Mute Swan*; last updated April 3, 2019[7]

Boston Globe; *Bird Lovers, Ct. Are at Odds on Swans*; Associated Press; retrieved April 7, 2009[8]

Boston Public Garden: 10 Fun Things for You to Do and See; Boston Discovery Guide website[9]

Walsh, Meredith; *European Starling*; Introduced Species Summary Project, Columbia University; last edited October 18, 2001[10]

U.S. Fish and Wildlife Service; *Lacey Act*; USF&WS International Affairs website[11]

Main, Douglas; *A Great Lakes Mystery: The Case of the Disappearing Species*; Purdue University News; May 28, 2008[14]
Great Lakes Environmental Assessment and Mapping Project; *Zebra and Quagga Mussels*; GLEAM website[15]

Macqueen, Kathryn; *Saving the Reef: Lionfish in Florida*; Changing Planet website; *National Geographic*; Aug. 29, 2016[17]

Blair, Kimberly; *Lionfish are Threatening Florida's Economy*; *Pensacola News Journal*; March 8, 2015[18]

Wikipedia; *Burmese Pythons in Florida*; last updated April 13, 2019[19]

Mettler, Katie; *Python Measuring 17 Feet and Carrying 73 Eggs is Largest Ever Found in Florida*; *The Independent*; April 8, 2019[20]

Wikipedia; *Invasive Species in the U.S.*; last updated January 3, 2020[21]

U.S. Coast Guard; *Standards for Living Organisms in Ship's Ballast Water Discharged in U.S. Waters*; Federal Register, 77R 17254; March 23, 2012[22]

Christiansen, Savanah; *As Eastern Hemlock Trees Die Off*; Public Radio International's Living on Earth website; Oct. 29, 2018[23]

Sidebottom, Jill; *Recommendations for Hemlock Woolly Adelgid Control in the Landscape*; North Carolina Cooperative Extension Service; retrieved Feb. 16, 2014[24]

Arbor Day Foundation; *Emerald Ash Borer*; arborday.org; April 2015[25,26]

U.S. Forest Service; Emerald Ash Borer Information Network website[27]

Odom, Jill; *The Threat of Spotted Lanternfly*; Total Landscape Care website; April 11, 2019[28,29]

Margolis, Jason; *Insects Slipping Into the U.S. are Causing Billions of dollars in Damage*; Public Radio International's The World website; Dec. 16, 2018[30,31]

Grebenstein, Emily; *Escape of the Invasives: Top Six Invasive Plant Species in the United States*; Smithsonian Insider website; April 19, 2013[32]

Vince, Gaiai; *Embracing Invasives*; *Science Magazine*; March 18, 2011; Vol. 331, pgs. 1383[33]

Bienkowski, Brian; *Baseball Bats Made from Ash May Fall Victim of Climate Change*; The Daily Climate; *Scientific American* website; March 31, 2014[34]

Chapter Nineteen: Nuclear Power: The False Promise

Wikipedia: *Nuclear Power in the United States*; last updated April 24, 2019[1,7,8,9]

Holt, Mark and Parker, Larry; *Nuclear Power: Outlook for New U.S. Reactors*; Congressional Research Service, #RL33442; March 7, 2007; pg. 3[2]

John Byrne and Steven M. Hoffman; *Governing the Atom: The Politics of Risk*; 1996; pg. 136[3]

Wikipedia; *Nuclear Power Debate*; last updated April 8, 2019[4]

Reindl, JC.; *Did We Really 'Almost Lose Detroit'?*; *Detroit Free Press*; Oct. 9, 2016[5,6]

History.com editors; *Three Mile Island*; History.com; last updated Aug. 21, 2018[10,11]

Johnson, Shane; *Nuclear Power 2010 Program Overview*; Office of Nuclear Energy; April 15, 2002[12]

World Nuclear Association; *Fukushima Daiichi Accident*; WNA website; updated Oct. 2018[13,14]

McCurry, Justin; *Fukushima Disaster: First Residents Return to Town Next to Nuclear Plant*; The Guardian; April 10, 2019[15]

Japan Fukushima Nuclear Plant 'Clean-Up Costs Double'; BBC News; Nov. 28, 2016[16]

Walton, Rod; *Vogtle Cost Upgrade Causes Rethinking of $25B Nuclear Plant's Future*; Power Engineering website; Aug. 9 2018[17]

Wikipedia: *Yucca Mountain Nuclear Waste Repository*; last updated April 30, 2019[18]

Clean Up the Mines website[19]

U.S. Energy Information Admin.; *Wyoming: State Profile and Energy Estimates*; EIA website[20]

Seacoast Anti-Pollution League; *Six Reasons Why Nuclear Power is Not Sustainable*; saplnh.org [21,22]

U.S. Energy Information Admin.; *Net Generation by Energy Source: Total (All Sectors), 2009-February 2019*; *Electric Power Monthly*, EIA website; April 24, 2019[23]

Beans, Laura; *300 Plus Groups Urge Climate Scientist Dr. Hansen to Rethink Support of Nuclear Power*; EcoWatch; Jan. 9, 2014[24]

Uranium 238 and 235: A Radioactive and Strategic Element; radioactivity.eu.com[25]

DiChristopher, Tom; *The Yucca Mountain Nuclear Waste Dump, a Political Hot Potato, is Back*; CNBC website; March 16, 2017[26]

Heller, Dean; *Once Again, Heller Successfully Stops Funding to Revive Yucca Mountain Project in U.S. Senate-Passed Conference Agreement*; Dean Heller Press Release; Sept. 12, 2108[27]

McKie, Robin; *Miami, the Great World City, is Drowning While the Powers That Be Look Away*; *The Guardian*; July 11, 2014[28]

Chapter Twenty: The Hummer is the Antichrist of the Environmental Movement

Wikipedia; *Hummer*; last updated April 1, 2019[1,2]

Melosi, Martin V.; *The Automobile Shapes the City*; The Automobile in American Life and Society Project, University of Michigan/Dearborn and Benson Research Center; Introduction[3,4]

Filler, Lane; *Long Island Traffic How to Fix It*; *Newsday* Opinion Column; December 29, 2015[5]

U.S. Department of Transportation; *Highway Statistics 2010*; USDOT Office of Highway Policy Information; transportation.gov[6]

Statista; *Number of Motor Vehicles Registered in the United States from 1990 to 2017*; Statista website portal[7]

Midwest Industrial Supply; *How Many Miles of Roads Are There in the U.S.?*; Midwest website; Dec. 28, 2015[8]

American Road and Transportation Builders; *How Many Miles of Road in the U.S.*; artba.org[9]

Wikipedia; *Climate Change Policy of the United States*; last updated March 25, 2019[10,16]

U.S. Environmental Protection Agency; *EPA and NHTSA Finalize Historic National Program to Reduce Greenhouse Gases and Improve Fuel Economy for Cars and Trucks*; EPA Office of Transportation and Air Quality Announcement; April 2010[11]

U.S. Environmental Protection Agency; *EPA and NHTSA Set Standards to Reduce Greenhouse Gases and Improve Fuel Economy for Model Years 2017-2025 Cars and Light Trucks*; EPA U.S. Office of Transportation and Air Quality Announcement; August 2012[12]

U.S. Department of Transportation; *Corporate Average Fuel Economy (CAFE) Standards*; transportation.gov; Aug. 27, 2014[13]

The White House Office of the Press Secretary; *President Obama's 21st Century Clean Transportation System*; The White House website; Feb. 4, 2016[14]

Kane, Joseph and Puentes, Robert; *Don't Dismiss Obama's Clean Transportation Plan*; Brookings Institution website; Feb. 8, 2016[15]

Bomey, Nathan; *What Gas-Mileage Standards Would Mean for Car and Gas Prices*; USA Today; March 16, 2017[17,18]

Trump to raise fuel economy standards by 1.5% per year through 2026; CBS News; Jan. 24, 2020[19]
Nanalyze Weekly; *How Many Electric Cars Are There in the USA?*; Nanalyze website[20]

Loveday, Steven; *Monthly Plug-In EV Sales Scorecard*; InsideEVs website[21]

Mitchell, Russ; *Americans Shun Electric Vehicles Not Named Tesla. Are American Car Makers Driving Off a Cliff?*; Los Angeles Times; Jan. 20, 2020[22]

Melosi, Martin; *The Automobile and the Environment*; The Automobile in American Life and Society Project, University of Michigan-Dearborn and Benson Ford Research Center; 2010[23,24]

U.S. Energy Information Admin.; *How Many Gallons of Gasoline and Diesel Fuel are Made from One Barrel of Oil?*; EIA website; June 29, 2018[25]

Rice, Doyle; *The USA's Long Battle Against Air Pollution Isn't Over Yet, As Air Quality Improvements are Slowing Down*; USA Today; April 30, 2018[26]

Stern, Perry; *Best-Selling Vehicles in America — 2019 Q1*; MSN Autos website; April 4, 2019[27]

The Environmental Literacy Council; *Rail Transportation*; ELC website[28]

Evans, David; *Planes, Trains, Cars and Buses – What's the Most Fuel-Efficient Way to Travel?*; International Council on Clean Transportation website; June 11, 2016[29]

Association of American Railroads; *Railroads and States*; AAR website[30]
Fuel Efficiency; csx.com[31]

Banker, Steve; *Rail Freight Is Losing Market Share*; *Forbes Magazine*; Oct. 21, 2017[32]

Fuel Cells; *National Geographic*; website reference[33]

California Air Resources Board; *Hydrogen Fueling Infrastructure*; ww2arb.ca.gov[34]

Pentland, William; *Wyoming Considers De Facto Prohibition on Solar and Wind Energy*; *Forbes Magazine*; Jan. 18, 2017[35]

Chapter Twenty-One: What in the World is McDonaldization?

Ritzer, George; *The McDonaldization of Society*; Sage Publications; 6th ed.; 2011[1]

Goyanes, Christina; *What's Really Inside McDonald's Chicken McNuggets?*; livestrong.com; Sept. 25, 2018[2,3,4]

A Nugget of Wisdom: Don't Eat Those Nuggets; Headline Health website; Jan. 18, 2019[5]

McCulloch, Marsha; *What Is Sodium Benzoate?*; healthline.com; Jan. 21, 2019[6]

Pollan, Michael; *The Omnivore's Dilemma*; Penguin Books; 2006; pgs. 113-115, pg. 68[7.8.18]
Sanburn, Josh; *America's Clutter Problem*; *Time Magazine*; March 23, 2015[9]

Mooallem, Jon; *The Self-Storage Self – Storing All the Stuff We Accumulate*; *The New York Times*; retrieved Feb. 1, 2012[10]

Harris, Alexander; *U.S. Self-Storage Industry Statistics*; SquareFoot.com; March 11, 2019[11]

Moss, Doug and Scheer, Roddy; *Use It and Lose It: The Outsize Effect of U.S. Consumption on the Environment*; *EarthTalk*; emagazine.com; 2009[12]

Semon, Jason Jeffrey; *If Everyone Lived Liked Americans, How Many Earths Would We Need?*; Science in Our World: Certainty and Controversy; Penn State; Oct. 24, 2012[13]

Statista; *Average Size of Floor Area in new Single-Family Houses Built For Sale in the United States From 1975 to 2017*; Statista website portal[14]

What is a McMansion?; wiseGEEK website[15,16]

MacDonald's; *About Our Food*; MacDonald's webstite[17]

Nelson, Samantha; *Where Does McDonald's Food Come From? Exploring the Supply Chain*; *Market Realist*; Dec. 27, 2018[19]

Brill, Steven; *How Baby Boomers Broke America*; *Time Magazine*; May 17, 2018[20]

Wikipedia; *The Affluent Society*; last updated Dec. 30, 2018[21,22]

BBC News; *Plan for Twenty-Five Percent of EU Budget to Fight Climate Change*; Reuters; May 8, 2019[23]

Benfield, Kaid; *What Does a 'Sustainable Community' Actually Look Like?*; *The Atlantic*; March 24, 2011[24]

Wallis, Jim; *Rediscovering Values*; Howard Books; 2010; pg. 180[25]

Warner, Melanie; *Would You Like a Gas Guzzler With That?*; *The New York Times*; Aug. 10, 2006[26]

Gläce Luxury Ice Co. website[27]

Chapter Twenty-Two: America the Wasteland – What a Mess We Have Made

Loki, Reynard: *America is a Wasteland: The U.S. Produces a Shocking Amount of Garbage*; salon.com; July 15, 2016[1]

Statista; *Municipal Solid Waste in the United States - Statistics & Facts*; Statista website portal[2]

Land of Waste: America Landfills and Waste Production; saveonenergy.com[3]

Hickman, H. Lanier; *American Alchemy: The History of Solid Waste Management in the United States*; Forester Press; 2003[4]

Energy Justice Network; *Commercial Trash Incinerators in the U.S.*; EJN website[5,8]

Farrell, John; *Report: Waste Incineration: A Dirty Secret in How States Define Renewable Energy*; Clean Technica website; Dec. 17, 2018[6,7]

Wikipedia; *Hazardous Waste*; last updated May 20, 2019[9]

U.S. Environmental Protection Agency; *Land, Waste, and Cleanup Topics*; epa.gov[10]

Johnson, David; *Do You Live Near Toxic Waste? See 1,317 of the Most Polluted Spots in the U.S.*; *Time Magazine*; March 22, 2017[11]

Beck, Eckardt; *The Love Canal Tragedy*; *EPA Journal*; Jan. 1979[12,13]

U.S. Environmental Protection Agency; *Learn the Basics of Hazardous Waste*; epa.gov[14]

Lallanilla, Marc; *All About Tire Recycling*; The Spruce website; Jan. 24, 2019[15,16]

Energy Justice Network; *Tires*; EJN website[17]

U.S. Environmental Protection Agency; *Tire-Derived Fuel*; EPA website archives; last updated Feb. 22, 2016[18]

Madrigal, Exis; Humans Have Made, Found or Used Over 50 Million Unique Chemicals; wired.com; Sept. 9, 2009[19]

Earth Over Us blog; *Pollution*; July 5, 2014[20,26]

Murray, Lindsey; *Here's Where You Can Buy a Couch Without Flame Retardants*; health.com; Jan. 31, 2017[21,22]

Dealing with Debris From Hurricane Harvey; environmenttexas.org fact sheet[23]

Ruiz, Rebecca; *Catalogs, After Years of Decline, Are Revamped for Changing Times*; The New York Times; Jan. 25, 2015[24]

U.S. Postal Service Reports Fiscal Year 2019 Results; usps.gov; Nov. 14, 2019[25]

Bryant, Kelly; *8 Surprising Facts and Misconceptions About Recycling*; Mental Floss website; April 22, 2016[27]

Sanchez, Rudy; *Norway Recycles 97% Of Their Plastic Bottles. Here's How They Do It.*; Dieline Media blog; April 16, 2019[28]

Goldstein, David; *U.S. Cities Scramble to Rewrite Rules on Recycling After China Restricts 'Foreign Garbage'*; Tribune News Service; July 3, 2016[29]

Semuels, Alana; *Is This the End of Recycling?*; The Atlantic; March 5, 2019[30,49]

Watson, Sara Kiley; *China Has Refused to Recycle the West's Plastics. What Now?*; NPR's Goat and Soda; June 28, 2018[31]

Kummer, Frank; *At Least Half of Philly's Recycling Goes Straight to an Incinerator*; The Inquirer Daily News; Jan. 25, 2019[32]

Kummer, Frank; *Philly to Stop Incinerating Recyclables by the End of the Month*; The Inquirer Daily News; April 18, 2019[33]

Leblanc, Rick; *The Decomposition of Waste in Landfills: A Story of Time and Materials*; The Balance Small Business website; May 16, 2019[34]

Save Our Planet; *Biodegradable Diapers*; Natural Environment website; Oct. 12, 2012[35]

Leblanc, Rick; *Knowaster Recycles Absorbent Hygiene Products*; The Balance Small Business website; Nov. 18, 2018[36]

The Amount of K-Cups That Have Been Trashed in Landfills Could Wrap Around the Planet 10 Times; the Story of Stuff Project website[37,38]

Larson, Janet and Venkova, Savina; *Plastic Bag Bans Spreading in the United States*; Earth Policy Institute; April 22, 2104[39]

Froelich, Amanda; *San Francisco Becomes First City to Ban the Sale of Plastic Bottles*; trueacitivist.com; Nov.11, 2015[40]

Doucette, Kitt; *The Plastic Bag Wars*; *Rolling Stone*; Aug. 2, 2011; pgs. 37-39[41]

Responding to Strategic Lawsuits Against Public Participation (SLAPPs); Digital Media Law Project; May 24, 2019[42]

Kinsella, Susan; *Paperwork: Comparing Recycled to Virgin Paper*; RePaper Project; April 2012[43]

Pittmoss.com[44]

Hagen, Paul, et al; *Basel Convention Recasts the Circular Economy for Plastics*; Beveridge & Diamond website; May 15, 2019[45,46,53]

Royte, Elizabeth; *Garbage Land*; Little, Brown and Company; 2005; pgs. 197 and 125[47,50]

Leblanc, Rick; *E-Waste Recycling Facts and Figures*; Investment Recovery Association website; Oct. 2017[48]

Mellino, Cole; *Find Out Which U.S. City Shames You Into Composting*; EcoWatch; Jan. 29, 2015[51]

Nave, Natalie; *More Printed Catalogs Mean More Energy, Water and Paper Gone to Waste*; Product Stewardship Institute blog; June 1, 2015[52]

Chapter Twenty-Three: Thirty Thousand Orangutans

Projections of Population Growth of World (2035); livepopulation.com[1]

Brush, Michael; *Why a New Age of Nuclear Energy Is About to Dawn*; *The Fiscal Times*; May 19, 2015[2]

How Many Roman Catholics are There in the World?; BBC News website[3]

Orangutan: An Endangered Species; bagheera.com[4]

United States Census Bureau; U.S. and World Population Clock[5]

Wikipedia; *Demography of the U.S.*; last updated May 27, 2019[6]

Cohn, D'Vera and Passel, Jeffrey; *U.S. Population Projections: 2005-2050*; Pew Research Center; Feb. 11, 2008[7]

Sesin, Carmen; *Over 200,000 Puerto Ricans Have Arrived in Florida Since Hurricane Maria*; NBC News; Nov. 30, 2017[8]

Kristof, Nicholas; *Food Doesn't Grow Here Anymore. That's Why I Would Send My Son North*; *The New York Times*; June 5, 2019[9]

Wikipedia; *List of Countries by Carbon Dioxide Emissions*; last updated May 24, 2019[10,12]

Wikipedia; *Land Use, Land-Use Change and Forestry*; last updated May 3, 2019[11]

U.S. Energy Information Admin, *What Is the United States' Share of World Energy Consumption?*; EIA website: last updated Dec. 26, 2018[13]

Moss, Doug and Scheer, Roddy; *Use It and Lose It: The Outsize Effect of U.S. Consumption on the Environment*; *Scientific American*; Earth Talk[14]

McDonald, Charlotte; *How Many Earths Do We Need?* BBC News; June 16, 2105[15]

Wessels, Tom; *The Myth of Progress: Toward a Sustainable Future*; University of Vermont Press; 2006; pg. 33[16]

Siciliano, John; *Mike Lee Says the Solution to Climate Change Is Having More Babies*; Washington Examiner; March 26, 2019[17]

Rosane, Olivia; *Washington Becomes First State to Legalize Human Body Composting*; EcoWatch; May 22, 2019[18]

Whiting, Kate: *This Is the Environmental Catastrophe You've Probably Never Heard of*; World Economic Forum; April 24, 2019[19]

Statista; *Consumption of Industrial Sand and Gravel in the U.S. From 2014 to 2018*; Statista website portal[20]

Chapter Twenty-Four: Nero's Fiddling While Rome Burns

Irfab, Umain; *Report: We Have Just 12 Years to Limit Devastating Global Warming*; vox.com; Oct. 8, 2018[1]

Griffiths, James; *Scientists: Global Carbon Dioxide Hits Record Level*; WRAL TechWire; May 13, 2019[2]

Goldberg, Suzanne; *Exxon Knew of Climate Change in 1981, Email Says – But It Funded Deniers For 27 More Years*; The Guardian; July 8, 2015[3,4]

Levine, Matt; *Exxon Is in Trouble Over Climate Change*; Bloomberg Opinion; Oct. 25, 2018[5]

McDonald, Jessica; *The Facts on Fuel Economy Standards*; factcheck.org; May 3, 2019[6]

U.S. Energy Information Admin.; *What Is U.S. Electricity Generation by Energy Source?*; EIA website; last updated March 1, 2019[7]

Pharm, Sherisse and Rivers, Matt; *China Is Crushing the U.S. in Renewable Energy*; CNN Business News; July 18, 2017[8,9]

Davidson, Jordan; *Scottish Wind Power Is So Efficient, It Could Power Two Scotlands*; EcoWatch; July 17, 2010[10]

Twelve Countries Leading the Way in Renewable Energy; clickeergy.org; Aug. 10, 2017[11,12]

ITV Report; *Britain's Power Grid Notches Up First Coal-Free Week Since the Industrial Revolution*; ITV News; May 8, 2019[13]

Pereda, Otto; *Costa Rica: World Power in Renewable Energy*; The Costa Rica News; Feb. 19, 2018[14]

Georgetown Utility to Be Powered by Solar and Wind Energy by 2017; georgetown.org[15,16]

Rainforest Action Network; *Banking on Climate Change 2019*; RAN website[17,18]

Environmental Policy Network; goldmansachs.com[19]

Smith, Adam; *2017 U.S. Billion-Dollar Weather and Climate Disasters: A Historic Year in Context*; National Oceanic and Atmospheric Administration; climate.gov; Jan. 8, 2018[20]

Smith, Adam; *2018's Billion Dollar Disasters in Context*; National Oceanic and Atmospheric Administration; climate.gov; Feb. 7, 2019[21]

Hurricane Barry Struck the Gulf Coast and Caused Flooding From Louisiana Into Arkansas; The Weather Channel Hurricane Central website; July 11, 2019[22]

Layne, Rachel; *Rising Seas Slash Homes Values by Nearly $16 Billion*; CBS News; Feb. 2, 2019[23]

Indonesia To Move Capital City; BBC News; April 29, 2019[24]

Jones, Nicola; *Redrawing the Map: How the World's Climate Zones Are Shifting*; Yale Environment 360, Yale School of Forestry and Environment; Oct. 23, 2018[25]

Sverdrup-Thygeson, Ann; *Humanity Must Save Insects to Save Ourselves, Leading Scientist Warns*; *The Guardian*; May 7, 2019[26]

Harvey, Chelsea; *The Biggest Coral Reef in the Continental U.S. is Dissolving Into the Ocean*; *The Washington Post*; May 4, 2016[27]

Healthy Oceans; *Six Reasons Why Coral Reefs Are Important*; healthypeople.gov; Jan. 7, 2019[28]

Brannen, Peter; *A Foreboding Similarity in Today's Oceans and a 94-Million-Year-Old Catastrophe*; *The Atlantic*; Jan. 12, 2018[29]

Pierre-Louis, Kendra; *Antarctica Is Melting Three Times as Fast as a Decade Ago*; *The New York Times*; June 13, 2018[30]

Climate Change; saveouroots.org[31]

Liberto, Tom; *High Temperatures Smash All-Time Records in Alaska in Early July 2019*; National Oceanic and Atmospheric Administration; climate.gov; July 16, 2019[32]

Radford, Tim; *Earth's Climate After 2030: Conditions Could Resemble Era 3 Million Years Ago, Scientists Predict*; Climate News Network; Dec. 31, 2018[33,34]

Farah, Nina; *Planned Changes to EPA Pollution Analyses Align with Industry Requests*; E&E News; May 31, 2019[35]

Farah, Nina; *To Kill Climate Rule, EPA Wants to Redefine Danger of Soot*; E&E News; Aug. 6, 2018[36]

Boggioni, Tom; *Trump's EPA Prevented NASA From Doing Cancer Research in Texas After Hurricane Harvey*; rawstory.com; March 5, 2019[37]

Hill, Joshua; *US Offshore Wind at Risk of Delays After "Redundant" Defense & Interior Appropriations Language*; Clean Technica website; May 24, 2019[38,39]

Decade-Long Gulf Oil Spill Caused by Hurricane Ivan; USA Today; Jan. 22, 2016[40]

Villafranca, Omar; *Fifteen-Year-Long Oil Spill is the Longest in U.S. History*; CBS News; March 16, 2019[41]

Brown, Nicole; *Williams Pipeline, Off New York shore, Would Be 'Monumental Step Backwards,' Stringer Says*; AM News; Nov. 5, 2018[42]

Stop the Williams Pipeline; surfrider.org[43]

New York Department of Environmental Conservation; DEC Statement on Denial of Water Quality Certification for the Proposed Northeast Supply Enhancement Pipeline; May 15, 2020[44]

Caldwell, Diane; *Nation's Largest Offshore Wind Farm Will Be Built Off Long Island*; The New York Times; Jan. 25, 2017[45]

Wikipedia; *Cape Wind*; last updated July 14, 2019[46]

Plumer, Brad; *We Fact Checked President Trump's Dubious Claims on the Perils of Wind Power*; The New York Times; April 3, 2019[47]

Clarke, Jack; *Climate Change Bigger Threat to Birds Than Windmills*; The New York Times; Nov. 14, 2018[47,48]

Roberts, David; *These Huge New Wind Turbines Are a Marvel: They're Also the Future*; vox.com; May 20, 2019[49]

Solar Energy in the United States; energy.gov[50,51,52]

Beans, Laura; *New Report Reveals Additional Fossil Fuel Subsidies Equaling $4 Billion Each Year*; EcoWatch; July 22, 2013[53]

Big Surprise: Fossil Fuels Win Under Tax Reform; earthtrack.net; April 29, 2019[54]

Rosane, Olivia; *Wildfires Force 10,000 to Flee as Alberta Repeals Carbon Tax*; EcoWatch; May 31, 2019[55]

Chapter Twenty-Five: Juliana, et. al. v. United States

Newspaper Clipping From 1912 Mentions Link Between Burning Coal and A Warmer Planet; Aug. 14, 2018[1]

Wikipedia; *Juliana, et al. v. United States*; last updated July 18, 2019[2,4]

Public Trust Doctrine Law and Legal Definition; uslegal.com[3]

Weiss, Debra Cassens; *Supreme Court Refuses Stay in Youths' Climate Change Suit, While Offering Advice to Trial Court*; ABA Journal; July 31, 2018[5]

Schwartz, John; *Judges Give Both Sides a Grilling in Youth Climate Case Against the Government*; The New York Times; June 4, 2019[6]

Griffiths, James; *Scientists: Global Carbon Dioxide Hits Record Level*; WRAL TechWire; May 13, 2019[7,21]

Wikipedia; *Fifth Amendment to the United States Constitution*; last updated July 19, 2019[7]

Juliana, et. al. v. United States; ethicsstupid.com; April 10, 2019[8,9]

Massachusetts v. EPA, 549 U.S. 497 (2007); justia.com[10]

White, Chris; *Climate Crusaders Take a Novel Approach to Their Newest Anti-Oil Lawsuit*; Daily Caller News Foundation; Nov. 15, 2018[11]

White, Chris; *NY Sues Exxon For Allegedly Defrauding Shareholders on Climate Change Risks*; Daily Caller News Foundation; Oct. 24, 2108[12]

Schwartz, John; *NY Sues ExxonMobil, Saying It Deceived Shareholders on Climate Change*; The New York Times; Oct. 24, 2018[13,14]

Grandoni, Dino; *ExxonMobil Prevails Over New York in High-Profile Climate Fraud Case*; The Washington Post; Dec. 10, 2019[15,16]

Corbett, Jessica; *Climate Liability Lawsuit Decision in Rhode Island a 'Welcome Sign' for Those Seeking Damages*; EcoWatch; July 24, 2019[17,18]

Savage, Karen; *Federal Judge Rules Against Big Oil, Sends Baltimore Climate Suit to State Court*; Climate Liability News; June 11, 2019[19]

Wikipedia; *Tobacco Master Settlement Agreement*; last edited July 25, 2019[20]

Evich, Helena; *Agriculture Department Buries Studies Showing Dangers of Climate Change*; Politico; June 23, 2019[22]

Higgins, Eoin; *We Can't Trust the Permafrost Anymore: Doomsday Vault at Risk in Norway*; EcoWatch; May 27, 2019[23]

Four in Five Parents Want Schools to Teach About Climate Change; ipos.com; April 22, 2019[24]

Perper, Rosie; *Satellite Photos Show Massive Swaths of The Arctic Engulfed in Flames By 'Unprecedented' Wildfires*; Business Insider website; July 24, 2019[25]

Paddison, Laura; *Earth Overshoot Day Shows We're Tearing Through Resources Faster Than Ever*; HuffPost website; July 29, 2019[2]

Chapter Twenty-Six: Going Carbon Neutral

Gaudelli, Janis; *The Truth Behind Millennials and the Green Movement*; adage.com; April 29, 2009[1]

Wilson, Mark; *Smartphones Are Killing the Planet Faster Than Anyone Expected*; fastcompany.com; March 27, 2018[2,3]

Bradberry, Danny; *How Much Power It Takes to Create Bitcoin*; theblance.com; Nov. 12, 2018[4]

Holger, Dieter; *Over 16 Million Now Own Cryptocurrency*; bitcoinist.com; March 19, 2018[5]

DePhillis, Lydia; *Delivery Now or Later? Your Next-Day Demands Come At an Environmental Cost*; WRAL TechWire; July 15, 2019[6,7]

Giving "Vast Wasteland" a Whole New Meaning; CNET News; July 4, 2008[8]

Rysavy, Tracy Fernandez; *Green and Climate-Friendly Televisions*; greenamerica.com[9]

Gillies, Trent; *Why California's New Solar Mandate Could Cost New Homeowners Up to an Extra $10,000*; CNBC News; Feb. 12, 2019[10]

California Aims to Become Carbon-Free by 2045; theconversastion.com; Sept. 12, 2018[11]

Wisconsin Aims to Fully Decarbonize Electricity by 2050; carbon-xchange.org; Aug. 27, 2019[12]

St. John, Jeff; *Hawaii Utility's 100 Percent Renewable Energy Plan Gets the Green Light*; greentechmedia.com; July 19, 2017[13]

Kaufman, Alexander; *Democrats' Green New Deal Wing Takes Shape Amid Wave of Progressive Climate Hawk Wins*; HuffPost website; Nov. 6, 2019[14]

U.S. Energy Information Admin.; *Iowa State Profile and Energy Estimates*; eia.gov[15]

Five Things to Know About Geothermal Power; energy.gov; Feb. 14, 2018[16]

Levine, Sandy; *Climate Problems of Expanding Natural Gas*; clf.org; April 21, 2014[17]

Salem Harbor Station; Footprint Power webiste[18]

Frazin, Rachel; *Bloomberg Pledges $500 Million To Close Coal-Fired Power Plants*; thehill.com; June 6, 2019[19,20]

Dzikiy, Phi; *Michael Bloomberg's $500 Million Beyond Carbon Plan Targets Natural Gas as Well as Coal*; electrek.co; June 7, 2019[21]

First Major U.S. Insurance Company to Stop Insuring and Investing in Coal; Insure Our Future website; July 1, 2019[22]

Hitt, Mary Anne; *Major Insurer Announces Policy to Ditch Coal*; Sierra Club website[23]

O'Doherty, Evelyn; *Outdoor Retailer Pulls Out of Utah Over Bears Ears*; *Standup Journal*; Feb. 19, 2017[24,25]

July Was the Hottest Month Ever Recorded; CNN Wire; Aug. 5, 2019[26]

Rosane, Olivia; *Second Major Heat Wave This Summer Smashes Records Across Europe*; EcoWatch; July 26, 2019[27]

Climate Central; *10 Hottest Years on Record*; climatecentral.org[28]

Smith-Schoenwalder, Cecelia; *EPA Proposes Rollback on Methane Emissions Regulations*; *U.S. News and Report*; August 29, 2019[29,30]

Hollis, Adrienne; *Top 10 Heat-Related Terms You Need to Pay Attention to While Reading Union of Concerned Scientists' Killer Heat Report*; EcoWatch; July 16, 2019[31]

Wallace-Wells, David; *The Uninhabitable Earth*; Tim Duggan Books; 2019; pg. 33[32]

Deutsche Welle; *Is Netflix Bad for the Environment? How Streaming Video Contributes to Climate Change*; EcoWatch; July 13, 2019[33]

Watkins, Morgan; *Kentucky Coal Mine Shifts to Solar Power*; *Courier Journal*; April 7, 2017[34]

Chapter Twenty-Seven: Changing the Rules of Capitalism

Illing, Sean; *Is Capitalism Worth Saving?* vox.com; Feb. 26, 2019[1,3,4]

Annual Message to the Congress on the State of the Union; The American Presidency Project; Jan. 22, 1970[2]

Gallagher, William; *Apple Backs Move to Make Corporations Accountable to Citizens, Not Shareholders*; appleinsider.com; Aug. 19, 2019[5]

Farand, Chloe; *Report: 90 Percent of World's Largest 200 Industrial Firms Are Using Trade Associations to Oppose Climate Policy*; desmogblog.com; Sept. 12, 2018[6]
Valueedge staff; *Shareholder Proposal Calls on Exxon to Disclose Lobbying Expenses and Policies*; valueedgeadvisors.com; April 1, 2019[7,11,12]

U.S. Chamber Key Vote Alert! on H.R. 205, H.R. 1941, and H.R. 1146; U.S. Chamber of Commerce; Sept. 10, 2019[8]

Stauffer, Peter; *House Passes Anti-Drilling Bills: Will the Senate Follow Suit?*; surfrider.org; Sept. 11, 2019[9]

A Sponge to Soak Up CO_2 Is in the Works; Energy Factor; exxonmobil.com; Aug. 26, 2019[10]

Exxon Shareholders Approve Measure on Climate-Change Report; CNBC; May 31, 2017[13]

Lavars, Nick; *Amazon Buys 100,000 Rivian Electric Trucks in Pursuit of Carbon Neutrality*; newatlas.com; Sept. 19, 2019[14]

Syymkowski, Sean; *These Twelve Cities Will Buy Only Electric Buses From 2025 On; More Expected to Join*; greencarreports.com; Nov. 14, 2017[15]

In Iceland, Hydrogen-Powered Buses Are Step Toward Oil-Free Economy; treehugger.com; Jan. 10, 2005[16]

Browning, Dominique; *Toxic Ignorance is Not Bliss*; edf.org blog; Dec. 7, 2009[17]

American Chemical Council Member Companies; americanchemistry.com[18]

Husted, Kristofor; *Supermarkets Waste Tons of Food as They Woo Shoppers*; NPR's The Salt; Sept. 25, 2014[19]

Balch, Oliver; *1.5 C Pledge From 87 Global Companies Fuels Hope of Bending Emissions Curve at Climate Week*; ethicalcorp.com; Sept. 22, 2019[20]

ADEC Innovations; *What is ESG?*; ADECI website[21]

American Council on Renewable Energy; *Decarbonizing Corporate Value Chains*; Market Review Report; Nov. 2018[22,23]

Blunt, Katherine and Gold, Russell; *PG&E Delayed Safety Work on Power Line That is Prime Suspect in California Wildfire*; The Wall Street Journal; Feb. 27, 2019[24,25]

Smith, Brad; *Microsoft Will Be Carbon Negative by 2030*; Microsoft.com\blog; Jan. 16, 2020[26]

Rosane, Olivia; *Coca-Cola Says It Won't Break Free From Plastic Bottles*; EcoWatch; Jan. 23, 2020[27]

Schooley, Skye; *What is Corporate Social Responsibility?*; *Business News Daily*; April 22, 2019[28]

Christie, Jim; *U.S. Jury Rules Against Bayer in Roundup Cancer Case*; Associated Press; March 19, March 28 and May 14, 2019[29]

Chapter Twenty-Eight: Avoiding Climate Chaos

Lent, Jeremy; *We Need an Ecological Civilization Before It's Too Late*; Patterns of Meaning, EcoWatch; Oct. 15, 2018[1]

The World Needs a New Worldview; newconsensus.com[2]

Sustainability; babcockranch.com[3]

Wikipedia; *Greensburg, KS*; last updated July 9,2019[4]

What is Carbon Pricing; worldbank.org[5,6]

McPhaul, John; *Costa Rica Aims to Win "Carbon Neutral" Race*; Reuters; May 24, 2007[7]

Huang, Echo and Rathi, Akshat; *The Complete Guide to the World's Largest Carbon Market That Just Launched in China*; qz.com; Dec. 18,2017[8]

Aggarwal, Sahil; *Singapore Plans Southeast Asia's First Carbon Tax From 2019*; californiacarbon.info; Feb. 23, 2017[9]

California Air Resources Board; *ARB Emissions Trading Program*; ww2arb.ca.gov[10]

Horowitz, Cara; *California Cap and Trade Survives Tax Challenge*; legal-plant.org; 2013[11]

Union of Concerned Scientists; *Existing Cap-and-Trade Programs to Cut Global Warming Emissions*; ucsusa.org[12]

The Regional Greenhouse Gas Initiative; rggi.org[13]

RGGI States Welcome New Jersey as Its CO2 Regulation Is Finalized; rggi.org; June 17, 2019[14]

Pricing Carbon Efficiently and Equitably; carbontax.org[15]

City of Boulder; *Boulder's Climate Action Plan*; bouldercolorado.gov[16]

Broder, John; *House Passes Bill to Address Threat of Climate Change*; The New York Times; June 26, 2009[17]

Wikipedia; *Bob Inglis*; last updated October 14, 2019[18,19]

Tayler, Timothy; *When Tradeable Pollution Permits Fall Short*; Conversable Economist blogspot; Oct. 12, 2012[20]

Weiss, Miles and Welch, David; *GM and Fiat Unmasked as Tesla's Secret Source of Cash*; Bloomberg; June 3, 2019[21]

Schildgen, Bob; *Does the Coal Industry Get Subsidies*; sierraclub.org; March 9, 2010[22]

Murse, Tom; *What Is the Citizens United Ruling?*; thoughtco,com; Oct. 22, 2019[23,24]

Roberts, David; *A Solar Future Isn't Just Likely – It's Inevitable*; vox.com; April 28, 2015[25]
Smart Grid; technopedia.com[26]

Nwanevu, Osita; *With the Green New Deal, Democrats Present a Radical Proposition for Combatting Climate Change*; The New Yorker; Feb. 7, 2019[27]

McDonald, Jessica; *The Facts on the Green New Deal*; factcheck.com; Feb. 15, 2019[28]

Here Are the 10 Electric Vehicles With the Longest Ranges; autotrader.com; April 2017[29]

Wikipedia; *List of Electric Vehicle Battery Manufacturers*; last updated Nov. 20, 2019[30]

Statistics of the Week: US Electric Vehicle Charging Stations/Outlets, Sites and Networks; evadoption.com; Dec. 30, 2017[31]

Born, Amy; *How Many Charging Stations Are Needed for the Growing PEV/PHEV Market?*; Engineering 360; Oct. 6, 2017[32]

Wagner, I.; *Projected Number of PEVs in Use in the U.S. by 2026, by Scenario*; statista.com; Jan. 29, 2018[33]

Frosch, Dan; *Coal Market Closures Shake Wyoming*; the Wall Street Journal; Sept. 4, 2019[34]

Ma, Jie and Stringer, David; *Where 3 Million Electric Vehicle Batteries Will Go When They Retire*; Bloomberg Businessweek; June 27, 2018[35]

Harvey, Chelsea; *Greenland Lost a Staggering 1 Trillion Tons of Ice in Just Four Years*; The Washington Post; July 19, 2018[36]

Roewe, Brian; *Would Pope Francis Back the Green New Deal?*; EarthBeat; April 15, 2019[37]

Gage, John; *Harris Announces, 'Landmark Bill' With AOC To Fight 'Environmental Injustice'*; *Washington Examiner*; July 29, 2019[38]

Heliogen Achieves Breakthrough Temperatures From Concentrated Sunlight for Industrial Processes, With Momentum Toward Commercial Hydrogen Fuel Creation; businesswire.com; November 19, 2019[39]

Saul, Michael, et. al.; *Grounded: The President's Power to Fight Climate Change, Protect Public Lands by Keeping Publicly Owned Fossil Fuels in the Ground*; Center for Biological Diversity; September 2015[40]

CPSIA information can be obtained
at www.ICGtesting.com
Printed in the USA
LVHW020951301020
670159LV00011B/348